About the Author

John Morton was educated at Merchant Taylors' School near Northwood, Middlesex. Through the R.A.F. Section of the Combined Cadet Force he won a Flying Scholarship and gained a Private Pilot's Licence before he could drive a car. He was commissioned during National Service in the Royal Air Force and trained as a pilot on piston Provosts and Vampires. He joined British European Airways in January 1956 and progressed through flying Herons, Viscounts, Comets and Boeing 707s to Lockheed TriStars. He was granted his first command in 1967 and culminated his career as a Route Training Captain. During thirty-seven years, he logged some 17,600 flying hours, covering an estimated eight million miles. He has recently published a small book explaining the operational aspects of airline flying for the layman and including a number of anecdotes from his long career. It is entitled *Whatever were you thinking of, Captain? A Handbook for Airline Passengers.*

Genuinely believing that his Queen's Scout Award was a major factor in his being selected for aircrew training, he has tried to put something back into Scouting. He was District Commissioner for Horsham, West Sussex, in the 1980s and has served over twenty-five years as a warranted Leader and in administrative roles in the Movement.

Following retirement, he studied for a BSc degree with the Open University, reading General Science, Astronomy, Geology and the History of Science. He edits *Stonechat,* the magazine of the Horsham Geological Field Club, and he is the author of *Strata*, a book on the life of the pioneer geologist, William Smith. Largely on the strength of this, he was, in 2001, elected a Fellow of the Geological Society.

King of Siluria

How Roderick Murchison

changed the face of Geology

John L. Morton BSc FGS

First published 2004

PUBLISHED IN THE UNITED KINGDOM BY:

Brocken Spectre Publishing
7 Windmill Close
Horsham
West Sussex
RH13 6BY

British Library Cataloguing in Publication Data.

A catalogue record for this book is available from the British Library.

ISBN   0-9546829-0-4

PRINTED AND BOUND IN GREAT BRITAIN

Front cover:
Portrait of Sir Roderick Impey Murchison with his great work *The Silurian System* (engraved by William Walker from a picture by W.H. Pickersgill, R.A.)
(© The British Museum).

Back cover:
Cartoon by Sir Leslie Ward depicting Murchison as 'King of Siluria'
(see page 149) (courtesy of The National Portrait Gallery).

Contents

Contents

Acknowledgements

I would like to express my gratitude to Dr. Ellis Owen, for many years a geologist and palaeontologist at the Natural History Museum, London, who encouraged me to write my first book, *Strata*, about the life of William Smith, which led on to my compiling this biography. My father, Leslie T. Morton FCILIP, has helped me with invaluable technical advice.

I also wish to thank Anthony Brook BA MA FGS, an independent researcher, for his advice and for allowing me to include his assessment of the state of geological knowledge at the start of Murchison's career in the discipline (page 11). He has also compiled, with a very small amount of help from myself, a comprehensive bibliography of Murchison's publications, amounting to over 350 items (twice the number in the Royal Society's published list!). Appendix 1 is his selection of the primary publications. In *Aspects of Murchison*, one of the Occasional Publications of the West Sussex Geological Society, (price £4.50), he has collected a number of papers and extracts from newspapers and journals, which have provided most useful material for this book. Both of these are available from him direct: tel. 01903 233418 or e-mail anthony.brook@amserve.com.

I am also grateful for their permission to reproduce the Stratigraphical Correlation Table (page 168) compiled by Dr. A.W.A Rushton and Dr. D.E. White of the British Geological Survey. Likewise for portraits of Murchison from The British Museum, The Natural History Museum, The National Portrait Gallery and The Illustrated London News. Sketches of fossils on pages 48, 53 and 55 are reproduced from *British Palaeozoic Fossils* (1969) (by kind permission of the Trustees of The Natural History Museum) and from *The Elements of Palaeontology* by Rhona M. Black (2nd ed.1988) (Cambridge University Press).

I have quoted extensively from Archibald Geikie's *Life of Sir Roderick Impey Murchison* (published in 1875) and have tried to copy the original faithfully. In some cases the punctuation, capitalisation and lack of italicisation differs from current practice.

Foreword

In his book entitled *Strata,* John Morton has already followed the footprints of the geological pioneer, William Smith, and has, once again, ventured into the extremely difficult realm of biographical research. This time the footprints are somewhat larger than those of Smith, as the almost unbelievable achievements of Sir Roderick Murchison, so lucidly recorded here, would eclipse many of those of the great explorers and adventurers of the time. In relating this amazing saga of one man's triumph over seemingly impossible difficulties and hazards, the author has amplified the strength of character and sheer determination of one of our greatest geological and geographical pioneers and explorers.

Ellis Owen

List of Illustrations

Geology and Evolution in the early 1820s, when Murchison took up interest in the subjects (Notes by Anthony Brook)

- There was no geological time scale.
- There were no geological periods.
- The vast extent of geological time was unrecognised.
- Individual strata had only occasionally been grouped into formations.
- International correlations of strata being extremely rare, there were no world-wide 'systems'.
- Uppermost layers of gravel and pebbles were regularly attributed to the Noachian Deluge.
- Other changes of strata (and most landforms) were also explained catastrophically.
- Thus, geological changes of almost all kinds were assumed to be rapid, violent, and devastating. But the nature of the catastrophe was often left unspecified.
- That fossils represented forms of past life was no longer doubted. Each stratum, moreover, had characteristic fossils, often unique to itself.
- The extinction of species was accepted but seldom emphasized.
- There was no prevalent theory regarding extinction.
- How species originated was equally unclear, but the already proposed idea that one kind of animal or plant might evolve into another was almost universally rejected. Animals and plants had no ancestors. Mankind had no predecessors.
- The great majority of known fossils were shells. Other invertebrates remained poorly known. Trilobites, for example, were still considered insects.
- Vertebrate palaeontology had scarcely begun. Only a few recently-extinct large mammals and a few exceptionally well-preserved Jurassic reptiles were known; interpretations of the latter were still controversial. Amphibians and, more importantly, dinosaurs had yet to be discovered. Even the abundant fossil fishes had not yet been closely studied. Almost nothing was known about either fossils or strata older than what we now call the Mesozoic.
- Gideon Mantell's *The Fossils of the South Downs* 1822 was a major contribution to the science of its day.

The Arms of Sir Roderick Impey Murchison, Bart.

Shield: or, a lion rampant sable, armed and langued gules between two pineapples slipped in chief, vert, and an escallop in base proper.

Crest: a dexter hand couped above the wrist, grasping a ducal coronet of three leaves both proper, enclosed between two laurel branches vert.

Motto: IMPAVIDO PECTORE (with a fearless heart)

Introduction

Roderick Murchison was a remarkable man. He was a prolific writer of reports and scientific papers; a new exhaustive bibliography compiled by Anthony Brook runs to 350 items. Appendix 1 (p.223) contains a selective list of his most significant publications. He was the author or co-author of two magnificent works, *The Silurian System*, which ran to four editions, and *The Geology of Russia in Europe and the Ural Mountains*. He became Director-General of the Geological Survey of Great Britain and later President of the Royal Geographical Society, in which role he worked tirelessly to support exploration of the unknown parts of the World. He was a Trustee of the British and Hunterian Museums and Vice-President of the British Association for the Advancement of Science. He was also a Member of the Imperial Academy of Sciences, and the Geographical and Mineralogical Societies of St. Petersburg. He was respected as a Corresponding Member of the Imperial Academy of Vienna, of the Royal Academy of Hungary, of the Institut de France, and was an Honorary Member of the Royal Academies of Berlin, Brussels, Copenhagen, Holland, Ireland, Munich, Rome, Stockholm and Turin, and of the scientific societies of Boston, Breslau, Edinburgh, Frankfurt, Moscow, New York, Philadelphia and Switzerland. He was President of the Hakluyt Society (founded in 1846 in memory of the 16th-century English geographer, Richard Hakluyt) and a Fellow of the Linnean Society (devoted to the natural sciences). From 1855, he was Director-General of the Museum of Practical Geology and Chief of the School of Mines. He was mainly responsible for the report of the Commission on the coal resources of Britain, a work of national importance.

Sir Roderick was invested with two orders of knighthood and created a Baronet by Queen Victoria; he was made a Knight Grand Cross of St. Stanislaus by Czar Nicholas I of Russia. He received many other medals and honours, including orders conferred on him by the sovereigns of Brazil, Denmark, Italy and Sweden. A list was compiled and published of the nineteen stars, crosses and other emblems of distinction awarded to him. It was said to constitute 'the largest number of honorary decorations which in modern times have been awarded by crowned heads to any individual for purely scientific attainments'.

Murchison was known across the World and several geographical features were named after him (see Appendix 2), together with several fossil species (p. 55). Though much of the family's wealth had been lost through their support of the Stuarts, Roderick's father was still a Scottish laird. He had made his own fortune in India under Warren Hastings and on his return purchased the estate of Tarradale, north-west of Inverness, from the Mackenzies. Roderick inherited this on achieving his majority. The income from it was not what it might have been; the impoverished tenants farmed the land inefficiently and were often unable to afford their rents. However, Roderick was to grow up into the life of a gentleman. He was educated at Durham Grammar School, where by all accounts he was not an outstanding pupil. Nevertheless, in later life he wrote letters, scientific papers and books with the highest standard of language and punctuation, often embellished with Latin phrases.

He showed his extrovert character and interest in a military career in his early 'teens by becoming a gang leader at school and drilling his fellow pupils in squads. He was mischievous and daring. In his 'teens he was academically lazy and more interested in the life of a playboy. He failed his first entrance examinations for the Military College but buckled down to enough work finally to be accepted and commissioned. He was posted under the command of Sir Arthur Wellesley to serve in the Peninsular War and fought in three important battles. However, after the Battle of Waterloo it became clear that there was no longer a good prospect of a rewarding career in the army and he resigned his commission.

In 1815 Roderick met and married Charlotte Hugonin, the daughter of a General and potential heiress. She was just under four years his senior and a very shrewd and clever lady. It is interesting to read that in the first few years of their marriage money was not plentiful, so, instead of settling in England, they went on a prolonged tour of the Continent! One hears today of pensioners finding the cost of living lower in, say, Spain, and settling there to enjoy a higher standard, but to go travelling would have to be much more expensive. When they returned, Roderick took to spending most of his time as a country gentleman, going out fox-hunting nearly every day and owning a stable of fine horses. The matter of wealth must have been purely relative!

Charlotte wanted more constructive things for her husband and directed him towards the study of science, which at that time was developing rapidly. He was introduced to geology and took up the subject with enthusiasm. He joined the newly-formed Geological Society in 1824, as Member number 624. Within two years he was serving on the Council, which he did for a further forty-three years, many of them as Vice-President. He was elected President only seven years after joining (1831–33) and held the Chair again from 1841 to 1843. He had begun work soon after William Smith published the first coloured geological map of any country and lived to see half the World surveyed geologically, having himself mapped a great part of eastern Europe in his identification of Silurian strata. He bequeathed to the Geological Society over 2500 letters, 140 field notebooks and twenty-six volumes of journals.

As a young man, Murchison was extremely fit and expended unbounded energy on field trips, looking in particular at older rocks. With Adam Sedgwick, the Woodwardian Professor at Cambridge, he developed knowledge of the Old Red Sandstone and proposed that it and associated strata be known as the Devonian System, since they outcropped significantly in that county. He spent months looking at the rocks below these in Wales and their equivalent in central

Europe, Scandinavia and Russia. He proposed the name Silurian, after the Silures, a tribe that had inhabited Wales and the western central counties of England, for the strata between his Devonian and the Cambrian, then thought to contain no record of life. A distressing dispute, detailed in the text, developed between Sedgwick and Murchison as to the dividing line between the Lower Silurian and the Upper Cambrian. This was not resolved until after their deaths, when a new system embracing part of both was established and named (by Charles Lapworth) the Ordovician, after the Ordovices, another ancient Welsh tribe who fought the Roman invaders. Appendix 3 provides a quick and convenient reference, listing the geological periods, their rocks and fossils.

Murchison was industrious, energetic and clear-headed, with a strong will and great tenacity of purpose. His military experience led him to be somewhat dictatorial. However, these attributes were matched with kindness, honesty and geniality, though these may have been disguised condescension, as he had great pretensions of grandeur and a tendency towards ostentatious display. His status and the economic value of his work led him to be granted audiences with several crowned heads and leading politicians of Europe. In 1840, he led an expedition, with the enthusiastic backing of the Czar, covering 14,000 miles in European Russia and the Ural Mountains. He suggested the name Permian, after the province of Permia on the western flank of the Urals, for the rocks immediately above the Carboniferous, which manifested themselves there. He took huge risks for his own security, exploring areas many miles from any possible emergency assistance, and he, his colleagues and his party of servants and assistants braved a very basic level of comfort and sustenance in undeveloped regions.

Sir Roderick Murchison's Will consists of nine pages of closely-written manuscript. As a legal document without punctuation, in places it is very difficult to read and it is hard to establish the correct spelling of names in some cases. Appendix 4 is an attempt to make the Will more readable. It makes an interesting document as the testament of a wealthy man in Victorian England. It is clear, for example, that he wished to provide for his servants, but he did not know exactly how many he had, nor how long they had been working for him! There was presumably a large number of them. The amounts he bequeathed to them were modest, but probably in line with current social practice. In contrast he spent a large sum on providing for his own tomb and left a substantial figure to both the Geological and Geographical Societies for the foundation of memorial awards to perpetuate his name. There are also numerous provisions for his friends and colleagues 'as remembrances'. He also directed that all his letters, books and documents (some twenty-six manuscript volumes) be handed over to Archibald Geikie, together with a bequest, for the preparation of his biography. This was duly published in 1875, four years after his death. Geikie, although his contemporary, was thirty-five years his junior and knew only those aspects of Murchison's early life about which he chose to tell him. Also, since he was paid to write the biography, he naturally did not include anything too detrimental to Murchison's character. Where appropriate, that task has fallen to later commentators. This book is an attempt to build on Geikie's work in the light of the passage of more than a century and a quarter, and to pay tribute to a man of outstanding achievement.

Chapter One
The Making of Roderick Impey Murchison

The name Murchison is a corruption of Murdochson. The Murdochs were a small clan in the wild Mackenzie country of Ross-shire, northern Scotland. The name derives from Mhurachaidh, recorded at least as far back as the sixteenth century, not long after surnames were first adopted in addition to personal (Christian) ones.

Roderick's grandfather, Alexander, was a third cousin of Colonel Donald Murchison, one of the most remarkable Highlanders of his day. He was an agent for, and a friend of, the Earl of Seaforth and protected his estates when he was forced into exile after the disastrous Battle of Sheriffmuir in the 1715 rebellion. The Colonel was buried on the shores of Loch Alsh, and some 140 years later Roderick Murchison raised a granite monument to him on the site. It is signposted from the A 87 a mile and a half east of Kyle and is reached along a short path through light woodland. Roderick's great-grandfather, John Murchison, died at Sheriffmuir and most of the ancestral property of the clan evaporated after the defeat at Culloden in 1745. Roderick's grandfather rented a farm at Auchtertyre by Loch Alsh, where his father, Kenneth, was born in 1751.

Kenneth studied medicine at Glasgow and Edinburgh and went out to India for seventeen years, where he found a lucrative appointment in Lucknow as physician to Warren Hastings. He amassed a fair fortune and returned home in 1786, when he purchased from his maternal uncle, Mackenzie of Lenton, the small estate of Tarradale (sometimes spelt Taradale) in Ross-shire (now Highland), about twelve miles west of Inverness. The house is accessible from the A 832 two miles east of Muir of Ord and stands in a delightful setting overlooking the Beauly Firth. It has been sympathetically modified and extended, but is still recognisable from a nineteenth-century sketch (pp 18 and 123). It is currently used by students from the University of Aberdeen. Kenneth Murchison devoted his later years to the gratuitous medical care of the poor. He planted a large number of trees and became an ardent antiquary and a Gaelic scholar. He was a zealous student of music and geology.

In 1791, he married Barbara, the eldest daughter of Roderick Mackenzie of Fairburn, Ross-shire. His first son, Roderick Impey Murchison, was born at Tarradale, on 19 February 1792. He was named after his maternal grandfather, his second name being in honour of an intimate friend of his father, Sir Elijah Impey.

Tarradale, Ross-shire, the Birthplace of Sir Roderick Murchison

The family spent three years at Tarradale, and Roderick soon had a brother, Alexander, who died young, then another christened Kenneth. Their father's health had been affected by his stay in India and they moved to Bath. In spite of the better climate, he died in 1796 of a liver disease and dropsy.

Mrs. Murchison took her two sons to live at 26 George Street, Edinburgh, where they were both tutored by Bishop Sandford. The site of this house is now the premises of the Royal Society of Scotland. In 1869, Roderick went back to visit the little chapel near Charlotte Square that he recalled from his boyhood. His mother soon found a second husband, Colonel Robert Macgregor Murray, one of the younger brothers of the Chief of the Macgregors. He and his brothers were old friends of Roderick's father from his days in India. In fact, the Macgregor of Macgregor, another brother, Colonel Alexander, and Sir Elijah Impey were left as guardians to the two boys. They had a governess, Sally, who came from Dorset and taught them an English accent.

Colonel Robert was called to Ireland to deal with a rebellion there and the boys' mother determined to accompany him. In 1799, at the age of only seven, Roderick was sent to Durham Grammar School. All his life he remembered the distress of leaving his mother and Sally.

Roderick was able to read and recite poetry before he went to Durham, but he did not do well academically. The headmaster's stern and morose manner did not help. Over six years, he struggled with the rudiments of an education, acquiring some French and Latin and reading Homer, but making heavy weather of geometry and arithmetic. He began to display leadership qualities, as he lived up to his second name and got into all sorts of mischief. He was the ringleader of the wilder boys, who nicknamed him 'Dick'. He would play with gunpowder or be seen sitting astride a gargoyle on the highest pinnacle of the cathedral. His first foray into subterranean exploration was to climb down a drain near the archway leading to Prebends' Bridge. Having entered the tunnel, he could not turn round, so was forced to continue, surprising the rats and tearing his skin and clothes, until he emerged at the level of the river 300 feet below, not exactly smelling of roses. His school friends were impressed!

During these years, his step-father and mother rented Newton House at Londonderry, near Bedale, eleven miles north of Ripon in North Yorkshire. This house was demolished following severe damage in a storm in December 1821 and replaced a year later. During his school holidays there he had the pleasure of exercising a pony and terriers. It was here that the idea of a military career gelled out in his mind, encouraged by his uncle, General Mackenzie of Fairburn, telling him he would make a good soldier. Later he said, 'From that day I read and thought of nothing but military heroes.' Back at school he drilled his fellow pupils in military exercises.

When he was thirteen, Roderick was taken to Great Marlow Military College in Buckinghamshire. He failed to gain entry at first, but following further study was eventually accepted as Cadet number C 26. Not surprisingly, he rapidly became the ringleader of the boisterous young men of the College, and he now found the academic side more interesting. He learned tactics and military drawing and developed a skill in assessing the lie of the land, a faculty which served him well later in his scientific career.

His time at Great Marlow instilled in him a military bearing, which he carried through into later life. Even though only fourteen, he acted the dandy. He noted the names of titled people he met, how he had been allowed to ride the chargers of some and how he played cards with young aristocracy. In January 1806 he visited his uncle, General Mackenzie, then commanding a force of the militia at Hull, who wrote in his diary, 'He is a charming boy, manly, sensible, generous, warm-hearted – in short possessing every possible good attribute. I think he has also talents to make a figure in any profession. That which he has chosen is a soldier.'

The following year, before he was sixteen, he was gazetted Ensign in the 36th Regiment, but was not assigned military duties for some time. He wrote, 'For the first six months after I became an officer, I was supposed to be completing my studies! In reality I was amusing myself with all sorts of dissipation at Bath, where I passed my holidays driving "tandems" [horses harnessed one behind the other] and wearing clanking spurs. On leaving Marlow I was removed to Edinburgh, where my mother and relatives lived, and was placed in the house of Mr. Alexander Manners, the respected Librarian of the Faculty of Advocates where I was associated with five or six other youths all older than myself. Having a recruiting party in the city under my orders, and with plenty of money to spend and balls to dance at, it may well be conceived that I did not gather together much knowledge. Still I picked up a few crumbs, which were destined to produce some fruit in after times. Unquestionably, this winter in Edinburgh materially influenced my future character. For example, I took lessons in French, Italian, German, and mathematics. I also attended a debating club, and wrote (such as they were) two essays on political subjects, of which of course I was profoundly ignorant. While the young powdered military fop (pig-tails and powder were then in the ascendant) affected to despise all dominies and philosophers, I could not be one of the table presided over by the bland and courteous old Manners without picking up many useful hints for future guidance.'

Roderick took lessons at Leatham's riding school and in fencing, before joining his regiment in Cork in late 1807. He was dismayed to find the other officers quite unlike himself. They were quiet and well disciplined, having seen active service in Europe, India and South America. He was impressed by the strictly disciplinarian Colonel Burne, who had trained his officers and men to become a 'crack regiment'. Burne was however able to relax off duty and, with his favourite port, could drink most men under the table. The 36th Regiment joined a small army of about eight thousand men, later to be reinforced to thirty thousand, under Sir Arthur Wellesley, which set sail from Cork to Portugal and the Peninsular War.

****

Following the Battle of Trafalgar in 1805, Napoleon, although he controlled practically the whole of Europe, was helpless at sea. He determined to create a land blockade of British sea-power and it was thus necessary to his schemes to control the ports of Spain and Portugal. He tricked King Charles IV of Spain and his son Ferdinand into a meeting at Bayonne, where, under threat of a firing squad, he forced them to sign documents of abdication and installed his own brother, Joseph, on the Spanish throne. When the Spanish people realised that their country was effectively annexed to France, they rose in revolt right across the country, an unprecedented event. The small province of Asturias expelled the French Governor and sent envoys to England to appeal for help. The British Foreign Minister, George Canning, and Robert Castlereagh at the War Office, were sympathetic to their cause and needed to keep the ports open. Thus began the Peninsular War.

The French had invaded deep into Spain with little effective opposition in a set battle but a population that gave no quarter in guerrilla skirmishes. Marshal Junot had entered Lisbon. However, General Dupont suffered a serious defeat and was forced by the Spanish insurgents to surrender with twenty-two thousand soldiers at Baylen, in Andalusia. This compelled Napoleon's army in Madrid to retreat to the north behind the Ebro, taking King Joseph with them. Junot was left isolated in Portugal, with a land retreat threatened by a hostile population and help from the sea unavailable.

The force in which Ensign Murchison was serving disembarked on the Mondego River, a hundred miles north of Lisbon. His General, Sir Arthur Wellesley, whose aide-de-camp was Fitzroy Somerset (later Lord Raglan), attacked Junot successfully at Roliça and again at Vimieira.

Two days after the Battle of Vimieira the sixteen-year-old Ensign wrote to his uncle, General Mackenzie, the following long letter:

'Vimieira, 23d August 1808

'My dear Uncle, - Having been prevented so very long a time from writing to you, on account of not knowing to what part of the Mediterranean you are ordered, I am resolved at last to send this letter to Sicily, and let it run the hazard of a ship sailing from Lisbon to that island. If you had been in England during the whole of the time in which we were acting against the French in this country, what pleasure it would have given me to have sent you from the scenes of action the last accounts of them; but in such ignorance was I of the country you were in, that in the only letter which I have had from my mother since I left Ireland, she informed me only of your having proceeded in the "Pomona" frigate to the Mediterranean; that it was probable you would touch at some of the Spanish ports, whither it was then supposed Sir Arthur Wellesley's expedition would proceed; and that in case of meeting with me, you intended taking me on with you as your aide-de-camp. I shall endeavour in this letter to give a detailed account of our proceedings, as I am certain you will be pleased with it, incorrect as it may be in some respects, and far as it must be from being a general one, on account of my humble situation in the army.

'Sir Arthur Wellesley, after having proceeded to Corunna in order to hear of the movements of the Spaniards, wrote to Admiral Sir Charles Cotton off the Tagus, and requested him to co-operate. The landing of the troops in Mondego Bay was then determined upon, and, on the 1st of August, the 36th and 40th infantry, and some rifles, disembarked on the south side of the River Mondego, under General Fane, exactly opposite the town of Figuiera. The troops passed the bar of the river chiefly in small schooners which trade along the coast, and also in Portuguese boats.

'The brigade being formed was then marched in open columns along the coast, chiefly through very heavy sands, about two leagues, and encamped near the village of Lavaos, where Sir Arthur established head-quarters for the night. As by his orders two shirts and two pair of stockings and a great-coat were to compose the whole of the baggage of officers and soldiers, and that not such a thing as a donkey or any other animal was procurable, our whole kit, including three days' provisions, was on our backs, which, with a brace of pistols and the 36th regimental colours, loaded me absolutely to the utmost of my strength.

Even our old Colonel was compelled to tramp through the sands this day, which he did with the greatest alacrity. In four days the whole of the troops and stores were landed without any loss. As we were now to wait at Lavaos for the arrival of General Spencer's force from Cadiz, we had it in our power to communicate with the shipping, and I was thus enabled to land my boat-cloak and a few other necessary articles, which have since been of infinite use to me on outlying picquets (under walls and without tents) and guards, and to buy a donkey to carry them, which little animal is with me at present. In the course of three days General Spencer's force arrived and immediately disembarked. The army being then arranged and divided into six brigades, we were placed under General Ferguson with the 40th and 71st regiments. The appointment of this excellent officer (who, I think, is your particular friend) gave us, the 36th, great satisfaction.

'Sir Arthur Wellesley's orders, previous to our landing, were most explicitly and clearly written, particularly in explaining to the troops the nature of the service they were about to enter upon, and directing the greatest attention to be paid to the religion and customs of the Portuguese. We were likewise given to understand by these orders, that through the whole of the war we should be en bivouac, and no tents allowed for officers or men. On the 10th the whole army directed its march to Leyria. It was intended at first to have marched only three leagues, but upon information being received that a force had proceeded by the sea-coast, in order to have surprised some of our outposts, our march was continued until three o'clock next morning. We then halted and took up our stations on a cold, bleak moor, about two leagues from Leyria, having marched upwards of twenty English miles. Next morning we marched to Leyria (where the inhabitants had been maltreated by Loison), and halted on the south side of the city, whence I went in to inspect it. There we were joined by the Portuguese army, which did not exceed in strength 3000 men. From what I could observe, there were about four squadrons of cavalry, good-looking, well-mounted dragoons, being the garde de police of Lisbon, who had made their escape from thence on hearing of our disembarkation. The Portuguese infantry was in a most wretched state of discipline. On the 13th the army marched two and a half leagues, and halted at Lucero, about a mile and a half on the south side of the beautiful ancient abbey of Batalha, where the Portuguese gained that celebrated victory over the Spaniards which secured the independence of their country. At this place, for the first time, we got hold of a few straggling Frenchmen. Next day, the 14th, we proceeded to Alcobaça, and halted near it. The abbey is most magnificent and delighted me more than any public building I have seen. The library and kitchen of the convent are well worthy of admiration. Part of the French army had just quitted this place.

'We had proceeded next morning about half-way between this town and Las Caldas; when, approaching the small town of Albaferam, the French appeared in sight. Their army was drawn up in close column, and was ready for action. They however continued their retreat, and we advanced and halted near Las

Caldas.

'Sir Arthur had received intelligence that the French General Laborde was strongly entrenched in the mountainous pass at the extremity of the valley in which the old Moorish fort of Obidos stands, and that General Loison was at no great distance from our right. The greatest part of the army was advanced from the valley to force the pass, while General Ferguson's brigade (with General Bowes's in its rear) was sent off to the mountains on the left, with the intention of cutting off Laborde's retreat. We were proceeding in this direction when the French appeared upon our flank, in consequence of which we formed line, and changing direction advanced, as the fog cleared, towards the enemy. We marched over about two leagues of hilly ground, and when within about a mile and a half of the pass we unexpectedly perceived the whole of the enemy in direct march to it, and immediately afterwards our riflemen opened their fire from the top of the hill upon one of the enemy's columns, who returned a volley and retreated a short distance.

'It fell to the lot of the Rifles, 5th, 9th, and 29th regiments, to force the pass, and to the last regiment especially, who, from the nature of the ground, could in some places only ascend up the hill in single files. It was on this account that the 29th lost so many officers and men, including the gallant Colonel Lake, who was some paces in front of his regiment when he fell. Just as we arrived at the foot of the mountains our artillery was brought into play, which no doubt annoyed the enemy's retreating columns, and three companies of our regiment were detached in order to support our light infantry, with the other light infantry of the brigade. The enemy had moved off, however, from the shots of the rifles, and the distant fire of a few pieces of our artillery. The 40th regiment was then detached from our brigade to cover the baggage, and as soon as the firing ceased we pursued our march through the pass. Swiss and Frenchmen were lying dead on all sides. As soon as we got through, General Ferguson's brigade, with the others which had not been much engaged, formed on a very extensive heath, and were advanced in front in order to charge the enemy if he would stand; but Monsieur would only permit a few stray shots to be sent into his solid columns – he had received beating enough to satisfy him for one day. [This was the engagement of Roliça or Roriça].

'On the 19th the army moved on to Vimieira, and passed over the very plateau on which we of the 36th were, two days afterwards, to have an opportunity of signalizing ourselves.

'The village of Vimieira is situated in a narrow valley, amid rising hills. In our front, on to the south-east, is a wood upon a low eminence; and in the rear, on towards the coast, are very high hills. On the summit of these hills, which lie exactly between Vimieira and the sea, the greatest part of the British army was posted. On a lower hill on the right, and a little in front of the town, was the Light Brigade, with the 20th regiment. This was an excellent post of observation. On the hill on the left was the 40th regiment, which was the left of our brigade, the 71st Highlanders on their right, and the 36th being in the hollow exactly in the rear of the village. Close to our front was a small river. The position was rather more than two leagues from the sea. . . . We discovered some squadrons and picquets of French dragoons. Several officers approached us, and one coming particularly near (I suppose he was sketching), Captain Mellish (General Ferguson's A.D.C.) offered the long odds to anyone that, if permitted, he would dismount him.

'On the following morning, the 21st, about nine o'clock, the drums of the 40th regiment beat to arms. This was occasioned by their outlying picquet being attacked by some small party of the enemy which was greatly advanced. In ten minutes we were formed. Our brigade, led by General Ferguson, immediately crossed the little river and ascended to the hill on which we were about to fight. We had hardly commenced our uphill move before the advanced posts of our centre, in the hollow near Vimieira, on our right, commenced a very heavy fire. We proceeded up the hill and formed line under its brow. A brigade of artillery was brought up with the greatest promptitude, and two guns, under Lieutenant Locke, being placed on the rising ground on our right, and the others on the left, three companies of the 36th were detached to the edge of the hill on our right, in order to protect the guns, which were soon annoying the advancing French close columns in the finest style with shrapnel shells, whilst our rifles and light infantry were firing in extended files as videttes.

'After some very hot and close work the centre of our army, at the village of Vimieira, repulsed the enemy. There General Anstruther's brigade, with the 50th regiment, received the enemy in front of the village. Colonel Taylor, who had charged with four troops, the only cavalry we had, viz., of the 20th Light Dragoons, was killed in a wood, whilst our heavy artillery, which was placed upon the hillock in front of the village, cut up the enemy most dreadfully. The 50th charged them with the bayonet; the 43d met them in a narrow lane when in open column, and gallantly repulsed them; the 52d and 97th were likewise warmly engaged and thus the enemy was quite routed in their central or main attack.

'To return to our part of the battle, i.e. to our left wing: the fire of the enemy soon became very hot, and even though the 36th were lying on their breasts under the brow, our men were getting pretty much hit, whilst the regiment in our rear, the 82d, which at that time could not fire a shot, suffered more than we did. General Spencer, who commanded the division, when moving about to regulate the general movements, was hit by a ball in the hand, and I saw him wrap his handkerchief round it and heard him say, "It is only a scratch!" Soon after, the Light Infantry in our front closed files and fell in; our guns were pulled back, and then came the struggle. General Ferguson waving his hat, up we rose, old Burne (our Colonel) crying out, as he shook his yellow cane, that "he would knock down any man who fired a shot."

'This made some merriment among the men, as tumbling over was the fashion without the application of their Colonel's cane. "Charge!" was the word, and at once we went over the brow with a steady line of glittering steel, and with a hearty hurrah, against six regiments in close column, with six pieces of artillery, just in front of the 36th. But not an instant did the enemy stand against this most unexpected sally with pistol-shot. Off they went, and all their guns were instantly taken, horses and all, and then left in our rear, whilst we went on chasing the runaways for a mile and a half, as hard as we could go, over the moor of Lourinhão. They rallied, it is true, once or twice, particularly behind some thick prickly-pear hedges and a hut or two on the flat table-land; but although their brave General Solignac was always cantering to their front and animating them against us, they at last fled precipitately, until they reached a small hamlet, where, however, they did make a tolerable stand.

'Here it was that Sir Arthur Wellesley overtook us after a smart gallop. He had witnessed from a distance our steady and successful charge, and our capture of the guns, and he now saw how we were thrusting the French out of this hamlet. Through the sound of the musketry, and in the midst of much confusion, I heard a shrill voice calling out, "Where are the colours of the 36th?" and I turned round (my brother ensign, poor Peter Bone, having just been knocked down), and looking up in Sir Arthur's bright and confident face, said "Here they are, sir!" Then he shouted, "Very well done, my boys! Halt, halt – quite enough!"

'The French were now at their last run, in spite of every effort of Solignac to rally them. Several of our bloody-minded old soldiers said in levelling, "they would bring down the ------- on the white horse;" and sure enough the gallant fellow fell, just as the 71st Highlanders, who were on our left, being moved round en potence, charged down the hill, with their wounded piper playing on his bum, and completed the rout of the enemy, taking General Solignac of course prisoner. [This appears to be a mistake. Solignac was wounded, but the French General taken prisoner was not he, but Brennier].

'Had we possessed a squadron or two of dragoons on the left wing, all the remaining force of Solignac's division, which had been driven two miles to the north, or away from the main body of Junot (which had retreated to the south), would have been captured, for they were then a rabble. But Sir Arthur knew his weakness in cavalry. He had defeated a very superior force in crack style; on our wing we had indeed taken the General, and all the guns brought against us; he also knew that the enemy had three full regiments of cavalry in the field, whilst he had none. Moreover, he was no longer commander, for old Sir Harry Burrard, already on the ground, was his senior and had ordered a halt.

'Think, my dear uncle, with what pleasure I got a sheet of long paper from the adjutant, and wrote my first account of this glorious victory to my mother on a drum in the field, in order that it might go home with the despatches. We shall soon go on to Lisbon, and then I expect we shall finish off Monsieur Junot. – I remain ever, my dear uncle, your most affectionate nephew.'

Junot negotiated a deal with Wellesley's superiors, the so-called Convention of Cintra, agreeing to evacuate Portugal, if the British transported him and his twenty-six thousand troops to Rochefort. This caused an outcry at home. Wellesley survived a military court of enquiry but his superiors were relieved of their commands.

Murchison, newly promoted to Lieutenant, served under their replacement, the extremely able Sir John Moore. To gain time for the Spanish to rally, Moore advanced to the north-west of Madrid, through Salamanca to Valladolid, threatening French lines of communication and preventing action against southern Spain and Portugal. The march started in September and ended in January, inflicting on the men great hardship in winter weather. At one point Murchison lost his boots in a quagmire with twenty miles to go to rejoin his regiment. Walking barefoot, he became exhausted and had reconciled himself to being taken prisoner, when he was revived and rescued by a young drummer of the 96th Regiment. From the junior officers' point of view Moore's generalship seemed questionable, but he was operating under extreme difficulties. Napoleon attacked him with fifty thousand men and he led a brilliant retreat to Corunna, where he was mortally wounded. However, having won a rearguard action, his men were transported home by a fleet of small ships commandeered for the purpose. They had embarked safely on the night of 16 January, 1809, but narrowly escaped shipwreck on the Cornish coast.

****

For the most part of 1809, Murchison remained with his regiment on home duties. He was stationed in Sussex at Horsham Barracks, which occupied some twelve acres of ground leased from the Denne estate to the south of the town. (The cricket ground now occupies a part of the site). London being only thirty-eight miles away, he made frequent visits to, among other places, a favourite haunt of the soldiery, Old Slaughter's Coffee House in St. Martin's Lane.

In the autumn, he achieved something on which he had set his heart and became aide-de-camp to his uncle, General Mackenzie. He joined him in Sicily, where he was provided with a house of his own and two horses. His duties included copying official correspondence between his uncle and the government of Naples, from which he learned of the double-dealing and broken promises with which the British in Sicily had to contend. There was a half-hearted belligerency across the Straits of Messina and the French Marshal Murat, King of Naples, threatened to invade Sicily but the idea was not pursued. Murchison found his life rather monotonous and turned to learning Italian and taking singing lessons.

In 1811, General Mackenzie's health deteriorated and they returned to England via Malta, Cagliari and Gibraltar. The General was appointed to a command in the north of Ireland, leaving little prospect of advancement in either his career or that of his aide-de-camp. Murchison at first went back to the tedium of barrack duty at Horsham with his old regiment, but soon rejoined his uncle in Armagh, where life turned out to be even more dull. He was promoted to Captain in 1812. Occasionally he obtained leave to go to England and fell into the habit of dressing in the height of fashion and of extravagant spending. Looking forward to his majority, he talked of selling his family home in Scotland. The idea horrified his guardian, who pointed out that as a laird he would have a voice in the community worth three times any sum in the bank that the sale might realise.

In January 1812, Captain Murchison became a Member of the Royal Institution and attended lectures by Sir Humphry Davy, the great chemist, inventor of the miners' safety lamp and science propagandist. He began to be persuaded of the mental stimulation and adventures of science.

On reaching the age of twenty-one, he travelled to Inverness to view his inheritance. On the way he ran into great difficulty with heavy snow, completing part of his journey on foot. He toured the Tarradale estate, which he perceived to be very poorly farmed by his impoverished tenants. He knew that they were only able to pay their rents by supplementing their income by the distillation of illicit whisky and he had not the heart to sell the estate over their heads. However, it was only a few years before the rents became so severely in arrears that he was eventually glad to sell Tarradale and see the back of it.

Back in Europe, Sir Arthur Wellesley had been elevated to the peerage, as Viscount Wellington, after his victory at the Battle of Salamanca in July 1812. He had driven the French out of both Portugal and Spain and Napoleon had abdicated and retreated to Elba. The whole campaign had ended without Captain Murchison being called to arms, which disappointed him greatly. He saw the peace of 1814 as a final blow to his hopes of military advancement. His uncle gave up his Staff appointment and Murchison returned to London on half-pay.

He crossed the Channel and stayed in Paris for a while, polishing up his French, taking dancing lessons, attending the theatre and studying the art treasures of the Louvre. He travelled to Tours, to visit his mother who was living there, and went on to Poitiers with a close friend, Francis Hare, who there introduced him to the English writer, Walter Savage Landor.

He was in Paris on his way home, when he heard that Napoleon had slipped away from Elba and landed in the south of France. There was some confusion as to what would happen, but it was clear that the French army would not stand by the King. It was obviously prudent for the young British officer to leave the country without delay. The road to Calais was already crowded, so he made a detour via Béthune and St. Omer to have a better chance of procuring post-horses. He had one or two close shaves with disorganised detachments of French soldiers and was only allowed through the gates of Arras because the captain of the guard had not yet received orders concerning the holders of British passports.

Murchison was looking for action and promotion, so determined to quit the infantry for the cavalry. In a letter to his mother, his uncle described this as a 'measure of the most stupid folly'. He joined the Enniskillen Dragoons, but to his chagrin only six troops were ordered out and his was not one of them. The hundred days of Napoleon's resurgence passed quickly, Waterloo came and went, and Murchison was left in the depot at Ipswich.

Chapter Two
An Interest in Art

Roderick's mother had left France to live at Ryde in the Isle of Wight. Early in the summer of 1815, he met there General Francis Lewis Hugonin and his wife Charlotte, together with their daughter, also Charlotte, whom he found 'attractive, piquante, clever, highly educated, and about three years my senior'. On 29 August they were married at St. Mary's, Buriton (near Petersfield, Hampshire), not far from Charlotte's home at Nursted House.

Murchison had already considered leaving the army, and his wife, having experienced some of the deprivations of a military career and believing her husband to have a higher calling than barrack life, added weight to the argument. The final straw was an order to join his regiment at Romford barracks; the thought of inflicting on Charlotte the boredom he had already experienced at Horsham and Armagh determined him to resign his commission. He had looked upon the army as a medium for channelling his physical energies and achieving distinction, however he was never more than an average young officer and he had not made much effort to study the art of war.

He was now influenced by a thoughtful, cultivated and affectionate woman and later he would freely acknowledge his debt to his wife for setting him on a truly remarkable career. He took her to Scotland, to show her Tarradale and to meet his friends and relatives there. They came south in October, setting out in a snowstorm.

At this stage he seriously considered entering the Church. He said 'I saw that my wife had been brought up to look after the poor, was a good botanist, enjoyed a garden and liked tranquillity; and as parsons then enjoyed a little hunting, shooting, and fishing without being railed at, I thought I might slide into that sort of comfortable domestic life.' He asked a friend to make enquiries as to how he should go about it. A letter from him shows how seriously he took the matter: 'In consequence of the peace we may expect an irruption of officers into the Church, which may produce an additional strictness of regulation. I am not aware in what time a degree may be taken at Cambridge; any Cambridge man would tell you. The examination is almost nothing. Not so at Oxford, where the whole system would present to you considerable difficulty.

'Surely as you are so well known in Ireland you might find a favourable bishop in that country, and the journey would be the work of a fortnight. At any rate, pray do not give up your excellent plans, dégoûté.

'I will in your absence, without mentioning your name, make every inquiry I can. The stability and well-being of our Church depends so much upon the respectability and fitness of its ministers that we can only quarrel with those forms and preliminaries to ordination when they come in competition with our own favourite wishes.'

Murchison had compiled in a notebook of 1815 the formidable list of books he might need for his clerical education. They were in Greek, Latin, French, Italian and English and in his methodical way he had classified them under Religion, Eloquence, History, Belles-Lettres, etc.

While still undecided about a life in the Church, he determined to take his wife on a long continental tour. This was largely forced upon them, the cost of living in other European countries being lower than in England and the revenues from the Tarradale estate having dwindled to a very low level. Charlotte had shrewdly assessed her husband's character and realised that he would be far more excited by new pursuits and friends abroad than in following a useless life at home. They spent the winter with her parents at Nursted House, while he improved his already good French and brushed up his Italian. They both read widely on the scenery and history of Italy, but Roderick was able to take the occasional break in the form of a day out with the Hambledon fox-hounds, beagles at Petersfield or shooting on his father-in-law's estate.

On Good Friday 1816 Roderick and Charlotte crossed from Dover to Calais with their own carriage and proceeded by easy stages to Paris. Many of the paintings previously displayed in the Louvre had been stolen and had now been returned to their rightful owners. Roderick, familiar with the gallery's previous contents, was, however, 'astonished to observe how rapidly the vacant places had been filled up, and not infrequently by good old Italian pictures, which had also been stolen, but which, not having been exposed in the Great Gallery, were not known to exist in France.'

They toured the sights of the city and Roderick attended a meeting of the Académie, which many years later was to enrol him amongst its foreign members. He met Georges Cuvier, Chancellor of the University of Paris, who talked of the influence that science could have on the working life of Man.

Leaving the capital, the couple took a leisurely journey through Dijon to Geneva. En route, Roderick started to make a point of meeting men of science and viewing their museums. In Geneva he made the acquaintance of Marc-Auguste Pictet, who had interests in geology, meteorology and astronomy. He had sustained intellectual contact between Britain and the rest of Europe during the Napoleonic Wars by means of his journal, the *Bibliothèque Britannique*. Roderick also met Augustin Pyrame de Candolle, Professor of Botany at Montpellier and later at Geneva.

The Murchisons rented a small villa on the north-eastern shore of Lake Geneva at Vevey, from where Charlotte's ancestors had come to England some hundred years earlier. They made many excursions in the surrounding area, Charlotte and some distant relations on horseback, while Roderick kept pace with them on foot. He made a number of long walking trips by himself, on one of which he covered 452 miles in fourteen days. On the last of these days he walked fifty-seven miles! On another outing to Mont Blanc, he took only three days to put 120 miles behind him. He gained great pleasure from these physical feats and his natural ability to grasp the main features of the countryside came to the fore. He described the Grindelwald glacier as a 'river of ice' and made copious notes on the processes employed at one of the Swiss salt mines.

Roderick and Charlotte were walking from Vevey along the shore of Lake Geneva to nearby Clarens, when they met Lord Byron. He had recently commemorated the captivity of the Protestant convert, François de Bonivard, who had opposed the Duke of Savoy, in his *The Prisoner of Chillon* (the castle farther round the lake beyond Montreux). That night there was a violent thunderstorm which Byron immortalised in his *Childe Harold's Pilgrimage*, written shortly afterwards.

The couple moved on to Genoa, where they kindled a passion for art. Roderick continued his walking expeditions, noting on one of them marine shells on the tops of hills, indicating to him that the region had once been under the sea. They reached Rome on 21 March 1817 and rented a house in the Via Condotti.

They visited numerous art galleries and churches, making elaborate notes on their contents. Roderick's journal showed a deep understanding and appreciation of the works. His comments on the Palazzo Colonna read: 'Four superb landscapes of Salvator Rosa (doubtful); marine views, with armed men and fishermen in the foreground. The light and distances have the light of Claude, the foreground less of the savageness of Salvator than usual. Two fine heads of Carlo Dolci, one St. Catherine, the other a saint chained. Some good heads of Guercino, and a fine small piece or two by Conca. Many good landscapes of Poussin in tempera, and one beautiful bluish landscape of Lucatelli, marine, with great depth: this is his best style. The Bella Cenci needs no description. Guido is more expressive here than in his fine exuberant Madonna above stairs. There are two little Claudes, and a Titian, etc. There are a good many pictures of the inferior and later Roman artists; some of these are pleasing. Gaetano Lapis (1776), a scholar of Conca; same light colouring, but no confidence in himself. His best picture here appeared to me a Lazarus with Christ (doubtful). The frescos of Stefano Pozzi in first room are bright and pretty (Turk smoking). The column of Bellona (twisted) of rosso antico, with Pallas on the top, very beautiful. A dead Christ by Franco Trevisani (d. 1746. Sc. Rom.), not Angelo Trevisani (Venet. Sc. same epoch). In this Christ the foreshortening is remarkable, the colouring Guidesco. He was a universal imitator.'

The most notable acquaintance that Murchison made in Rome was that of

Antonio Canova, regarded as the founder of a new neoclassical school of sculpture, who, four years earlier, had begun one of his most famous works, *The Three Graces.*

In early June, Charlotte contracted malaria and was so seriously ill that Roderick feared for her life. However by the end of the month, she rallied and they moved to Naples to benefit from the sea air. This move gave Roderick a chance to take a number of trips out to the islands, where he witnessed an eruption of Vesuvius. He later climbed the mountain at night to observe the showers of red-hot stones and the lava streaming out of the side of the cone. His notes, however, show that he was just an intelligent spectator without any particular geological interest.

In October, the couple returned to Rome to spend the winter there, during which they investigated the remains of temples and public buildings, including the Baths of Caracalla and the Roman Forum. Of the last Roderick wrote: 'Old Horace could not have enjoyed his evening walk there more than I do, and one great delight consists in the imagining that I behold some relics of those very buildings which he admired. Away then, ye cold sceptics who drive everything to such an extreme that at last ye begin to doubt whether ancient Rome did really exist here, or whether the Tiber may not have changed its course! They will tell you (even Nardin and others) that most part of the columns have been re-erected in subsequent ages on or near the spot where they had fallen or been pulled down. But, oh ye learned sceptics! What Pope, Antipope, or Goth, may I humbly crave, would ever have had the genius of architecture and the love of classical remains impressed so deeply on his mind that he should wish to raise up broken entablatures of colossal size, and mutilated columns, in order that he might be called a man of taste? If, therefore, none of these re-erections took place in the dark ages, which I think any reasonable man will allow, we can have little difficulty in proving that such attempts have not been made since the revival of letters in the fifteenth century. Private and public history are both silent on this point, whilst on a number of trivial little subjects, such as that Lorenzo di Medici robbed the Dacian captives on the Arch of Constantine of their heads, and other similar facts, we have abundant details.'

In March 1818, the Murchisons left Rome on a leisurely homeward trek, lingering for three weeks in Florence, where Roderick made copious notes on the art treasures there, being particularly critical of Michelangelo. They continued their journey via Bologna, Modena, Parma and Turin, to cross the Alps by the pass of Monte Ceneri, thence by Lyons to Paris and home.

They had spent over two years on the continent, during which Roderick had learned the rewards of intellectual pursuits rather than the frivolous way in which he had previously passed his time. In this Charlotte had played no small part. In fact he had tried her strength and stamina, as he chased energetically round churches and galleries, pursuing a new interest with which he had become absorbed.

They now had to make a decision as to where they would live. Charlotte had some income, but Roderick's collectable rents from the Tarradale estate, which should have been around £500 per annum, had dwindled to only £250. In August 1818 he sold the property to Baillie of Dochfour for £27,000. Charlotte's grandfather had just died. He had spent the last twenty years of his life in a sizeable eighteenth-century house, 21 Galgate, Barnard Castle, County Durham. Joined to number 21 by a graceful stone arch was number 19, which was probably the servants' quarters. Roderick and Charlotte decided to settle there. They were well received by the landowners of the county, but the rather boring life of visiting and receiving guests was no substitute for the intellectual pursuits which had excited them on their continental tour. Charlotte had a collection of plants and minerals but it was not extensive enough to show Roderick how stimulating real scientific study could be. He expressed some interest in politics by actively supporting the Tory candidate in an election for the county of Durham, but ended up being hounded by the voters and pelted with cabbages and rotten eggs.

Over the next five years, Roderick took up fox-hunting and became one of the leaders of the sport in the north of England, reflecting the pursuit of physical activity which formed such a significant part of his character. To the mortification of his wife, in 1822 he determined to move south to Melton Mowbray in Leicestershire, where he rented a house and kept eight hunters and two other horses for his wife and himself. He subscribed £50 a year to a pack of hounds. All this was more than he could afford but he speculated with some success in foreign bonds. To please his wife and to preserve some intellectual content in his life, he kept his daily hunting journal for the winter of 1822-3 in French.

During these years he wrote frequently to his younger brother, Kenneth, in the East Indies, expressing tender affection towards him and an interest in his affairs. Kenneth became Governor of Singapore and later of Penang. Roderick and Charlotte were also charged for a short time with the care of their little niece, Charlotte (whose mother had died), from whom they derived great delight.

Some forty years later, he wrote: 'As the time rolled on I got blasé and tired of all fox-hunting life. In the summer following the hunting season of 1822-3, when visiting my old friend Morrit of Rokeby [Hall, three miles south-east of Barnard Castle], I fell in with Sir Humphry Davy [President of the Royal Society], and experienced much gratification in his lively illustrations of great physical truths. As we shot partridges together in the morning, I perceived that a man might pursue philosophy without abandoning field-sports; and Davy, seeing that I had already made observations on the Alps and Apennines, independently of my antiquarian rambles, encouraged me to come to London and set to at science by attending lectures on chemistry, etc. As my wife naturally backed up this advice, and Sir Humphry said he would soon get me into the Royal Society, I was fairly and easily booked.

'Before I took the step of making myself a Cockney I sold my horses. The two best were put up at auction in the ensuing autumn, after dinner, at the Old Club at Melton, and were brought into the room after a jolly dinner, Maxse acting as auctioneer. In fact I threw them away, and Maker who bought the "Commodore," named him "Potash," as a quiz on me for taking so much of that alkali after our potations.'

It may well have been that Roderick's decision to sell his horses was one of prudent necessity, for, when they left Melton Mowbray he did not set up another household, but went to live with his parents-in-law at Nursted House. However, he still had a substantial independent income and he could, after all, continue to indulge in hunting with the Hambledon hounds and shoot pheasant in the grounds of nearby Up Park. He bought a new modestly-priced horse and then spent the summer shooting with friends in Scotland. It was as though he had forgotten his meeting with Sir Humphry Davy.

Chapter Three
Takes up Geology

However, in late 1824, Murchison was quite suddenly taken up with interest in science in general and geology in particular. This branch of science was considered at the time to be a most suitable vocation for a gentleman. Its protagonists became known as 'knights of the hammer'. Roderick and his wife moved up to London, renting No. 1 Montagu Place, half a mile north of where the Marble Arch now stands. He sold his horses, except for a pair which he kept for his wife's carriage.

On his rambles in the Alps and the Apennines he had come across marine shells in rocks high above sea level and the recollection of these had triggered questions in his mind. Advised to do so by Sir Humphry Davy, he attended lectures by Dr. Brande on chemistry and geology at the Royal Institution. He took full and careful notes from day to day. On one occasion when Dr. Brande did not give the lecture, his young assistant took his place, timidly at first but later with great success, achieving a round of applause. It was Michael Faraday and this was his first public appearance.

Murchison attended debates and heard papers presented at the then premises of the Geological Society of London at 20 Bedford Street, Covent Garden. The Society had been founded in 1807 by a small group of enthusiasts, with the resolution 'That there be forthwith instituted a Geological Society for the purpose of making geologists acquainted with each other, of stimulating their zeal, of inducing them to adopt one nomenclature, of facilitating the communication of new facts, and of ascertaining what is known in their science, and what remains to be discovered'.

In his *Life of Sir Roderick Impey Murchison*, published in 1875, Archibald Geikie says: 'Of the men on whom the progress of geology mainly depended at the time when Murchison joined them to become their life-long associate and friend, something should be said here. Some of the band of enthusiasts by whom the Geological Society of London was originated still lived, and took an active share in the Society's work. Among them were Greenough, the true founder and first President of the Society – amiable, yet shy, and somewhat hesitating in manner, full of all kinds of miscellaneous knowledge, obstinately sceptical of new opinions, a kind of staunch geological Tory, and playing the part of objector-general at the evening discussions; and Babington, a kindly, bland, and courteous veteran, who, well versed in the mineralogy of his time, had gathered at his house the few like-minded friends from whom the Geological Society sprang, who introduced the practice of discussing the papers read at the meetings, and who even when nearly fourscore years of age found a congenial occupation in the Society's museum. Other names which had long been associated with the progress of the Society still had an honoured place on its list. Such were those of Wollaston – admirable mineralogist, sternly upright in his search for truth, quiet, reserved, serious, looking like a Greek sage, and deservedly regarded as a general arbiter in the scientific world of London, yet, to those who were privileged with his more intimate friendship, fond of a joke and of a quiet corner in a pheasant cover, where his gun seldom failed to tell; Warburton – cautious and uncommunicative; Fitton – friendly and painstaking, an active leader in the affairs of the Society, but somewhat hasty in temper, and prone to what some of his colleagues thought "red-tape" formality, yet an admirable observer in the field, a most gifted debater, and one whose clear and elegant pen did good service to the infant science in popular journals, and whose house formed a pleasant centre for the geologists of the town; Conybeare – clear-headed, critical, full of quaint humour and wit; Buckland – cheery, humorous, bustling, full of eloquence, with which he too blended much true wit, seldom without his famous blue bag, whence, even at fashionable evening parties, he would bring out and describe with infinite drollery, amid the surprise and laughter of his audience, the last "find" from a bone cave; Leonard Horner – mild, unpretending, and deferential, yet shrewd and systematic, a valuable member of the council of management of the Society; Sedgwick – with his well-remembered hard-featured yet noble face, and eyes like an eagle's, manly alike in body and mind, full of enthusiasm, ready and graphic in talk, generous and sympathetic, often depressed by a constitutional tendency to hypochondria, yet, when in full vigour of health, shrinking from no toil, either at home or abroad, in furtherance of his chosen branch of science, and laying up year by year a store of facts and of brilliant deductions from them, which have given him one of the most honoured places in the literature of geology.'

Although the science of geology had started with the ancient Greeks, progress had been slow and, from the knowledge we have today, unacceptable by modern standards. The teaching of the Church was that the World was created in 4004 BC. This was based on a literal interpretation in 1650 of the Book of Genesis by James Ussher, a Protestant Irish prelate working in London. They also believed that all sedimentary rocks were the result of Noah's Flood in 3290 BC!

Abraham Gottlob Werner, an expert mineralogist of Freiberg in Saxony, had a strong following for his belief that the older rocks had precipitated from a universal ocean. His disciples were, not surprisingly, called the Neptunists. His estimate for the age of the Earth was something over a million years. He knew only the rocks in his own native region, where there were no volcanics (except isolated patches of columnar basalt capping the hills), and presumed that his theories applied to the whole globe. He stated that the rocks were all laid down in the same order, the unfossiliferous granites, gneisses and schists first, followed by what he called 'Transition' rocks - those with few fossils, the slates, limestones and greywackes (poorly sorted sediments with rock fragments in a mud matrix). Next came the highly fossiliferous sandstones and younger limestones, and finally the unconsolidated clays, sands and gravels.

James Hutton, on the other hand, had experience of extinct volcanoes in the area around his home in Edinburgh. His followers were known as the Vulcanists or Plutonists. He believed in uniformitarianism (paraphrased as 'the present is the key to the past' or that evidence in the rocks shows us that geological processes we see today have happened throughout the history of Earth). In 1785, he presented to the Royal Society of Edinburgh a sketch entitled *A Theory of the Earth*, or *An Investigation of the Laws observable in the Composition, Dissolution and Restoration of Land upon the Globe*. He used this as a basis for his famous work *The Theory of the Earth, with Proofs and Illustrations*, published in Edinburgh in two volumes later that year. Hutton introduced for the first time the idea of igneous rocks and their erosion over a vast period to form sedimentary deposits, which became consolidated and then in turn were uplifted again by volcanism. He realised that this would take a great deal longer than the 5,800 years since the Earth was supposed to have been formed and suggested that its history had developed across almost limitless time.

Probably unaware of the work of either of these important geologists was William Smith, the son of a country blacksmith, who had developed his pioneering ideas from his own observation. He was the first to realise that the strata were laid down in the same order right across Britain and that they could be identified by the fossils they contained. In 1799 he published a list of twenty-five strata in the region of Bath from the Chalk to the Coal. Two years later, he produced the first ever geological map of any country and steadily improved it until he was able to publish in 1815 his magnificently detailed *Delineation of the Strata of England and Wales with part of Scotland; exhibiting the Collieries and Mines, the Marshes and Fen Lands originally overflowed by the Sea, and the Varieties of Soil according to the variations in the Substrata, illustrated by the Most Descriptive Names*. This map, of which about a hundred copies are extant, measures six feet by eight feet six inches (1·8 by 2·6 metres). One was, until recently, hung by the eastern stairway of the premises of the Geological Society of London in Burlington House, Piccadilly, (Morton, 2001).

This was the essence of the development of the science of geology when Roderick Murchison attended his first meeting of the Society in January 1825. The Neptunists had lost ground to the Vulcanists, and Murchison soon saw that his time would be well spent determining the order of succession of Werner's 'Transition' rocks. Meanwhile, Poulett Scrope had claimed in 1822 that the valleys of central France had been cut out by running water. Murchison believed that valleys had been formed by major convulsions of the Earth's crust on a cooling globe. There was of course no concept of Continental Drift, which was not evenmooted until 1915 (by the German meteorologist and geophysicist, Alfred Wegener) and not widely accepted until United States Navy submarine observations of the bottom of the Pacific Ocean were released after the Second World War. Although the relative ages of fossils could be determined by the order of the strata in which they were found, their actual age had to wait for Ernest Rutherford and Frederick Soddy's proposed theory of radioactive decay in 1902 and its refinement by others in the following decade.

Murchison heard Charles Lyell, five years his junior, present his first technical paper (on the marl-lake at Kinnordy, Scotland), and in December 1825 read to the Society a paper entitled *Geological Sketch of the North-western Extremity of Sussex and the Adjoining Parts of Hants and Surrey*. Murchison and Lyell were to become the two most prominent British geologists of the mid-nineteenth century. For the most part their rivalry was friendly, but from time to time over the years Murchison showed an undue jealousy of the success of Lyell's theories. Meanwhile he had made not only the acquaintance but close friends of many famous people, including Dr. William Hyde Wollaston, a highly successful research worker in chemistry and optics, Professor William Buckland, first President of the Geological Society, Adam Sedgwick, the Woodwardian Professor of Geology at Trinity College, Cambridge, William Whewell, a fellow of the same college, Thomas Peacock, the poet and novelist, Charles Babbage, the mathematician who invented the first calculating machine, and others.

At this time William Buckland invited Murchison to hear some of his lectures at Oxford and took him out on horseback to Shotover Hill, three miles east of the city centre, where he spelled out for him the geological structure of the landscape. This fired Murchison's enthusiasm and, with his wife, he set out on a nine-week tour of the south coast of England from the Isle of Wight to Cornwall. Charlotte avidly collected fossils and made sketches of the more striking geological features, while Roderick exerted great energy in exploring the region's geology. In a quarry he met accidentally William Lonsdale, a veteran of the Peninsular War, who passed on to him much of his considerable knowledge of the fossils of the neighbourhood, particularly of corals.

Murchison became one of the two Honorary Secretaries of the Geological Society, replacing Charles Lyell, who at that time was fully occupied with his studies as a law student. In the spring of 1826, Murchison was elected a Fellow of the Royal Society of London, an honour rather more easily obtained then than it is now. He received encouragement from Dr. Wollaston and his old friend, Sir Humphry Davy, who, as President, 'explained to him that he had not been elected for his scientific work, but because he was a man of means and leisure and so might be expected to be a profitable Fellow of the Society' (Lyons, 1944).

Following his successful observations along the south coast, Murchison was encouraged to visit the coalfield of Brora, north-east of Dornoch in Highland, rather mysteriously in much younger strata than the usual Carboniferous deposits. On the way north, he met John Phillips, then the Curator of York Museum, which had a good collection of oolitic fossils. Phillips strongly recommended him to visit his uncle, William Smith, in Scarborough. Murchison and Smith took a boat trip together from Scarborough to Whitby. Smith was able to point out to him the principle results of his comparison of the oolitic and lias strata of Yorkshire with those of the south of England. Murchison was interested in establishing a connection between these Jurassic sediments and those at Brora, and he took note of the position of the outcrops of poor quality coal on the eastern moorlands of Yorkshire.

He and his wife continued northwards, but on reaching Edinburgh, turned westwards towards Arran and the Inner Hebrides. Here were rock structures quite new to him – schists, granite, rhyolite, basalt, gabbro, many dykes, and red sandstone. He visited Staffa (Fingal's Cave), climbed Ben Nevis, went half way up the Great Glen, then turned westwards through Glen Garry to Skye, where Charlotte found a large number of fossils. They were particularly useful in comparing the rocks of western Scotland with those of England. Later James Sowerby, publisher of *The Mineral Conchology of Great Britain*, named one of them after her – *Ammonites murchisoniae*.

They took most of the summer to traverse the western Highlands, visiting friends and relations, enjoying the scenery and shooting the odd grouse. When they did reach Brora, Roderick found his task easier than he had expected. He was able to recognise the similarities of the strata with the oolitic series of Yorkshire. They were mostly the Kimmeridge Clay that he had seen south of Scarborough and on the south coast of England, just north of Chesil Beach. So the coal was a local peculiarity. Again he collected some fossils, useful to confirm his findings and provide evidence for a paper he presented to the Geological Society entitled *On the Coal-field of Brora, in Sutherlandshire, and some other stratified deposits in the north of Scotland*. He sent a copy to William Smith, whose principles he had applied to the oolitic rocks.

The rapid solving of this problem gave Roderick and Charlotte time to go further north through Caithness (now Highland) and over to the Orkney Islands, before turning for home. From Inverness they cut across to Aberdeen and down the east coast. At St. Andrews they heard that Charlotte's father was seriously ill and proceeded rapidly by the mail coach back to Nursted House. In fact the old General recovered and lived for another ten years, dying on 29 March 1836 at the age of eighty-five.

****

Rotherhithe, on the south bank of the Thames, was a flourishing suburb with mills, wharves and factories. St. Katherine's, London and West India Docks were on the north side. To avoid a four-mile journey via London Bridge, the lowest river crossing at the time, it was thought desirable to build a tunnel under the river from Wapping. Marc Brunel, the brilliant French engineer, had conceived a tunnelling device which was jacked forward hydraulically as material was removed. Work started on the shaft for the tunnel (now the access to Wapping Underground station) on 2 March 1825. In January 1826 the Thames broke in, but the seepage was contained and work continued until well beyond the half-way mark. Leaks continued, however, and the workmen were finding china, wood and coal towards the top of the tunnel, indicating that it was dangerously close to the river-bed.

Dr. Buckland organised a party, which included Murchison and Charles Bonaparte (later Prince of Canino), to inspect the work. Murchison reported, 'The first operation we underwent (one which I never repeated) was to go down in a diving-bell upon the cavity by which the Thames had broken in. Buckland and Featherstonehaugh, having been the first to volunteer, came up with such red faces and staring eyes, that I confess I felt no great inclination to follow their example, particularly as Charles Bonaparte was most anxious to avoid the dilemma, excusing himself by saying that his family was very short-necked and subject to apoplexy, etc.; but it would not do to show the white feather; I got in, and induced him to follow me. The effect was, as I expected, most oppressive, and then on the bottom what did we see but dirty gravel and mud, from which I brought up a fragment of one of Hunt's blacking bottles. We soon pulled the string, and were delighted to breathe the fresh air.

'The first folly was, however, quite overpowered by the next. We went down the shaft on the south bank, and got, with young Brunel [Isambard], into a punt, which was to steer into the tunnel till we reached the repairing shield. About eleven feet of water were still in the tunnel, leaving just space enough above our heads for Brunel to stand up and claw the ceiling and sides to impel us. As we were proceeding he called out, "Now, gentlemen, if by accident there should be a rush of water, I shall turn the punt over and prevent you being jammed against the roof, and we shall then all be carried out and up the shaft!" On this C. Bonaparte remarked, "But I cannot swim!" and, just as he had said the words, Brunel, swinging carelessly from right to left, fell overboard, and out went of course the candles, with which he was lighting up the place. Taking this for the sauve qui peut, fat C.B., then the very image of Napoleon at St. Helena, was about to roll out after him, when I held him fast, and, by the glimmering light from the entrance, we found young Brunel, who swam like a fish, coming up on the other side of the punt, and soon got him on board. We of course called out for an immediate retreat, for really there could not be a more foolhardy and ridiculous risk of our lives, inasmuch as it was just the moment of trial as to whether the Thames would make a further inroad or not.'

****

Murchison spent the spring visiting at Oxford Dr. Buckland, and, at Lewes, Dr. Gideon Mantell, whose wife had reputedly in 1820 found the tooth of the first described dinosaur. Over the next twenty-seven years, he wrote no less than fifty-three letters to Mantell, and Charlotte wrote to him six times between 1825 and 1840 (East Sussex Records Office has these documents on microfilm). During 1826, Murchison also did some more field-work around his home near Petersfield, ensuring that he understood the full succession of the Cretaceous strata.

Adam Sedgwick had commanded Murchison's respect for some time, not only for his knowledge but also for his wit, charm and sense of fun. He had already distinguished himself in his understanding of older rocks and Murchison proposed to him that they go to the west coast of Scotland to complete his unfinished business with the red sandstones there. Some work had been done by Macculloch and others, but basically little was known of the geology of this region. Sedgwick was able to help Murchison to understand things which had puzzled him earlier. He taught him, among other things, to recognise the phenomenon of cleavage (the splitting of crystals along planes of weakness in the atomic structure of a rock).

While they worked their way, sometimes against adverse weather, through the Highlands, they made sure they enjoyed themselves at the same time, accepting Scots hospitality and merrymaking. On the way they had a few risky adventures, not the least of which was finding themselves in a leaky boat near Ullapool and Sedgwick having to bail it out with his hat. Geikie mentions another incident: 'His [Murchison's] mother, as we have seen, was a Mackenzie of Fairburn, born in the ancestral Tower. There had been a tradition in the district to the effect that the lands should pass out of the hands of the Mackenzies, and that "the sow should litter in the lady's chamber." The old tower had now become a ruin, and the two travellers turned aside to see it. "The Professor and I," says Murchison, "were groping our way up the broken stone stair-case, when we were almost knocked over by a rush of two or three pigs that had been nestling up-stairs in the very room in which my mother was born."'

They returned via Carlisle and Newcastle, visiting some of Murchison's old fox-hunting friends en route, to spend the winter in London.

****

The President of the Geological Society, Dr. William Fitton, was very demanding and Murchison, as one of the Secretaries, rather insubordinate; they fell out for some months, the rift being healed by much correspondence and the intervention of friends. Murchison had much else to do. He and Sedgwick were to produce two memoirs for the Society – one on Arran and the other on the conglomerates of the northern and eastern counties, but his friend was busy at Cambridge and delayed their completion. The first was read to the Society in January 1828, the second not until May, by which time Murchison had left for the Continent. The task of presenting the second part had been left to Sedgwick who split it into two, so large had it grown. Later in their lives they were able to admit that several errors had been made and that to expect to sum up the geology of Arran and the north of Scotland after only a few traverses was rather too ambitious.

In the winter of 1827-8, Murchison began to think about applying to the continent of Europe the same geological survey technique as he had used in Scotland. He persuaded Charlotte and his friend, Charles Lyell, to accompany him, and in April they set off. They looked first at the Paris basin, studying the alternation of freshwater and marine strata with Constant Prevost, who had surveyed the area in detail. In the city they met several important scientific figures, including

Georges Cuvier, the Chancellor of the University of Paris, and Alexandre Brongniart, Professor of Mineralogy at the Natural History Museum in Paris, who had together, in 1808, published their *Essai sur la géographie minéralogique des environs de Paris*. They also spoke to Nicolas Desmarest, an inspector of industries for the French Crown, who in 1763 had visited volcanoes in the Volvic area and the following year begun to prepare a map of them, returning several times to the region to ensure his observations were complete. He linked a sheet of black columnar basalt with the crater of one of the Puys, so proving it had been erupted from the volcano as a lava. He had also looked at the processes of erosion by which they were destroyed and had come up with the then novel conclusion that streams eroded their own valleys instead of flowing through gorges or lowlands which they found ready-made.

They went south to investigate the geologically-recently extinct (200,000 years) volcanoes of Auvergne and found one that Desmarest had missed! They had taken with them a memoir on the area by Poullet Scrope, and were invited to the home of Count Montlosier, who had devoted himself to the study of the volcanic rocks of the district. The party of four went out on horseback to look at the fresh cones, craters and lava streams. They spent the next six weeks exploring the region, noting in one instance where a lava flow had blocked a channel and diverted a stream. They climbed up the side of an old, silent volcano, looking down into a crater now carpeted with grass and wild flowers. They marvelled at the still perfect cones of the Puys, half expecting steam, smoke or sulphur fumes to burst out from them. All this made the basis of papers which would be read before the Geological Society on their return *On the excavation of valleys, as illustrated by the volcanic rocks of Central France*.

The party then turned east and south to follow the valley of the Rhône down to Montpellier, then across via Nîmes to Aix-en-Provence. On leaving Toulon, en route for Nice, Roderick suffered a bout of malaria, which weakened him for about three weeks, but he recovered more easily than Charlotte had done in Rome. Nevertheless he was able, with the guidance of a local conchologist, to scour the area for interesting fossils.

While at Nice, Murchison wrote an account of the tour to Adam Sedgwick, '[In Central France] we left various things undone, consoling ourselves that such a case was to be worked out by [you] next year. And here let me, by the way of parenthesis, invoke the philosophical spirit of enquiry which prevails at Cambridge, and urge you, who are almost our only mathematical champion, not to let another year elapse without endeavouring to add to the stock of your British geology some of the continental materials. Pray do it before you marry and settle for life; pray even do it before you bring forth that long-expected second volume on the Geology of England and Wales [William Conybeare and John Phillips's influential *Outlines of the geology of England and Wales* (only Part 1 of which had been published in 1822) being considered the first]; your comparisons will then have a strength and freshness which will quite electrify us.

'We met with splendid cases of basalt and trap [lava], rivalling in an antiquity of aspect our northern acquaintances, splendid proofs of the extraordinary amount of excavation in the valleys, two thousand feet or more of fresh-water strata, with apparently everything which characterizes even the older secondaries – red sandstones, grits, shales, an excellent cornstone, and beneath this lymneae and planorbes; little coal-fields – true chips off the old coal-block. In dust and insufferable heat, which have never quitted us since, we descended the Rhône. The only cool place we could find was Buckland's hyaena cave at Lunel [between Montpellier and Nîmes]. Our journey across to Aix en Provence was most interesting, and that place offered so much that we halted a week, our work being now reduced to four or five hours in the morning, from four to nine, and a little in the evening. We hope to show you twenty or thirty species of insects!! from the gypsum quarries there. In this city of idleness we have been pent up during ten days, not daring to travel into Italy with these heats: it has not rained one drop here for eight months.'

They had discovered many fossils, which Mrs. Murchison had carefully packed for them. The work no doubt stimulated Murchison's already excessive appetite for huge meals. In spite of his wife's pleadings for him to exercise moderation, he brought down upon himself chronic indigestion, which he tried to combat with pills.

They continued across northern Italy to Vicenza, where Lyell, having finally resolved to abandon law and devote himself entirely to geology, left them to go further south to explore more extinct volcanoes, examine their cinder fields and trace the effects of ancient earthquakes. On the island of Ischia, off the Bay of Naples, he discovered marine shells two thousand feet above sea level.

Murchison was not blessed with a great imagination, nor was he a profound thinker, however he was a keen-eyed and careful observer. He was full of energy and enthusiasm, rushing from site to site, whereas Lyell was rather more slow and methodical. This may have been why Lyell chose to go his own way! In his excellent booklet *Aspects of Murchison* (2001), Anthony Brook says that after this tour their careers diverged 'Murchison into unravelling the intricacies of the old hard "Transitional" rocks, whilst Lyell stayed with the Tertiary and developed fundamental principles. As [Leroy E.] Page [1976] clearly shows, Murchison, although recognised as one of the greatest geologists of his day and age, was nevertheless incandescent with astringent jealousy over Lyell's conceptual prowess and public honours. All his life he disparaged Lyell's innovatory paradigm of geology, and ensured he matched his rival every step of the way. Murchison came to personify the vigorous Science of Geology to the Victorian public, mainly as a role model for the hero in geology; on the other hand, Gideon Mantell considered him to be "too omnivorous of fame".'

The Murchisons then went on eastwards to Venice but they found the July heat oppressive, the temperature exceeding 30° C daily. They turned north into the

Alps. At Bassano, in the foothills, Murchison examined the secondary and tertiary rocks to provide material for a paper which he read to the Society the following spring. At Bolzano there were well-known earth-pillars – tall pyramids of stony clay, each with a stone or large boulder on the top of it. He surmised that they had been formed by 'powerful torrents coincident with the elevation of the chain'. At that time it was not known how far the glaciers had extended, nor was it realised that *they* had formed these pyramids.

At the little mountain village of Seefeld, they found bituminous schists containing so many fish remains that the locals had for generations heated pieces of the stone to obtain oil for their lamps and cart-wheels. This information made another subject for a subsequent paper for the Society.

They proceeded through the Brenner Pass, stopping frequently to collect rock samples and make sketches, finally dropping down to the Vorarlberg and into Switzerland. Now they were looking to establish the sequence of the rock formations. Near Stein-am-Rhein they explored the quarries of Öningen, famous for their collection of fossils of freshwater plants, insects and vertebrates, indicating a once warm, humid climate. There had been found there a skeleton at first gravely described as 'Homo diluvii testis' (a human witness of the Flood) but later determined to be that of a salamander. A doctor and silversmith of Stein had recently acquired a remarkable fossil on which Murchison counted twenty-three vertebrae. It resembled a dog or fox, possibly a wolf, and the doctor was asking £30 for it. Murchison expressed his intention of buying it, providing Cuvier in Paris confirmed its value. Charlotte crept in early the next morning, before the doctor was up, and made a sketch of it. Cuvier later said he thought it was a fox, and being an old fox-hunter Murchison was determined to acquire the first fossil of one! He wrote to the doctor from Paris and had it sent to him. He gave it to the British Museum where Richard Owen, later to become the most prestigious zoologist of Victorian England, pronounced it to be more like a civet than any other living animal, and named it *Galecynus öningensis*.

The Murchisons made their way slowly home via Basle, the Vosges Mountains and Strasbourg, observing the geology and visiting museums. By October they reached England, having been away six months. Roderick had worked tirelessly, having produced two memoirs and, jointly with Charles Lyell, three papers for the Society. The winter of 1828-9 was a busy one, with a lot of time spent on his secretarial responsibilities with the Society, but he still was able to fit in some field-work and some visits to friends. He made plans for a new foray into the Alps to determine their structure, this time in the company of Adam Sedgwick.

They set off in June via Bonn and Koblenz, then turning north-eastwards to Kassel and Göttingen, where they met two old Prussian geologist friends, Oeynhausen and von Dechen, before continuing over the Harz mountains to Halle and Berlin. En route they found the 'interminable grauwacke' rather tedious. Little did they know that in years to come their world-wide reputation would come from these rocks. They then turned south via Dresden and Vienna to the caves at Adelsberg and Trieste.

Their route home lay by the Austrian Alps to Lake Constance and Strasbourg. In Carinthia they were cordially received by the Archduke Johann, the most scientific prince in Europe. He showed them the waterfalls near the Nassfeld Pass, the washing out of gold at the village of Bockstein and mapped out for them the passes in the surrounding mountains. Later they found thick beds of good coal, large amounts of millstone grit and oolite, which they determined to be much younger than expected, contemporary with the Tertiary sands and clays in England. They were taken aback by the amount of erosion they witnessed, many fast streams carrying debris down to the Adriatic. During their travels they had made several useful contacts with geologists in Germany and France. The winter was again a busy one with the preparation of papers and administration of the Society.

In 1830, Murchison, with Mountstuart Elphinstone, John Cam Hobhouse (later Lord Broughton) and Robert Brown, set up under the guidance of Sir John Barrow, the constitution of the Geographical Society. Murchison became a member of the Council the following year and Vice-President five years later. He was first elected President in 1843 and subsequently occupied the Chair at intervals for fifteen years. He obtained for the Society a Charter of Incorporation from the Crown in 1859.

There had been a number of criticisms of Murchison and Sedgwick's reports in both British and foreign journals and it became clear that they should carry out more surveys in localities which it had been suggested did not reflect their findings. To this end, Roderick and Charlotte set out in June 1830 via Ostend, Antwerp, Brussels, Namur and Liège. En route they made new geologist friends. They went on via Cologne and Bonn, rapidly up the Rhine, then struck eastwards through Aschaffenburg, Bamberg, Bayreuth and Ratisbon to Vienna, stopping at all the museums on the way to see if they could cast any light on the structure of the Alps. At Bamberg they had the good fortune to meet Leopold von Buch, who had studied under Abraham Werner but later contradicted his teaching, accepting basalt as a product of volcanic activity. He had, in 1826, published the first coloured geological map of Germany in forty-two sheets. He had made important early studies of Alpine geology and discussed with Murchison the process of dolomitization (the transformation of limestone to dolomite by the addition of magnesium).

In Vienna, Murchison renewed his acquaintance with Archduke Johann and dined with Prince Clemens Metternich, who confided in him that he preferred science to politics, having obtained an honours degree in scientific studies, but was obliged to follow the latter because of his noble birth. He was interested in the application of geology to the development of the mineral wealth of Austria.

Murchison now made several excursions around Vienna, accompanied by Professor Paul Partsch, an active geologist from the city. He then went south-westwards to Graz and thence westwards into the Alps. He was detained at first by the Tertiary basins of Carinthia and their occasional thick masses of lignite, but he soon moved on to the Salzkammergut, where he hoped to throw light on the Tertiary strata of Gosau, with its peculiar assemblage of fossils, and the secondary rocks of the region.

The following year, Charlotte Murchison published in London a book of sketches entitled *The valley of Gosau in the Salzburgh Alps, drawn from Nature on Stone.* There were two impressions.

Murchison wrote to Sedgwick from Bad Ischl, 'O, what would I give that our sketch of the Alps was not out! I could make it so much more perfect in details and sections. I am working out the details of the upper beds (upper grits and marlstones of the Alpen-kalk), which by a charming accident I have got within half a mile here.' He was able to make four parallel sections near Hallein, with lias shells and enough fossils to prove them correct. He worked through the flanks of the Bavarian Alps, noting extraordinary inversions and contortions of the rocks, then turned homewards via Munich, Nuremberg, Gotha and Göttingen. Roderick and Charlotte left Rotterdam on 1st October, having achieved the aims of their journey, seen much new country and made many new acquaintances.

Late in 1830, before publishing all his recent findings, especially those bearing on English geology, Murchison went to Paris to compare a collection of fossils from Germany with those in the museums there. He made the acquaintance of Baron Alexander von Humboldt, the great explorer, who happened to be in the city. Humboldt had just returned from Central Asia, where he and his companions had examined strata which produced gold and platinum. They had also made magnetic observations and collected geological and botanical specimens.

Referring to his forthcoming presentation to the Geological Society, Murchison wrote the following letter, dated 28 January, 1831, to his friend Sir Philip Egerton: 'I am quite vexed that I should fire off all my Alpine crackers without your hearing the report of one. I finish on Wednesday next, when the whole of the meeting-room will be hung with sectional tapestry of the manufacture of Lonsdale [the Curator of the Society's collections] and Co., magnified from my smaller designs. If, therefore, you have any intention of being in town for the meeting of Parliament, being Friday, perhaps you can accelerate your movements (particularly as it freezes hard), and be with us; otherwise you will miss a golden opportunity of learning how much deposit took place between the periods of our English chalk and London clay, and throughout such extensive regions that I verily believe our case in Western Europe will prove to be the exception and not the rule. Besides this, I will warm you with basaltic eruptions which, though they only show the tips of their noses, have heaved up mountains of gneiss and granite against the greensand series, setting it, and the tertiary strata above it, all on end.

'I was out of town for a fortnight, shooting at Charles Lefevre's, and at Up Park about the Christmas time, since when I have been working like a slave, previous to quitting office – not with disgrace, however, as my friends are going to vote me into the President's chair, in which case I shall request you to be one of my councillors - a post well befitting so grave a senator. Our anniversary, when all the jollification and election take place, is the 18th February – so you may bow to the Queen in the morning, and to me at night.'

Some Fossils mentioned in the Text

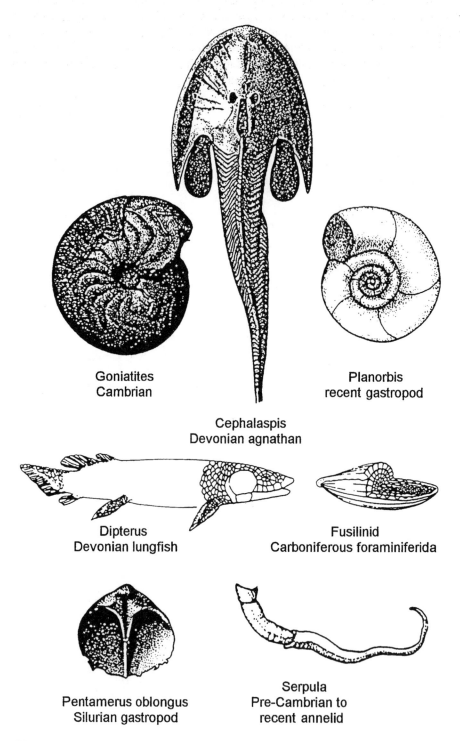

Goniatites
Cambrian

Planorbis
recent gastropod

Cephalaspis
Devonian agnathan

Dipterus
Devonian lungfish

Fusilinid
Carboniferous foraminiferida

Pentamerus oblongus
Silurian gastropod

Serpula
Pre-Cambrian to
recent annelid

Chapter Four
Grauwacke

'Grauwacke' was the name given by German miners to a particular group of rocks in what Abraham Werner had called the Transition series, i.e. those strata that had been formed at a period of the World's history transitional between the time when they were laid down (as he thought) all over the globe by chemical precipitation from a hot ocean and when conditions more like those of today allowed the existence of living creatures on Earth. Because little work had been done on this series and it looked to be uninteresting, the whole group came to be classed together under the rather unattractive name. It was very misleading, because the same name was given to rocks of different character and there was no distinction between similar rocks of different ages. This term does not seem to have the same meaning as what we today call 'greywacke', whose dictionary definition is 'texturally and mineralogically immature sandstones that contain more than 15% clay minerals. They may consist of angular to sub-rounded grains of quartz and feldspar, small pebbles, and a fine matrix of clay minerals, chlorite, and carbonate.' Presumably they can be of any age.

Charles Lyell's *Principles of Geology* devoted three hundred pages to the Tertiary deposits and only twelve lines to all fossiliferous rocks older than those just above the Coal. Leroy E. Page (1976) says, 'Murchison's review of Lyell's book in his anniversary address in February 1832 was, unlike that of Adam Sedgwick the year before, entirely favourable. Nevertheless, Lyell was displeased by Murchison's attempt to reflect some of the credit for Lyell's work on to himself by implying that Lyell's uniformitarian views and the "first idea" for his book had originated during their joint tour in 1828. Lyell "quietly protested" against this "great anachronism" by adding to the preface for his third volume a detailed account of the origin of his book, emphasizing that the "original MS.", or "first sketch", had been sent to the publisher the year before his trip with Murchison ....

'Lyell at this time contrasted himself favourably with Murchison, who he felt had "worked at science chiefly for the rewards". Later, apparently downcast about poor attendance at his King's College lectures, Lyell related his embarrassment at a well-meant, but typically patronizing, statement by Murchison to the Council of the Geological Society.

'Lyell's friends kept him aware that Murchison was continuing to claim "a much greater influence in the shaping of my geological career and in contributing towards the planning and execution of my work" than he considered Murchison "entitled to". After Murchison had persuaded the Editor of the Edinburgh Review to add a footnote on the subject to Scrope's review of the third edition of the Principles in 1835, Lyell drafted a new preface for his fourth edition in which he dissociated himself from Murchison in stronger terms than before. When Lyell sent the draft to him, Murchison objected, declaring that his advice had "induced" Lyell "to abandon the Law for Geology" and proposing that Lyell acknowledge that Murchison had "zealously promoted" his journey to Sicily, which would, Lyell replied hotly, "induce half the world to think you had contributed toward part at least of my pecuniary expences [sic]". In his letter Lyell rejected Murchison's claims and went over the facts of their relationship in detail. Murchison replied that he had been misunderstood and protested his innocence of the charge that he had, in private conversations, unduly magnified his role in Lyell's achievement. Lyell professed himself satisfied by Murchison's disclaimer and removed the objectionable passages from his preface. The preface, as printed, merely thanked Murchison and others for their "zealous co-operation" and displayed the clear intent of dating the beginnings of Lyell's uniformitarian beliefs as early as possible, giving credit for inspiration to Scrope's work.

'Although relations between Lyell and Murchison never again came so close to the breaking point as they did in 1835, Lyell privately expressed to Charles Babbage his contempt for Murchison during a serious controversy between Babbage and Murchison in 1838 and 1839. However Lyell refused to allow Babbage to draw him into a public dispute with Murchison.

'In 1839, in his Silurian System, Murchison turned against uniformitarianism and embraced catastrophism and the theory of a cooling earth.'

In the third edition of his *Geological Manual*, Sir Henry De la Beche (pronounced 'Beech'), who had described in detail the Secondary strata on the Dorset coast near Lyme Regis, included all the fossiliferous rock in the 'Grauwacke Group', which he suggested was 'a large stratified mass of arenaceous [sandy] and slaty rocks, intermingled with patches of limestone, which are often continuous for considerable distances.' He listed 126 genera and 547 species of fossils from the grauwacke rocks of Britain and foreign countries.

However, in his *Down to Earth – one hundred and fifty years of the British Geological Survey*, H.E. Wilson says, 'The conventional view of De la Beche as an innovator of geological science, trying endlessly to advance his infant survey for the benefit of society, must be amended somewhat when we read the comments of some of his contemporaries. Murchison, for instance, writing to Sedgwick: "De la Beche is a dirty dog, there is plain English and there is no mincing the matter. I know him to be a thorough jobber and a great intriguer". Or Ramsay, who noted that though he pretended to be open, frank and cordial, he was really " – an artful dodger, forever working for his own interest, heedless of that of others".'

A large part of Murchison's research had been carried out on the Secondary rocks, generally undisturbed in central and southern England, but strongly folded in the Alps. The brilliant insight of William Smith had enabled them to be identified and traced right across the country. Smith had also noted the Carboniferous deposits – as a surveyor his advice was frequently sought about where speculators might prospect for coal – and the Old Red Sandstone of Wales. Beneath these rocks, in Wales, Somerset, Devon, Cornwall, the Lake District and widely on the Continent, were enormously thick layers of relatively unexplored deposits, though yearly more and more fossil crinoids, corals, shells and other organisms found in them were being reported. As these rocks clearly did not predate the advent of life on Earth, it was rapidly becoming clear that that event was a lot earlier than had previously been thought. Remember that the Church objected to the study of geology and was teaching that all sedimentary rocks were the result of Noah's Flood just five thousand years before. It was, after all, logical from their point of view that animal life came after the creation of the Earth and these remains could not have sunk through rocks, so they must have been buried as the result of the only world-wide event chronicled in the Bible.

The fossils contained in the grauwacke were quite different from those found in the younger strata above them, so it became clear that, if the fossils were to be of any use, the order of succession of the rocks had first to be established. No one had been able to do this so far and Murchison, with his characteristic energy and enthusiasm, determined to attempt it. In the spring of 1831, he, Charlotte and her maid set off in a small carriage towards Oxford. Here he was received by his old friend, Professor Buckland, from whom he gleaned all he knew about the grauwacke. The Professor suggested that he would find a good illustration of the succession of the strata on the banks of the River Wye east of Builth Wells.

Further westwards, the Murchisons visited their old friend, the Rev. William Conybeare, one of the joint authors of the first volume of *Outlines of the geology of England and Wales*, apparently obtaining from him 'some good advice', although the second part of this work, intended to cover the stratigraphic sequence below the Old Red Sandstone was never published. They also received help from several local observers, in particular the Rev. Thomas T. Lewis, curate of Aymestrey (north-west of Leominster). Lewis had already determined the arrangement of rocks in his district and recognised their characteristic fossils, before Murchison had even begun to study the subject.

He also had available to him some of the findings of Arthur Aikin, who had been forced to abandon a survey of Shropshire in 1816 through lack of financial backing. He had published part of his discoveries in the *Transactions of the Geological Society*. Some four years later, Aikin gave up any idea of further publication and handed his notes and drawings to Murchison. These were acknowledged in the introduction to his *The Silurian System*, published in 1839, but in his *Arthur Aikin's mineralogical survey of Shropshire 1796-1816 and the contemporary audience for geological publications* Professor Hugh Torrens concludes that 'Murchison made a quite unjustifiable claim about the demise of

Aikin's Shropshire survey: "In truth at the early period when Mr. Aikin undertook the task it was almost hopeless to attempt to unravel the structure of Shropshire; for that county not only contains every sedimentary formation from the lias to the slates inclusive but is also rendered most complex by the numberless dislocations of the strata through the agency of volcanic rocks". Yet, as we have seen, Aikin's Proposals of 1810 already contained a highly creditable sketch of the structure of that part of the country from the Longmynd to the ridge formed by the Aymestry Limestone, and correctly separated and stratified from the unstratified volcanic rocks of the area. Murchison's suggestion that geology was not sufficiently advanced to investigate Shropshire in Aikin's main period of survey over 1809-1816 must thus be rejected – the use of fossils to identify the relevant rocks was already becoming known and was practised by Aikin in Shropshire. It is far more likely that the "hopelessness" of Aikin's attempt had financial and not scientific causes as inferred by Murchison.

'Although Aikin, according to Fitton, "disclaimed any previous knowledge of the stratigraphic system described by Mr. Murchison" in 1839, his work does demand a reassessment of this claim above, and [so does] Murchison's other claim that "no one was [previously] aware of the existence below the Old Red Sandstone of a regular series of deposits containing peculiar organic remains".

'Other work contemporary with Aikin's in Shropshire also suggests that Murchison's claims are overstated. John Farey (1766-1826) wrote on June 14, 1812: "Shropshire . . . I have not seen except in the distant horizon", yet within one month he was there in person. He visited Croft Ambrey Park limeworks, southwest of Ludlow, where he collected the index fossil *Pentamerus [= Kirkidium] knightii* from one of the three limestone rocks he was able to trace in the Ludlow area and which he discovered underlay the Clear Hill [= Clee Hills] Coal Measures to the east. Most significantly he correctly correlated this Croft Ambrey [= Aymestry] limestone with outliers of the same limestone on Tinkers Hill and Caynham Camp [= Cairbairn Hill] to the southeast of Ludlow. This was achieved within a two- or three-day visit and it is clear he was able to identify, separate and follow the discontinuous outcrops of limestone rocks later named Carboniferous, Aymestry and Wenlock Limestones in this area in this short time using the same techniques he had used elsewhere on other rocks in England. We must conclude that Greenough's claim in the introduction to this present paper has much to support it from the work of Aikin and Farey alone [that adequate enquiry alone was wanting to prove the existence of a succession of strata in the west of England, and in Wales].

'We must agree with Laudan that the small size of the audiences to which the geological maps and memoirs of Aikin, Smith, Greenough and Macculloch appealed are significant, and note that such projects were financially crippling unless subsidised in some way. We may leave the final word on this to John Farey, writing in January 1817 of an intended Mineralogical Survey of Perthshire to architect William Atkinson (c.1773-1839): "The art of mineral surveying is at present so much in its infancy that the public in general are not sufficiently

Fossils first described by Murchison

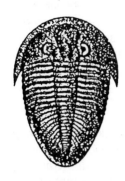

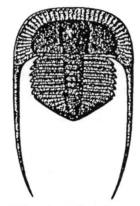

Basilicus tyrannus
Ordovician trilobite

Trinucleus fimbriatus
Ordovician trilobite

Megalaspidella murchisonae
Cambrian/Ordovician trilobite

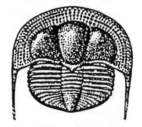

Salterolithus caractaci
Ordovician trilobite

Acaste downingiae
Silurian trilobite

Bumastus barriensis
Silurian trilobite

Ischadites koenigi
Silurian coral

acquainted with its value to give the same extended encouragement to its professors as they do to other arts of longer established *publication* of large mineral maps, but in prudence must look for real employers before commencing such works". He might well have had Aikin's Shropshire survey in mind while writing this.

'When Murchison started work fifteen years later over a much larger area he brought no new techniques to the unravelling of Siluria but boundless energy, sagacity and the necessary financial resources. The volte-face that had taken place in the appreciation of geology over the twenty years is shown by the fact that, instead of Aikin appealing in the newspapers to potential subscribers to come forward in 1811, we find the potential subscribers themselves appealing to Murchison to make his researches available in book form so that they could purchase copies. This was a truly remarkable revolution in the public attitude to geological publication and its financing.'

****

When Roderick and Charlotte finally reached Swansea, they turned northwards into the hills behind the coalfields, where, armed with Greenough's geological map of 1819 (which turned out to be rather inaccurate), they found the Transition rocks of South Wales. The strata dip steeply southwards here, so that as they descended into the valley of the Afon Tywi, they found under the Coal, the Carboniferous Limestone, then the Old Red Sandstone and finally near Llandeilo the Transition rocks they were seeking. Farther to the east, Murchison made the following observation: 'Travelling from Brecon to Builth by the Herefordshire road, the gorge in which the Wye flows first developed what I had not till then seen. Low terrace-shaped ridges of grey rock dipping slightly to the south-east appeared on the opposite bank of the Wye, and seemed to rise out quite conformably from beneath the Old Red of Herefordshire. Boating across the river at Cavansham Ferry, I rushed up to these ridges, and to my inexpressible joy found them replete with transition fossils, afterwards identified with those at Ludlow. Here then was a key, and if I could only follow this out on the strike of the beds to the north-east the case would be good.'

Hawley (1997) says, 'This is the classic version of Murchison's deliberate "discovery" of what were later to be named the Silurian rocks, as related to and recorded by Murchison's biographer and disciple, Archibald Geikie, in the later years of Murchison's life. However, in an analysis of the events surrounding that fieldwork tour of 1831, Secord [1986] argues that the Silurian discovery at Cavansham Ferry was not deliberate and that Murchison did not immediately realize the importance of what he had observed on that morning of July 11, 1831. Secord (1986, p. 55) suggests that it was not until some months later, reflecting on the notes of the summer's field season back in London, that Murchison made a decision that the main thrust of his geological endeavours should be directed toward the stratigraphical ordering of the greywacke.

'Nevertheless the location made sufficient impact on Murchison for him to make a careful note of the names of the surrounding hills in his notebook, thereby enabling its location to be properly charted at a later date. At some later stage he wrote in his field notebook "N.B. This was the first true Silurian".

'Whatever his original intentions, and whilst other locations in the Welsh borders assumed more important stratigraphical significance in Murchison's delineation of the Silurian System, it is clear that he came to regard his field work at Cavansham Ferry in the Wye valley as a major turning point in his scientific career. Given the magnitude of Murchison's influence over the development of geology in the nineteenth century and the widespread implications of the establishment of the Silurian System, Cavansham Ferry is therefore of great historical and cultural significance to the science of geology.'

Nevertheless, after reading an account of the discovery in manuscript five years later, Sedgwick wrote to Murchison, 'Starting then without any anticipation of ample harvest after enormous labours. This kind of statement takes not away one jot from your discoveries. As the passage now stands, you assume a prescience I don't believe real – and you set down as little better than a pack of

Fossils named after Murchison and his wife

Didymographus murchisoni
Ordovician graptolite

Murchisonia bilineata
Devonian gastropod

Megalaspidella murchisonae
Cambrian/Ordovician trilobite

asses everyone who had preceded you.' Secord (1986), quoting this, observes, 'Of course, these remarks are touched by more than a shade of jealousy, as by this date the definitive quality of Murchison's work was already evident. Sedgwick recognised that the discovery account had been aimed not only at predecessors like the provincial clergyman Lewis and the metropolitan specialist in Shropshire geology, Arthur Aikin, but also against himself. This made it all the more necessary that Murchison put his accomplishment in proper perspective. Otherwise Sedgwick feared appearing in the roll call of scientific worthies as little more than the leading "ass" in the pack.'

In his field notebook, Murchison refers to Trericket Mill. Duncan Hawley goes on to say, 'Trericket Mill is still located by the side of the road [SO 1125 4140]. Immediately to the southeast of the Mill, the road descends from an upper river terrace (c. 20-30m above river level) to a lower, narrower terrace about 10m above river level. The soil on the upper terrace is dark red, similar to that typically found covering the Old Red Sandstone, and no doubt Murchison observed this. By contrast, the soil in the bank which descends to the lower terrace is buff yellow with small exposures of grey Upper Silurian rock. It is here that Murchison decided he had "quit the Old Red Sandstone". Confirmation of the change in the underlying geology may well have been realised by his observation of grey beds forming a small waterfall in the Sgithwen Brook, which are easily seen from the bridge at Trericket Mill.'

The bridge to which he refers is not the one on the main highway, but a parallel structure on the service road leading to the mill. The old building, currently used as a bunk house and camping centre, stands on the west side of the A 470, a little way south of a narrow suspension bridge over the Wye, carrying a minor road across to the east side of the river. On the south side of this bridge can be seen the remains of a beaching area for small boats.

Cavansham Ferry was not a place on the river. The Welsh cafan means a boat and Shaan (Siôn) is equivalent to John, so the name was probably an anglicised version of the Welsh for 'John's boat'. Five hundred yards north-west of Trericket Mill, upstream from the modern suspension bridge, is a stretch of the river known as 'Boat Pool'. It is almost certain that it was here that Murchison crossed the river to make his first detailed examination of the Grauwacke. Just above this, the river flows over Hiro Rocks, prominent ledges of Upper Silurian strata, but Murchison looked first at the active Llanstephan quarries on the eastern side, in which there were numerous fossils, many of them new to him. Later he found he was able to use them to locate and correlate beds of the same age within complicated structures, an important conclusion. In subsequent years he returned to the area several times.

Beyond and above the quarries he expected to find the Old Red Sandstone lying conformably on the Grauwacke. He recorded a micaceous greenish hard grit sandstone dipping under it. He then recrossed the river and followed the road upstream, where he came upon the Grauwacke again in the Gromaen quarries, lying unexpectedly almost horizontally some hundred and thirty feet above the water. He found the Old Red Sandstone again at Erwood in the bed of a tiny tributary of the Wye, the Cletwr Brook, and concluded that the rocks had been folded into an anticline and Greenough's map was inaccurate. Further up the Wye he discovered at another ferry point (now replaced by Erwood bridge) Grauwacke slates on both banks. He was able to confirm this by the fossils they contained, similar to those he had found in the Llanstephan quarries.

Murchison worked his way to and fro through the Welsh and English border counties, as far north as the Cheshire Plain, with great success, for he had stumbled on some prime exposures of the strata and their conjunctions. He wrote, 'For a first survey, I had got the upper grauwacke, so called, into my hands, for I had seen it in several situations far from each other all along the South Welsh frontier, and in Shropshire and Herefordshire, rising out gradually and conformably from beneath the lowest member of the old red sandstone. Moreover, I had ascertained that its different beds were characterized by peculiar fossils. I had, therefore, quite enough on hand to enable me to appear at the first meeting of the British Association, which I had promised to join at York in October, with a good broad announcement of a new step in British geology.'

****

Roderick and Charlotte made leisurely progress from Wales to York. On the way, they visited old north-country friends and made copious notes of the geology en route and as far north as the coast of County Durham. On arrival in York, they were the guests of the Archbishop. Murchison preserved the following recollections of the meeting:

'FIRST MEETING OF THE BRITISH ASSOCIATION AT YORK,
27th September to 3rd October 1831

'This first gathering of men of science to give a more systematic direction to their researches, to gather funds for carrying out analyses and inquiries, to gain strength and influence by union, and to make their voice tell in all those public affairs in which science ought to tell, came about in this wise: - Assemblies of "Naturforscher" had been for two years in existence in Germany, having begun in Hamburg. Thereon Sir D. Brewster wrote an article in the Edinburgh Philosophical Journal suggesting that such a meeting should be tried in Britain. On this the Rev. William Vernon (afterwards Vernon Harcourt), the third son of the Archbishop of York, and a Prebendary of York, not only made the real beginning by proposing that we should meet at York, but by engaging his father to act as a patron, and by inducing Earl Fitzwilliam to be the President, he gave at once a locus standi and respectability to the project. But he did much more; for he elaborated a constitution of that which he considered might become a Parliament of Science, such as Bacon had imagined, and was thus our lawgiver.

'The project thus elaborated having been transmitted to me in London in the spring of 1831, when I was President of the Geological Society, I at once eagerly supported it. Nay, more, I wrote and lithographed an appeal to all my scientific friends, particularly the geologists, urging them to join this new Association. But notwithstanding my energy, the scheme was for the most part pooh-poohed, and, among my own associates, I only induced Mr. Greenough, Dr. Daubeny, Sir Philip Egerton, and Mr. Yates, to follow suit. John Phillips of York, the nephew of William Smith and the Curator of the York Museum, had very much to do in the origin of this concern, for he co-operated warmly with William Vernon, and, when we got together at York, was the secretary and factotum. He had previously corresponded with me in London, and stimulated me with a ready-made prospectus. I may say that it was the cheerful and engaging manners of young Phillips that went far in cementing us; and even then he gave signs of the eminence to which he afterwards arose in the numerous years in which he was the most efficient assistant-general-secretary of the body, until when, as the distinguished Reader of Geology in the University of Oxford, he presided over the British Association at Birmingham.

'When, however, we were congregated from all parts, the feebleness of the body scientific was too apparent. From London we had no strong men of other branches of science, and I was but a young President of the geologists; from Cambridge no one, but apologies from Whewell, Sedgwick [who was busy among the rocks in North Wales], and others; from Oxford we had Daubeny only, with apologies from Buckland and others. On the other hand, we had the Provost of Trinity College, Dublin, Dr. Lloyd, Dr. Dalton, from Manchester, and Sir David Brewster from Edinburgh. Thus there was just a nucleus which, if well managed, might roll on to be a large ball. And admirably was it conducted by William Vernon, for, after opening the meeting in an earnest, solemn manner, the good Lord Fitzwilliam handed over the whole control to Harcourt and left us.

'On my own part I had plenty of matter wherewith to keep my geological section alive, as, besides those I have mentioned, we had a tower of strength in old William Smith, the Father of English Geology, and then resident at Scarborough; James Forbes, Tom .... the mineralogist, and Johnston the chemist from Edinburgh, to say nothing of Harry Witham of Lartington (now an author on fossil flora), and others, including William Hutton of Newcastle-on-Tyne, then strong upon his "whin-sill." After all, however, we were but a meagre squad to represent British science, and I never felt humbler in my life than when Harcourt, in his opening address, referred to me as representing London!

'Indeed, William Conybeare, afterwards Dean of Llandaff, had quizzed us unmercifully, as well as W. Broderip and Stokes, and other men of science. The first of these had said, that if a central part of England were chosen for the meeting, and the science of London and the south were to be weighed against the science of the North, the meeting ought to be held in the Zoological Gardens of the Regent's Park! It required, therefore, no little pluck to fight up against all this opposition, and all I can claim credit for is, that I was a hearty supporter of the scheme – coûte que coûte.

'This first gathering was in short much like what takes place at small Continental meetings – we had no regular sections, but worked on harmoniously with our small force in cumulo. The excellent Archbishop was of great social use, and gave a dignity to the proceedings, whilst Lord Morpeth, then the young member for Yorkshire, incited us by speeches as to our future. It was then and there resolved that we were ever to be Provincials. Old Dalton insisted on this – saying that we should lose all the object of diffusing knowledge if we ever met in the Metropolis.

'With all our efforts, however, we might never have succeeded had not my dear friend Dr. Daubeny boldly suggested (and he had no authority whatever) that we should hold our second meeting in the University of Oxford!! It was that second meeting which consolidated us, and enabled us to take up a proper position. Then it was that, seeing the thing was going to succeed, the men of science of the metropolis and those of the universities joined us.'

Murchison had not had time to prepare a paper on his recent discoveries, but he displayed some maps he had used during the summer, on which he had coloured 'the Transition Rocks, the Old Red Sandstone, and Carboniferous Limestone', which strongly suggested that he was some way towards unravelling the relationships of the Transition rocks. Earlier that year, he had come across William Gilbertson, a 'little druggist' of Preston, and he was pleasantly surprised that he attended the meeting. Murchison introduced him to the assembly in an impromptu lecture 'with all the éclat he merited'. Gilbertson had amassed a magnificent collection of limestone fossils, which he had made available to James Sowerby, for illustrations in his *Mineral Conchology*, and which was to prove invaluable to John Phillips for his *Illustrations of the Geology of Yorkshire: Part II, The Mountain Limestone District*.

After the meeting, Roderick and Charlotte travelled in their small carriage to visit William Smith at Scarborough and to have another look at the coastal rocks. In a letter to John Phillips, Roderick said, 'I have had a nice field-day with your uncle at Hackness. What is your opinion, your real opinion, as to what I or my friends could really do for him (i.e. for his benefit)? On his return to London, Murchison wrote again to John Phillips: 'You know all my heart's desire for our good old father in geology. I propounded the same (as expressed to you) to the Council of the Geological Society at our first meeting in November, and I only waited for the gathering of the men of office to sound Lord Morpeth on the feasibility of my plan, and, if approved of by him, then to throw in a strong memorial to the Government. Judge of my delight then, when I found that Lord Morpeth had anticipated my wishes, and had already written to Lord Lansdowne, arguing Smith's merits, and asking for a small pension. This application I was asked to second, which I have done by letter a few days ago to Lord Lansdowne; but in doing this I have deviated so far from the original request, as to point out to Lord L. that Mr. Smith was still capable of doing the state a good service. I went into an exposé of the whole thing, and proposed the creation of a new appointment, with some such title as "Geological Colourer of the Ordnance Survey Maps" – thereby meeting all the objections of the Humists [he may be referring here to a small group who considered themselves and their friends a cut above everybody else] which might be directed against sinecure places or pensions, but which could not hold good with respect to an office so connected with the development of the mineral wealth of the country as that which I have suggested. We shall see what the Lords will do, and in the meantime we had better say nothing of it to Smith.'

Very shortly afterwards the Government granted William Smith a pension of £100 a year without stipulating that he should colour any Ordnance Survey maps (Morton, 2001 p.129).

Murchison spent the winter enthusiastically and successfully chairing the Geological Society. On 17 November he wrote to Dr. Whewell, Professor of Mineralogy at Cambridge: 'We had a capital meeting last night. 1st, A memoir on the gigantic Plesio of Scarborough. 2d, Old Montlosier on Vesuvius, which drew out a long and lucid explanation from Neckar de Saussure; Lyell, Buckland, Fitton, Greenough, De la Beche, and others being orators. Buckland filled up all the parts wanting in the Plesio, and perfected a monster for those who in a snowy November night were disposed to nightmare.'

****

Roderick and Charlotte had moved to No. 3 Bryanston Place, north-east of the Edgware Road, in 1826, and now hosted a number of gatherings to which they invited both scientific men and those of rank and fashion without such interest. This had an important influence on the position of science in society.

In the autumn of 1831 a keen battle developed over candidates for the Chair of the Royal Society and Murchison involved himself with some ardour. He afterwards wrote: 'On the retirement of Mr. Davies Gilbert from the chair, a certain clique in the Society got up the notion that the Duke of Sussex would be the best person we could fix upon. As soon as the plot got wind, the indignation of all the real men of science knew no bounds, and they resolved to start Herschel [the astronomer son of Sir William, Sir John, who had five years earlier won the Gold Medal of the Royal Astronomical Society] as an opponent to the Royal Duke. We subscribed our names to a public protest; about eighty or ninety names were appended, including those of nearly all the notable and working men in science. It was resolved to beat us, and the greatest influence was used politically, royally, and socially to bring up voters for the so-called royal cause. I became an active canvasser for Herschel.

'At that time the Royal Society was very differently composed from what it now is. Any wealthy or well-known person, any M.P. or bank director, or East Indian nabob who wished to have F.R.S. added to his name, was sure to obtain admittance, by canvassing and by being elected at any ordinary meeting. The consequence was that over all that class of our body the Royal and Government influence of the day was overpowering, and even Lord Holland, though the gout was on him, was carried up into our meeting room, where he had never been before, to vote for his royal friend!

'I stood at the top of the stairs at Somerset House, doing my best to catch a vote as any friend ascended. We were beaten by 119 to 111. Many persons who had seen our public declaration had felt so sure we should be victors that they did not come up from the country. But so it was. The election over, the good Duke found himself in a dilemma. He wisely saw that he could not govern the Society if he could not make up a better Council than he came in with in 1830. He therefore resolved to choose his advisers from among those who had stoutly opposed him, and who in fact mainly represented the science of the body. Overtures were made to myself, and I deemed it to be my duty to accept office under a Prince who could act so liberally and kindly towards his opponents.'

In his address to the Geological Society in February 1832, in summing up the progress of geology at the time, Murchison was able to cite Adam Sedgwick's work in Cumberland and Westmorland, Joshua Trimmer's discovery of marine shells on Moel Tryfane in Wales, and three recently published books, *Fossil Flaura* by John Lindley, Professor of Botany at University College London, written jointly with James Hutton, John Macculloch's *System of Geology* (based solely on mineralogy, as though William Smith had never lived!) and the second volume of Charles Lyell's *Principles of Geology*.

****

Murchison spent the summer resurveying the 'Transition Rocks' in Wales and the English border counties. He determined to plot them, but the Ordnance Survey of the country was far from complete (the first sheet having been published only in 1801) and he had some difficulty in finding suitable maps. This, however, meant that he had to explore many obscure sites, some of which turned out to hold the key to the geological structure of the district.

On his return, he wrote to Sir Philip Egerton: 'I have done a fine stroke of work. I have coloured up all the Ordnance Maps I could procure, describing a zone of about twenty or thirty miles in breadth, from the Wrekin and right bank of the Severn to the mouth of the Towey, and I hope to show you four or five distinct natural fossiliferous formations of great thickness in our neglected "grauwacke", in which I have got abundance of fossils – many quite new; indeed I have fished some out of the genuine Old Red Sandstone which overlies all my system.'

Throughout the winter, he was very busy attending to his duties as President of the Society and sitting on a number of committees for dispensing appreciation of good works, yet found time to pursue country sports as the guest of several landed friends. Probably the most important event to require his attention was the founding of the Geological Survey, over which twenty-two years later, he was to preside. Henry De La Beche had been appointed, in connection with the Ordnance Survey, 'to affix geological colours to the maps of Devonshire, and portions of Somerset, Dorset, and Cornwall'. He later became Director of the Geological Survey.

Chapter Five
The Silurian System

Around 500 million years ago, what is now England and Wales lay at about 70° south of the Equator. A shallow sea covered almost all of Wales except its south-east corner and spread as far as a north-east/south-west line across the north Midlands to Cleveland. Shelly sediments marking the shoreline are traceable today. The Iapetus Ocean was closing erratically, giving rise to widespread volcanic activity, a lot of it underwater, producing pillow lavas. There were great thicknesses of volcanic lavas and ashes over Wales, together with ordinary marine sediments. Over the next sixty million years southern Britain moved some 1750 miles (2800 km.) northwards and sediments about 7500 feet (2286 metres) thick were deposited. It was these that formed the Silurian rocks. Planktonic-like animals called graptolites evolved strongly during the period and made it possible for careful observers to differentiate between the strata and determine their relative ages. It was into this difficult arena that Murchison threw himself. He worked downwards from the Old Red Sandstone, while his friend Sedgwick worked upwards from the Cambrian.

There was a preconceived opinion, based on inadequate observation, that few organic remains were likely to be detected below the Old Red Sandstone, the lower rocks having been altered so much that evidence of their origins had been obliterated. It was expected that there could be no extension of identification by fossils in these older strata. Macculloch, Greenough and Sedgwick had studied these ancient rocks and found no complete sequence of fossiliferous strata beneath and connected with the Old Red Sandstone in Scotland, the Lake District or Yorkshire. Sedgwick tried to correlate the rocks on the basis of their colour and texture alone (lithostratigraphy). No one was aware that an unbroken fossiliferous series did occur in Wales. Just to complicate matters there were numerous intrusions of volcanic origin (trap rocks) – basalts, greenstones, porphyries, and syenites.

It was not too surprising that the Lower Silurian became the subject of dispute between Murchison and Sedgwick, as we shall see, but after their deaths it was, from his interpretation of the structure of the Southern Uplands of Scotland, identified fully by Professor Charles Lapworth. By identifying and differentiating graptolites in the strata he showed that Murchison's Lower Silurian and Sedgwick's Upper Cambrian were one and the same. In 1879 he proposed to rename the period the Ordovician, after a local tribe, the Ordovices. Although widely recognised in Europe from the 1880s, this was not formally accepted by the British Geological Survey until the early 1900s.

Murchison's two-year tenancy of the Chair of the Geological Society enhanced his standing in the scientific world and developed his character so that he could carry off his position particularly well. He did not yet fully appreciate the significance of his work on the 'grauwacke'. Many new fossils appeared in the Silurian period, including lamellibranches (comparable to the modern cockle or oyster) and cephalopods (ancestors of the cuttle-fish and pearly nautilus). Murchison presented another paper to the Society, which, albeit partly erroneous, was a first attempt to classify these rocks. He listed: Upper Ludlow Rock; Wenlock Limestone; Lower Ludlow Rock; Shelly Sandstones, 'which in Shropshire occupy separate ridges on the south-eastern flanks of the Wrekin and the Caer Caradoc'; Black trilobite Flagstone, whose 'prevailing trilobite is the large Asaphus Buchii, which, with the associated species, is never seen in any of the overlying groups'; and Red Conglomerate Sandstone and Slaty Schist, several thousand feet in thickness. In fact he had confused the Wenlock Limestone with that that he had found fifteen miles farther south at Aymestrey and as a result placed the Lower Ludlow Rock below instead of above the Wenlock (see p. 170).

On his expeditions he lodged mainly at inns, but occasionally stayed with friends, often the local gentry. However, he found that he achieved only half as much work if he did so! One particular friend, Thomas Frankland Lewis, suggested that he should not restrict himself to presenting his findings to the limited audience of the Society, but should make them known to a wider public. This idea was warmly supported by Lord Clive of Powis Castle and Murchison promised him that he would go ahead with publication of a book. Within months, Lord Clive was able to assure him of at least eighty subscribers. However he wrote to John Phillips, saying that, although he had spent seventeen weeks studying the rocks, he was not yet ready to venture into print on a subject on which nobody else had written a line. He also said, 'Each succeeding year in which I propagate the principles of our craft, and enlist raw recruits in provinces where the sound of the word geology was never heard before, I find on revisiting my fields of battle that my aides-de-camp have collected facts, and facts alter preconceived notions.'

While Sedgwick was looking at rocks of similar age in Cumberland, Murchison spent the summer of 1833 continuing his surveys right across South Wales. He was encouraged by George Greenough, a one-time Chairman of the Society, John Phillips, now Professor of Geology at King's College, London, and particularly by the Society's Curator, William Lonsdale, whose help and advice he readily acknowledged. Murchison was able to produce the first published table of the Transition rocks of England and Wales, which he called the Upper Grauwacke series. Under the Old Red Sandstone he placed the Ludlow Rocks (2000 feet), subdivided into the Upper Ludlow, the Aymestrey and Sedgeley Limestone and the Lower Ludlow. Then came the Wenlock and Dudley Rocks (1800 feet), differentiated into Limestone and Shale, followed by the Horderley and Mayhill Flags, later named Caradoc (2500 feet), Sandstone Grits and Limestones. Finally there were the Builth and Llandeilo Flags characterised by *Asaphus buchii* (1200 feet), and the rocks of the Long Mynd and Gwastaden (many thousands of feet thick and described as unfossiliferous).

In 1834, Murchison let it be known that he was preparing a substantial book on the subject, but a further four years' work was going to prove necessary before it was actually published. Sedgwick had moved his surveys into North Wales, and they now got together to crosscheck each other's work and agree boundaries for their researches. They worked in unison through Hereford, Brecon, Carmarthen, Montgomery and Shropshire. Murchison learned from Sedgwick what he had gleaned a couple of years earlier from the Berwyn Mountains in southern Denbighshire (now Clwyd). He had, for example, found a repetition of his Llandeilo 'black flags' on the east side of them. This convinced Murchison that his groups of rock tied in with Sedgwick's discoveries to the north. He later published this concept without protest from Sedgwick, but many years later friction developed between the two, when time had blurred their memories.

They climbed to the top of the Berwyns from the east and Sedgwick explained that they were standing on slate immediately above the Bala Limestone (his upper base-line), which dipped steeply to the west. It reappeared, dipping to the east, at Meifod, thirteen miles to the south-south-east, and his conjecture (later to be proved correct by the Geological Survey) was that this suggested an eroded anticline. Murchison had just placed the Meifod Limestone in his Caradoc formation in the middle of his Lower Silurian series and the similarity of fossils between the two seemed to confirm the connection. Neither realised at the time the huge overlap of their respective subject strata, because the premise from which they started was that all of Sedgwick's rocks were beneath those of Murchison. They were unable in the short time available to find enough petrographic evidence to refute this and they discounted the palaeontological clues.

Sedgwick's account of their work together was somewhat different from Murchison's. He wrote, 'There were early difficulties, both physical and palaeontological, in distinguishing the Lower Silurian from the Upper Cambrian groups, and in fixing their true geographical limits, and it was partly in the hopes of settling such points of doubt that in 1834 I went, during six weeks, under my friend's personal guidance, to examine the order of succession as established by himself in the typical Silurian country. Beginning therefore at Llandeilo, and ending the first part of our joint work at Welsh Pool, we examined many of his best sections. Occasionally, while he was working out minute details, I spent some days in collecting fossils. . . . I believed his sections, so far as I saw them, to be true to nature; I never suspected (nor had he then suspected) any discordancy or break of continuity amongst his typical rocks from the Upper Ludlow down to the Llandeilo groups. I adopted all his groups, I may say, with implicit faith, never dreaming of a chance (during a rapid visit) of correcting those elaborate sections on which he had bestowed so much successful labour. . . .We never examined or discussed together the Silurian base-line in the country south of Welsh Pool; and whatever be the merit or demerit of the base-line afterwards published in the map of the 'Silurian System' belongs exclusively to my friend. As to this base-line, I never gave nor had I an opportunity of giving any opinion, either good or bad. . . . North of Welsh Pool we reached a country (east of the Berwyns) with which I was previously acquainted. . . . My friend now made use of and interpreted some of my field sections of 1832. . . . I guided my friend (as he in his Silurian country had guided me) over the Berwyn chain to the Bala limestone, along the high road from Rhaiadr to Bala. We made no mistake in the section. . . . My friend then declared that the Bala limestone was no part of his Silurian system.'

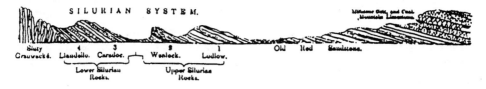

The first Silurian Section

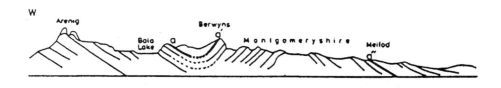

Sedgwick's traverse section across the Berwyns in 1832, illustrating his tentative correlation between the Bala Limestone and the beds near Meifo

In the autumn, Sedgwick recommended Murchison for a Royal Medal of the Royal Society, endorsing the accuracy of his work from 'a personal examination of a considerable part of the country described by Mr. Murchison'.

Reporting in the *Journal of the Geological Society* eighteen years later, Murchison said 'I believed it [the Bala limestone] to plunge under the true Llandeilo flags with Asaphus Buchii which I had recognized on the east flank of that chain. Not seeing, on that hurried visit, any of the characteristic Llandeilo Trilobites in the Bala limestone, I did not then identify that rock with the Llandeilo flags, as has since been done by the Government surveyors.'

Sedgwick then claimed that classifying the Bala rocks as underlying all the Silurian groups was an error, since they should be identified as the equivalent of the Caradoc rocks in the Lower Silurian series. He blamed Murchison entirely for this error, which in fact was hardly avoidable at the time. This accusation was unfair, because even if Murchison initiated the error, Sedgwick had adopted it and believed it for years, and evidence existed in his own territory to put things right at once. Sedgwick said in 1855 in *British palaeozoic fossils*, 'A single traverse from Glyn Ceiriog to the northern end of the Berwyn chain would have settled this question on evidence not short of a physical demonstration. But we did not make this traverse.' Sedgwick's letters suggest that he was clearly under the impression that the rocks he had surveyed in Wales were older than those of Murchison. In February 1833 he had written to Murchison, 'The upper system of deposits, with its subdivisions, is as plain as daylight, and entirely under your set.'

The 1834 meeting of the British Association was held in Edinburgh and both Murchison and Sedgwick attended it. Afterwards, Murchison wrote to Sir Philip Egerton, 'The meeting was most successful in every way. .. . .I may say, without vanity, that we geologicals were all the fashion, and engrossed by far the greater share of attention. [Louis] Agassiz [Professor of Natural History at the University of Neuchâtel] has pronounced that not one of the fossils of the Burdiehouse limestone are reptiles, but all belong to fishes. You will be amused to read old Buckie's lecture, given two nights before Agassiz made his decision against the reptiles, for in it the reptiles made a grand figure. My fishes in the Old Red are baptized Cephalaspis, from their horse-shoe heads. . . . I was a day at Lord Melville's, after which Sedgwick and self moved on together to Sir John Hall's at Dunglass to look at St. Abb's Head and the Siccar Point, both famous by the writings of Hutton, Playfair, and Hall. Whilst at Dunglass I fell in with my old friend Lord Elcho, who has set up a very crack pack of fox-hounds, and he so tempted me with the offer of a mount on his best nag, that I could not refuse; and I am still suffering from the stiffness incident to this frolic, not having been accustomed to screw to my seat for the last ten years. Sedgwick and myself explored the headland together, and in the boat we had with us our host, Sir John Hall, and Archibald Alison, a clever young Scotch advocate, who made sketches of the rocks in my notebook.'

Murchison readily acknowledged the help he received from friends living amongst the grauwacke, even from children who collected fossils for him. He had now learned enough to divide the rocks into four distinct formations, each defined by mineral and fossil content. It was clear that the name grauwacke, which did not differentiate between fossiliferous and barren rocks, was now far too misleading. A new name was needed and Murchison wrote, 'At this time I proposed the term "Silurian," and it came about this way. My friend, the eminent French geologist, Élie de Beaumont, seeing what a clear classification I had made out by order of superposition and characteristic fossils in each descending formation, earnestly urged me to adopt a name for the whole of the natural groups. Seeing that the region in which the best types of it occurred was really the country of the Silures of the old British King Caractacus, I adopted that name [Silurian]. I had seen that all geological names founded on mineral or fossiliferous characters had failed to satisfy, and that fanciful Greek names were still worse. Hence it seemed to me that a well-sounding geographical term, taken from the very region wherein the classification had been elaborated, and where every one might go and see the truthfulness of it, was the best.'

Murchison first published this new name in 1835 in the *London and Edinburgh*

Philosophical Magazine. He defined two major subdivisions of the system, the Upper Silurian (the Ludlow and Wenlock beds), and the Lower Silurian (the Caradoc sandstones and the Llandeilo flags). He had selected names from places where examples of each stratum, with its characteristic fossils, were best observed. He said, 'The term "transition" might indeed have been retained, if for no other reason than to impress upon foreign geologists, (the Germans particularly,) how vast a difference exists between the geological horizon of the mountain or carboniferous limestone and that of the limestones of Ludlow and Wenlock, which are not only separated by many thousand feet of strata from the limestone of the carboniferous system, but, further, contain an entirely distinct class of organic remains.' He went on, 'In various memoirs read before the Geological Society I have described these rocks as "fossiliferous grauwacké," but this term is in reality a misnomer, as the group contains few if any strata of the true grauwacké of German mineralogists. But whilst this system contains no such beds, it is underlaid and sometimes in discordant stratification, by a vast series of slaty rocks, in which much genuine grauwacké is exhibited. It was therefore manifest that if used at all in geological nomenclature, the term "grauwacké" must be rejected as inapplicable to the first great system below the old red sandstone, and restricted to rocks which were now proved to be of much higher antiquity. My friend Professor Sedgwick will doubtless soon dispel the obscurity which hangs over these grauwacké rocks, with which his labours in Wales and Cumberland have so well enabled him successfully to grapple ....

'I further propose that the system be subdivided into "Upper" and "Lower Silurian rocks," the former embracing the deposits of "Ludlow" and "Wenlock," the latter those of "Caradoc" and "Llandeilo." By this arrangement the observer will not be embarrassed when he finds that certain typical strata have disappeared. Thus, for instance, when the zones of limestone thin out, by which the formations of Ludlow and Wenlock are subdivided, it is no longer practicable to mark lines of separation between them. Under such circumstances the united mass will simply be described as "Upper Silurian rocks," whilst, wherever similar causes prevent the separation of the "Caradoc sandstones" from the "Llandeilo flags," the two will be termed "Lower Silurian rocks." To illustrate his article, he included a woodcut section showing the relationships of the rocks. This was the basis of all subsequent Silurian sections.

Before taking up further studies of rocks, Murchison headed a deputation to the Government suggesting the urgent requirement for an accurate map of the northern half of Great Britain. The Chancellor of the Exchequer, an Irishman, Spring Rice, fobbed them off, saying that Ireland, which was also so deprived, must have one first.

Murchison and Sedgwick attended the 1835 meeting of the British Association in Dublin, where they gave a joint account of their activities amongst the 'grauwacke' rocks. Sedgwick gave the name of Cambrian to those he had studied in Cumberland and Wales, including the greater part of the chain of the Berwyns, and clearly believed that they were older than the Silurian. He said, 'it is connected with the Llandeilo flags of the Silurian and expanded through a considerable part of South Wales.' He stated that the 'Middle Cambrian Group' comprised the higher mountains of Caernarvonshire and Merionethshire; the 'Lower Cambrian group' occupied the south-west coast of Caernarvonshire and consisted of chlorite and mica schists with some serpentine and granular limestone. He continued by explaining the mode of connecting Murchison's researches with his own, so as to form one general system.

Murchison stated that he had identified the base of the Silurian and explored downwards into what was now to be called the Upper Cambrian. He said, 'Although two or three species of shells of the Upper Silurian rocks may be detected in the Lower Silurian, the mass of organic remains in each group is very distinct.' There was no disagreement between them, but it was later shown that they were both in error, in that the Silurian rocks went lower than either of them had believed and the two systems overlapped.

Murchison crossed back to Tortworth (north-east of Bristol), where he spent four or five days making a map. This small area had been the subject of upheaval by volcanism, which had thrown up a band of elevated Silurian rocks between Bristol and Hereford. Within a very short distance there were many different geological formations from the Inferior Oolite to the Lower Silurian. Working downwards it was possible to identify the Lias, the New Red Sandstone, dolomitic conglomerate, coal measures (unconformable with their overlying rocks) Carboniferous Limestone, Old Red Sandstone and, in the Silurian System, small developments of Ludlow and Wenlock formations and Caradoc Sandstone.

Murchison then turned westward to Pembrokeshire, where he spent three strenuous weeks consolidating his work on the Silurian rocks. He established that they outcropped in three bays. He remarked how absurd the name 'grauwacke' was to describe so wide a range of deposits. He returned home with the intention of concentrating exclusively on his great book on the subject. In fact the size of the work grew beyond all original concepts and it was another three years before it was published. He needed to return occasionally to the field to confirm his findings. Some of his geological friends were becoming impatient and he wrote to his friend, John Phillips, in the spring of 1836, 'There are at least three reasons why I cannot bring out the "Silurian System" with that promptitude with which you have issued your monograph of the "Carboniferous Limestone," – 1st, I have not the same facility of composition. 2dly, I depend on others, and not as you do on yourself, for the description and figuring of the organisms. 3dly, The work is so multifarious, being, besides the history of the rocks beneath the Carboniferous system, an attempt to work out all the general relations of the Lias, New Red Sandstone, and Coal-measures of those central counties. . . The work is entirely written save the descriptions of the organisms – a very large salvo this! I cannot shove [James] Sowerby [publisher of *Mineral Conchology*] on, and when he is shoved on I am not so sure of him as I could wish. My corals I have no doubt will be beautifully distinguished by Lonsdale; my fishes by Agassiz; plants I have none; my graptolites by Dr. Beck of Copenhagen. What would I not give, my dear friend, for your powers in the descriptions of the mollusca!

'The correspondence [with the Council of the British Association on the subject of the delay in completing the Ordnance Survey] is ordered to be printed for the use of the House of Commons, who now begin to feel (railroads cutting into their senses) that physical geography is of some importance even to senators.'

In the spring of 1836, Murchison was concerned over the health of his mother and went to visit her in Cheltenham. While his wife went to see her own mother at Nursted House, he continued westwards to join Sedgwick exploring the geology of Devonshire, the results of which expedition they reported to the British Association at their annual meeting in Bristol. After the meeting, Murchison heard that his mother's health had deteriorated and rushed to join his half-sister, Jeanette, at her bedside. She died at the age of sixty-five and he said of her 'No man ever had a more affectionate mother than myself, her only defect being over-indulgence of her children.' He buried her beside his father at Bathampton. The family tomb is in the north-east corner of the churchyard of St. Nicholas. Ten years later his brother Kenneth's wife, Anne, and seven years after that, his uncle, General Sir Alexander Mackenzie, were interred at the same spot. Murchison had put up inside the church, under the tower, a plaque commemorating his uncle, 'the senior General of H.M. Service'. After his death another plaque was placed underneath it, in memory of Roderick himself, to explain that he and his wife were buried in Brompton Cemetery, London.

Sedgwick went back to Devon and Cornwall, while Murchison met John Phillips at Brecon, from where they went north-west up the Afon Ysgir to Corn y Fan. Phillips wrote, 'Welsh ponies were in requisition, and we reached the hill, hoping to escape the jealous company of the Welsh farmer, who looked upon the men of the hammer as some kind of miners secretly prowling for gold or coal. Murchison had paid many visits, and had tried to explain to the inquisitive agriculturalist why the barren grey rocks prominent above the "Old Red Sea" had so much interest in his eyes. On this occasion I also had to encounter "the old man of the mountain," because my clinometer was in great use in respect of dip, cleavage and joints. "Axes of elevation," "direction of fault," "extent of throw," "envelope of old red," and other strange phrases, made our friend very angry, so that, unlike Welshmen in general, he offered us no kind of welcome or refreshment, but appeared to rejoice in our going away as a relief from some positive evil.'

Back in London, Murchison wrote to Sir Philip Egerton, 'I am going through my heavy work, and am just sending to press all that I mean to say of the "New Red System." . . . .

'My bone-bed in the Ludlow rocks is turning up trumps – jaws with teeth complete, carnivorous shark-like little fellows, with loads of coprolites, indicating that my Silurians digested even harder stuff than your Liassic friends, viz., Pentacrinites, etc.! This is beautiful, at some 8000 or 10,000 feet below the fish-beds at which Buckland begins his transition stories about the oldest fishes. But it will do for his third or fourth edition [of his well-known *Bridgewater Treatise*]. He has been in town last week, and was one day closeted with Babbage eight or nine hours, to get his siphuncle into order. It appears that Sedgwick and others, on reading the Nautilus Theory, at once saw there was a screw loose in the mechanics, and that if the animal got down to depths unknown he never could get up again. I know not how it is to end, but I hope our friend will be able to sing Resurgam. On the whole the book pleases most people.

'We are going on swimmingly, with bumper meetings. I am working from six A.M. till dark.'

Sedgwick had promised to help prepare a memoir on the Devonshire geology, but kept postponing the completion of his part. Frustrated by this, Murchison spent part of the winter producing, in conjunction with Hugh E. Strickland, a memoir on the New Red Sandstone, in which he showed a correlation of the English deposits with the Keuper and Bunter formations of Germany. The Council of the Society referred the paper to Sedgwick, who gave his opinion direct to Murchison, 'I have reported favourably on your paper on the Keuper, and said that it ought to be printed. But was ever a blotched, patched, botched, scratched, blurred, bothered thing sent to an arbitrator! with a prospectus, too, of certain plates affixed like a tin case to its tail, I suppose to make it go. It made me mutter bad words through my teeth many times over before I got to the end of it. Perhaps I did not swear outright; but you have no right to tempt me.'

In his *Life of Sir Roderick Murchison*, Geikie comments, 'This description of the author's style of calligraphy is not more graphic than true. His manuscript as it went to the printers was so scored, and crossed, and rewritten, as to be sometimes with difficulty legible even by himself. When the proof came back it soon grew under his pen nearly as bad as the original manuscript, and many a time had to be set up afresh.'

Murchison spent the remainder of the summer of 1837 and most of the following year seeing *The Silurian System* through the press. In between all this he carried out his exacting duties as General Secretary of the British Association, organising their meeting this year in Liverpool. The delay in publishing the book allowed him to improve its scope and accuracy, in particular in respect of the coverage of organic remains, which formed the second half. When it finally appeared on January 1 1839, it consisted of no less than 768 pages, with 112 coloured geological sections and 31 pages of drawings of fossils. There were numerous sketches of scenic landscapes, several by Charlotte Murchison. The book also featured a map on a scale of one inch to three miles.

The book's full title was *The Silurian System founded on geological researches in the counties of Salop, Hereford, Radnor, Montgomery, Caermarthen, Brecon,*

Pembroke, Monmouth, Gloucester, Worcester, and Stafford, with descriptions of the coal-fields and overlying formations. Murchison dedicated it to 'Rev. Adam Sedgwick FRS VPGS, Woodwardian Professor, Cambridge'. He wrote: 'To you, my dear Sedgwick, a large portion of whose life has been devoted to the arduous study of the older British Rocks, I dedicate this work. Having explored with you many a tract, both at home and abroad, I beg you to accept this offering as a memorial of friendship, and of the high sense I entertain of the value of your labours.'

He presented a copy to the Geological Society. It was a landmark in the history of geology. For the first time, it listed the succession of strata laid down before the Old Red Sandstone, together with details of the fossils found in them. Murchison had succeeded in unravelling what had previously been considered as the almost hopeless confusion of the so-called 'Transition' rocks. He had also found the sites of some of the submarine volcanoes of that great age and discovered the considerable thickness of the lava flows and ash deposits on the seabed. He included details of some of the younger rocks overlying his Silurian – the coalfields and other deposits up to the Oolitic Limestones. Dr. William Whewell, Professor of Mineralogy at Cambridge and the current President of the Geological Society, spoke of it as 'an admirable example of the sober and useful splendour which may grace a geological monograph'.

In his Introduction, Murchison said of Sedgwick, 'In speaking of the labours of my friend, I may truly say, that he not only shed an entirely new light on the crystalline arrangement or slaty cleavage of the North Welsh Mountains, but also overcame what to most men would have proved insurmountable difficulties in determining the order and relations of these very ancient strata amid scenes of vast dislocation. He further made several traverses across the region in which I was employed; and, sanctioning the arrangement I had adopted, he not only gave me confidence in its accuracy, but enhanced the value of my work by enabling me to unite it with his own; and thus have our joint exertions led to a general view of the sequence of the older fossiliferous deposits.'

Murchison described thirty-seven species of trilobites and also acknowledged the wealth of assistance he had received from others – Agassiz on fossil fish, Sowerby on brachiopods, Lonsdale on the corals, and many more, including the Rev. T.T. Lewis of Aymestrey. Murchison was somewhat overactive in trying to obtain favourable reviews in *The Times* and elsewhere. This was driven by the need to recoup some of the large sums of money that he had expended on the publication. He argued the necessity of knowledge of geological structure for the development of the country's mineral resources and the benefits of publicity about recent researches.

Murchison's term 'Silurian' was accepted in many countries, including France, Scandinavia, Turkey and the United States. He now looked upon 'Siluria' as his domain and a kind of personal property, the knowledge of which he worked to extend further afield.

Chapter Six
The Devonian

The followers of Werner had established that their Transition rocks, upturned semi-crystalline schists and slates, were overlain by sandstone, on top of which was the coal, then another layer of sandstone. We know now that what we call the Old Red Sandstone accumulated around 400 million years ago, when the Iapetus Ocean finally closed and England and Scotland came together. In its long drift northwards from near the South Pole, Britain was then situated at about 25° south of the Equator and experiencing a generally arid climate somewhat equivalent to the Kalahari of today but with flash floods. The presence of fossil leaves from this period indicates that the climate was not entirely without moisture.

The subduction of Scotland under northern England gave rise to mountain-building of Himalayan proportions and volcanic activity in the Lake District and North Wales. The Caledonian Mountains eroded at an almost unbelievable rate of one centimetre in fifty years, from some 8000 metres to near enough sea-level in forty million years, giving rise to a vast amount of sediment. Over the next hundred or so million years Britain moved northwards, experiencing equatorial rainfall, which brought tropical forest and swampland, the origin of most of our coal measures. Further northerly drift brought a return to arid conditions similar to that of today's Sahara and Negev deserts and the formation of the New Red Sandstone.

Of course none of this was known to geologists in the nineteenth century – all they could observe was the result, but they did understand the economic significance, as the coal could be found sandwiched between two layers of sandstone. Back in 1831, Murchison, with his experience of it in Scotland, had identified the importance of the Old Red Sandstone and its great thickness (some 3000 metres or more), together with the remarkable character of its fossil fishes. He realised that it should be seen as a separate series. However, this was not accepted on the Continent because the rocks, save a small outcrop in Belgium and possibly in Russia, did not occur. Geologists there considered them as group peculiar to Britain and an extension, either upwards from the 'grauwacke' or downwards from the Carboniferous.

Sedgwick and Murchison had hitherto generally worked separately in the north and Wales, nevertheless comparing their findings. Sedgwick had struggled to unravel the physical structure of the rocks and Murchison had had the good fortune to find a region whose structure was simple and which yielded abundant fossils, giving good grounds for distinguishing the strata. Now they combined their knowledge and energies in Devon. Their immediate task was to discover the age of some anthracitic coal-dust measures, but this led on to wider investigations in Cornwall and on the Continent, which eventually established the Devonian System.

Murchison explained, 'The origin of this joint survey [of Devonshire] came about in this way. In the preceding winter [December 1834], Mr. (afterwards Sir Henry) De la Beche had sent up specimens of small fossil plants from the culm [coal-dust] rocks of North Devon, which he described as belonging to the Grauwacke formation. At the evening meeting of the Geological Society I opposed this view, on the ground that my Silurian rocks, both upper and lower, contained no land plants whatever. Moreover, I thought I recognised a complete similarity between these common specimens of North Devon and those which I had explored in the opposite coast of Pembroke, and which I knew were superposed to the Millstone Grit and Mountain Limestone. I therefore urged Sedgwick to join me in a campaign to settle the question. He agreed to do so. So off we went; and first we looked through the rocks of North Somerset, Ilfracombe, Morte Bay, Baggy Point, and Barnstaple. As we went on, a good, steady, southerly dip continued until we reached the edge of the famous Culm tract, into and under which the older strata pitched at a rapid inclination. I there saw that the game was won, and, drawing a section, in which I reversed De la Beche's hypothetical diagrams, I called out to Sedgwick from the rock on which I was sitting, - "Here it is! Look at my section of the North Devon coal-field – the youngest instead of the oldest rocks of the county – our job is done!" Still he was a little incredulous until we advanced southwards (for I had sketched this from the north side of the bay), and then when he saw the actual order he entirely assented, saying what a crow we should have over De la Beche. The truth I can only surmise to be, that De la Beche, who was certainly a very able geologist, had never really looked carefully at the consecutive sections in nature, but seeing the Culm strata in a state of great contortion in a low tract, he had presumed that they passed under the higher country in the north. I also believe that he was so much occupied in writing that remarkably skilful and ingenious work (the best he ever wrote), Theoretical Researches in Geology, that in doing so, and carrying out his first map of Devon and Cornwall, he really worked very little in the field.

'At the Bristol meeting of the British Association, the chief business of Sedgwick and self was to establish the point regarding the great change we proposed in the structure of Devonshire; and though Greenough, Buckland, and the old hands made some resistance, and did not like to see the ancient "Shillats" and "Gossans," [visible guides to sulphide mineralization] believed to be the most ancient rocks in Britain, so modernized, it was evident that truth would prevail.'

After the meeting, Murchison returned to clerical work while Sedgwick went back to Devon to spend many weeks establishing a broad base for the paper the pair had arranged to read to the Geological Society. Their findings were not generally accepted at first, several members of the Society being strongly opposed to their propositions. Murchison really needed the support of Sedgwick, who was somewhat of a hypochondriac and used all manner of presumably imaginary ailments to excuse himself for not travelling from Cambridge to London to back him up.

On 30 January 1837, Murchison wrote to him, 'My dear Sedgwick, - I worked all day yesterday to make the sections, and to have them correspond with our long Bristolian coupe. I was in great hopes to have your dispatches before now; but I wait patiently like a lamb for the sacrifice; - and sacrificed I most assuredly shall be without your aid. However, I will drink the best part of a bottle of sherry to screw me up to face Buckland, Greenough, Yates, and the Ordnance forces which are to be brought against us. In anticipation of the memoir, I must take this chance of a vale from you before the fight.'

They had worked together for six years and had advised the British Association in a brief note of their discoveries. A date was set for them to present their joint paper, but neither Sedgwick nor the memoir from him materialised. Murchiston wrote from 3 Bryanston Place on 2 February, 'My dear Sedgwick, - The part of Hamlet being omitted, the play was not performed, and all the scenic arrangements which I had laboured at were thrown away, though the room looked splendid. The morning's arrivals certainly surprised me. Ten o'clock brought me your double letter; eleven o'clock by the same mail the maps, and a little note to Lyell, but in vain I looked through the parcel for the document to be read. I read and re-read your letter, and still I could not understand it. One thing I clearly perceived, and with great regret, that you were seriously out of sorts, and had been suffering; so after waiting till two, I journeyed down to the Society, still thinking that a third package with the paper might be sent to Somerset House, - not so, however. These things going on; the whole room decorated for the fight; Buckland arrived, Fitton present, and a large meeting expected, - what was to be done? Fitton and Lonsdale . . . counselled me to give up the thing, which I resolved to do, to the very great annoyance of the President [Buckland], and of all the others who came to hear. . . .

'I am mortified that the memoir did not come; of course I blame myself somewhat for having thrown in doubts on some points, because I see that ill as you have been, and without the power on my part of talking the case over, we mutually misapprehended each other. But enough of what is past. The thing now to consider is when to have the paper out. I should certainly not wish to have it done till you are present, because we must have a fair stand-up fight and knock the -------- and Greenough down.

'Did you really imagine that I was to dramatize the whole thing without a sermon before me? or have you been written to by Greenough or some of the dark school? or was the paper unfit to be sent? or was it omitted by accident or mistake? The President stated the last as the cause, and I said not a word about it, for with Lonsdale's help in construing your letter, we were unable to understand it. I think that the delay occasioned by my doubts and your influenza and state of the stomach are the true causes; but if you had sent it in ever so unfinished a state, the heads would have been read, and an abstract made, which would have served all purposes.'

The paper was eventually read to the Society well into the summer. There was in fact a series of presentations which settled the age of the coal-measures of Devonshire. This was important in itself, but led on to more momentous discoveries. The pair needed to establish a baseline for their Carboniferous formations, which would in other parts of the country be the Old Red Sandstone. However, in Devon and Cornwall the rocks were much distorted and altered, as we know now, by the Variscan Orogeny (which followed the closure of the Rheic Ocean and the formation of one supercontinent (Pangea) at the end of the Carboniferous period about 290 million years ago). This meant that they had considerable difficulty in establishing their correct succession. They contained much limestone and many fossils and they thought at first that they fitted into the middle and upper levels of Sedgwick's Cambrian series of North Wales.

Several collectors had amassed a large number of fossils quite different from those found in the Silurian rocks, though they had some similarities. Equally they showed a relationship with those found in the Carboniferous strata, so should have been placed in some intermediate category, e.g. the Old Red Sandstone. However, Murchison and Sedgwick found this hard to accept, because they did not tie in with their observations in Wales and the north.

A Scottish bank accountant, Hugh Miller, who later became famous as a writer, had started his working life apprenticed to a stonemason and developed an interest in fossils as a teenager. He had made important discoveries of fossil fish from the Devonian rocks of Scotland. Having heard of Murchison's researches, he sent him a number of fossils eventually destined for Louis Agassiz in France. He asked Murchison if he could say whether they were of fresh-water or marine species, as he was writing a series of articles for the Scottish 'Evangelist' newspaper, *The Witness*. He requested him to forward the fossils to Agassiz, when he had inspected them, and offered to send him others, of which he had duplicate samples.

In reply, Murchison said, 'Although my work was intended to be exclusively devoted to Silurian (or Transition) rocks of England and Wales, I have made a few allusions to other tracts, and, among these, to the Old Red Sandstone of Scotland, in doing which I have, in the descriptions of the organic remains, briefly alluded to your labours. Now that I know the fidelity and closeness of your research, I shall endeavour to introduce another allusion in the Appendix, which is all that remains unprinted.

'I am delighted with your clear and terse style of description, and beg to assure you, that if you could send us, in the course of the summer, any general and detailed account of both the Sutors, and all their contents, I shall have the utmost pleasure in communicating it to the Geological Society, to be read at the November meeting.

'You write and observe too well to waste your strength in newspaper publications, and a good digest of what you have done ought to be preserved in a permanent work of reference. I can give you no positive answer as to whether the Old Red Sandstone of Scotland was formed in a lake or in the sea. I have, however, strong reasons for believing that it is a marine deposit, for in England we find marine shells in it to a considerable height above the uppermost beds of underlying Silurian rocks. . . .I much long to visit the shores of Caithness and Cromarty with my increased knowledge, and with the conviction that I should learn so much from you, but I fear it is hopeless.'

It was later shown by the military surveyor, Colonel Henry Godwin-Austen, and others that the fossils were more probably of fresh-water origin.

The astronomer Sir John Herschel had reviewed his father's great catalogue of nebulae, adding 525 new ones, and in order to extend the survey to the southern hemisphere had spent four years in South Africa, observing a further 1708, the majority previously unseen. He also added to his father's work on double stars and catalogued over 1000 objects in the Magellanic Clouds. On his return to England in 1838, his friends determined to give him a public dinner and present him with an inscribed vase. Murchison accepted responsibility for organising this event, which he did with meticulous care. It involved him in a mound of correspondence and associated work.

On 16 January 1838, Mrs. Charlotte Hugonin, Murchison's mother-in-law, died at Nursted House after some months of illness. He kept the letter he wrote to Sedgwick the following day amongst his papers, and later in his life wrote on it 'My Creed in 1838'.

'My dear Sedgwick, - I have not for the last many months found an hour so vacant, that if I abstracted it from the book, or any other avocation, I did not reproach myself, so heavily has the incubus pressed upon me. Here, however, . . . I am free to occupy an hour, and I give it to you as the man of my heart. 1st, Talking of this last mentioned member of our frame in a physical sense, I must crave some of that sympathy from you which I have often felt for you when you have described to me your own sensations in its region. The scene here has altogether been trying and harassing for my wife and self – several times up and down from town, and, on the last occasion of my visit, I returned only to Eccleston Street [Belgravia] to hurry off Mrs. M. at a moment's notice, as I feared she would be too late to close her mother's eyes. This, however, was happily not the case. The old lady made a wonderful rally, her mind became quite composed, and she took the sacrament with her daughter in full confidence of a change to a better world. These are agreeable reflections. Tomorrow I attend her body to the grave. The will gives to my dear wife a most ample income for her life.

'I do not mean to relax one jot in my search after natural knowledge; nay, being now a free agent for the first time these twenty years, I shall, I hope, be enabled to employ all my leisure hours more effectively in pursuing my favourite study.

'But this is not enough. I have one deep-seated source of personal unhappiness in my thoughts of the future. To go we know not where, may be viewed calmly and resignedly by many philosophers, trusting as they do to the wise dispensations of Providence, yet unable to believe in the great 'Atonement for the sins of man. Alas! I am (for I need scarcely confess it again to you, for you know me) one of those half-instructed wandering beings who sufficiently know and feel what they ought to believe, yet cannot overcome the force of habit and a long-continued apathetic indifference to the vital point. Doubtless I perceive much to admire, nay, nothing to cavil at, in the precepts of Christ, though I cannot bring my mind to acquiesce in His divinity. Still less can I confide in and give my common sense to adopt all the historical details of the Old Testament. You will refer me to Paley [who, in 1802, published *Natural Theology, or Evidences of the Existence and Attributes of the Deity*], while ------- professing to be a Christian, will refer me to Fellowes. I do not require a stimulus to induce me to adopt natural religion, for I have it strongly implanted in me; and if geology has done me no other good, it has, at all events, strongly fortified me in this sense.

'But here I halt. Most unwillingly it is true, for few people have a higher respect for sincere believers than myself, and no one would more stoutly fight for the Church, as a great and essential moral engine, than myself. When, however, I see men of powerful minds and great integrity, who are strict believers in Christ, I am roused to a perception of the chance there is that the defect is in my own capacity and heart. I hope the former only. Your example has made more impression upon me than all that was ever said or written; for nothing has more alienated me from Christian belief than the constant exposure (which history and our own experience affirm) of hypocrisy, cant, and all the worst passions veiled under the garb of religion. You might well say to me, "Look at home;" for if there ever existed a thoroughly pious, yet unobtrusive Christian, that person is my excellent wife. Seeing the tranquillity with which she views her passage from this world, and knowing how the best Christian principles are ever her guides, albeit without a tincture of fanaticism or exclusive sanctity, I cannot but hope that the day will come, when, striving to follow out the dying wishes of my own beloved mother, I may become a true believer. Alas! I am a short way yet upon the road. ----- Ever yours, my dear friend,   Rod. I. Murchison.'

****

In May 1838, Sedgwick reported to the Geological Society on the Cambrian rocks of North Wales and divided them, without referring to characteristic fossils, firstly into 'the Primary Stratified Groups, including gneiss, mica schist and the Skiddaw slates'. He provisionally called them Protozoic, which he said 'included the Highlands of Scotland, the crystalline schists of Anglesea and the Southwest Coast of Caernarvonshire.' He added, 'The series is generally without organic remains; but should organic remains appear unequivocally in any part of this class they may be described as the Protozoic System.'

Secondly, his Palaeozoic Series included the Lower Cambrian (which he had named Middle Cambrian in 1835), the Upper Cambrian, and Murchison's Silurian. Without comparing fossils, it was impossible to relate the two systems. Yet he went on to say, 'The Upper Cambrian, which commences with the fossiliferous beds of Bala, and includes all the higher portions of the Berwyns and all the slate-rocks of South Wales which are below the Silurian System, appears to pass by insensible gradation into the lower division of the Upper System (the Caradoc Sandstone) and many of the fossils are identical in species with those of the Silurian System.'

In spite of intense work in co-operation with Sowerby and Lonsdale during the winter of 1838-9, Sedgwick was still, in March, convinced that there was no Old Red Sandstone in Devon. In the spring, De la Beche published a Geological Report on Cornwall and Devon, still failing to admit that the Culm rocks were true coal-measures and retaining the name 'grauwacke' for the older strata. Murchison and Sedgwick were irritated because it appeared to overlook the important work they had done in the two counties.

In April 1839, Sedgwick and Murchison published in the *Philosophical Magazine* a paper, 'On the classification of the older stratified rocks of Devon and Cornwall', which formally proposed the name Devonian to apply to all the rocks between the Silurian and the Carboniferous systems. Lonsdale had originally restricted the name to the limestone of South Devon, but now they had widened the definition and also anticipated that it might apply to strata on the Continent. Dr. Buckland expressed the opinion that this was 'undoubtedly the greatest change which had ever been attempted at one time in the classification of British rocks'.

In the paper they stated, 'In attempting to classify the oldest rocks of Devon we fell into some false conclusions from imperfect data. These we have corrected, and the whole series of Devonshire and Cornwall is now, we trust, exhibited in harmony; the lower sandstones and slates being the equivalents of the old red sandstone, the next natural group beneath the great coal-bearing strata of the British Isles, and the whole being exhibited under peculiar mineral types.

'In asserting that the older stratified rocks of Devonshire and Cornwall are upon a broad scale the equivalents of the carboniferous and old red systems, we do not however deny that in some tracts the lowest members of these rocks may represent the upper division of the Silurian System: for although we have as yet found few if any of the fossils most typical of that system, we admit that when the sediments of a given epoch have been accumulated under peculiar conditions, we must expect to find considerable variations in the forms of animal life....

'The present opinions of Mr. De la Beche are before the public, and we have no right, perhaps, to be his interpreters. He puts forth several hypotheses, without positively adopting one of them. He must, however, (after the recent publication of such large groups of Silurian fossils) before long perceive that the formations of South Devon not merely contain fossils approaching those of the mountain limestone (a fact long known), but that their whole suite of fossils is intermediate between those of the Silurian and Carboniferous Systems; a fact which at once defines their true place in the sequence of British rocks....

'So long as we were unprovided with a typical suite of fossils from the older system of Devon, it was impossible to propose for it any name; but now, having discovered a great many of its fossils, and that too in regions wherein the red arenaceous character gives way to the slaty impress, and a very different mineral aspect; the necessity of adopting a new name becomes apparent, and we propose the term "Devonian System" as that of all the great intermediate deposits between the Silurian and Carboniferous Systems. The "Devonian System" is so far unexceptionable, that it may be applied, without any contradiction of terms, to rocks of every variety of mineral structure which contain the characteristic series of organic remains.'

A meeting was arranged on 10 April for the purpose of hearing a paper by one of their opponents, the Rev. D. Williams. Sedgwick was not able to attend and Murchison wrote to him the following day, 'My dear Sedgwick, - The fight is over. It lasted till near midnight, and, all things considered, we have come off remarkably well. Parson Williams, who was present, had prepared an Ordnance map of Devon and Cornwall coloured on his own mineralogical plan. . . . Immediately after the memoir was read, De la Beche, who came up per mail for the nonce, rose, and holding in his hand our memoir, commenced an exculpation of himself from the charge we bring against him in our conclusion. . . . He spoke calmly, and without going into the memoir of the evening. I immediately replied by first assuring the Chair that I had no hesitation in expressing my regret that a word or two had been made use of in the hurry of composition which both of us were sorry for. . . . Disavowing the least personality, I immediately got D. with me, and having thus cleared the course, I opened the discussion on Williams' paper, and went "the whole hog," as well as I could, touching the Devonian case. De la Beche then replied, but did not attempt to shake one of our positions, did not place a veto on one of my assertions, and least of all, on that which laid claim to the originality of the Culm-trough. He bothered about a point or two near Chudleigh, as difficulties, and ending by saying it was immaterial to him what the things were called.

'Lyell then spoke, and very adroitly put the case as one most agreeable to him, now that he perceived that Mr. D. not only acknowledged that the view which we took at Bristol was original, but also that he (D.) was by no means indisposed to adopt our new views, which get rid of all the anomalies and difficulties (about plants and fossils). Fitton rose in great solemnity, and with deep pathos impressed on the meeting the propriety of restraining the too pungent expression of controversial writing among geological friends, alluded to my having called him "my geological father," and only wished that I had submitted the paper in question to his parental revision before it was published. He acknowledged, however, that the explanation had quite rectified the case, and then he went on to expatiate on the value of our doings, giving us superlative praise, and bringing out Lonsdale in the foreground.

'Greenough made his oration as I expected, was very ingeniously sophistical, tried to throw all into chaos, saw nothing new in our views, adhered to his old belief – Greywacke for ever! – and sustained old Williams by casting fossil evidence overboard.

'Featherstonehaugh spoke well on the great subdivisions of the old rocks of North America, and said they were distinctly the same as ours....

'These and many other things being said and done, Buckland summed up at half past eleven, and though he evidently wished to shield De la Beche, he ended by approving highly of "Devonian" – he now saw light – that light he referred to W. Lonsdale, and henceforth, said he, there will be two great names in English geology – W. Smith and W. Lonsdale; he adhered entirely to the fossil evidences, did not give us the credit we deserved for our coal-trough (which is the key to the whole thing), nor did he do justice to my Siluriana, without which, as you have justly said, no one could have started this new hare.

'The room was a bumper. Warburton, who sat it out, assured me . . . that he looked upon the case as settled, as it was quite evident that Buckland had completely given in, De la Beche was ready to do so, and Greenough alone held out, standing like a knight-errant upon his "antiquas vias" [old ways]. 'I had forgot to tell you that Lord Northampton also spoke to a point of conciliation; in fact, there was too much of this, for I sat next to De la Beche, never lost my temper for an instant, asked him to dine with me, and all ended "à l'aimable," and would have done so without any of the surpassing efforts of these "good Samaritans."

'Buckland was particularly happy in assisting to demolish "Greywacke" by pulling old Greenough up, who with himself had declared a mass of rock in the Alps to be good "grauwacke," which proved to be full of Tertiary shells; that he had seen very good "grauwacke" in oolites, in red sandstone, in coal – in short, in everything, and therefore he did think with Conybeare that it was "Jupiter quodcunque vides," [King of the Gods wherever you look] and agreed with us in the fitness of using it hereafter entirely as an adjective or expletive. Q.E.D.

'It was right well that I was not absent in Paris, or things in your absence also might have gone pro tempore against us. – Ever yours, Rod. I. Murchison.'

The nomenclature was soon recognised and accepted across the World. Geikie (1875) says, 'And yet we must admit that, though exceedingly ingenious, it was based rather on what seemed probable than what had been proved to be the case. Had the authors simply declared that their Devonian rocks occupied a place somewhere between the base of the Coal-measures, or upper part of the Mountain-Limestone and the Silurian system, their position would have been unassailable. Their identification, however, of the Devonian slates, limestones, and sandstones, as the true equivalents of the Old Red Sandstone of other regions, left out of sight the fact that a great thickness of Lower Carboniferous rocks was on this view unrepresented in the south-western counties, and hence that a portion at least of their Devonian series might really be Carboniferous.'

The distortion of the rocks in the two counties resulting from the Variscan Orogeny had caused considerable problems. The Old Red Sandstone was characterised by Ichthyolites (primitive fish), which were perfectly distinct in form from any remains of that class in the Carboniferous beds above or in the Silurian strata below. It had yielded no remains of mollusca at that time. In case the distinctions were only local ones, Murchison and Sedgwick suggested that investigation of the continental deposits of similar age might well clarify the situation. They even indicated their intention of looking into the matter personally. Murchison considered Scandinavia, Belgium, the south of Ireland and parts of Germany as appropriate starting points. He had been advised, particularly in a letter from Leopold von Buch, that in Russia there were large areas of sedimentary rocks, undisturbed by Earth movements. He begged Sedgwick to try to release himself from his obligations at Cambridge, so that they could conduct the surveys together. Three weeks later, he told him that he wished to make an early start, and that, if he could not come straight away, he could perhaps meet him at one of the sites. He visited Dr. Buckland at Oxford and listened to all he could tell him about Normandy and Brittany, acquiring some maps from him. He told Sedgwick of his final plans in early April, advising him that he intended to leave in the first week in May for Antwerp and Liège, go on via Spa and Trèves (Trier), looking quickly en route at the Eifel district (where rocks such as peridotite and garnet from the Earth's mantle forty miles or more deep may be found on the surface), then to Paris to catch the geologists before they left for the summer. He would then go straight to Caen and meet Sedgwick there in the first week of June. However, the whole itinerary was changed; the pair would now work together on the banks of the Rhine. The object of the exercise was to see whether there was a series of rocks between the Silurian and the Carboniferous, containing an assemblage of fossils which would justify them being classed as Devonian.

Murchison left for Paris and attended there a meeting of the Société Géologique de France, of which he had become a member. His claim that his Devonian rocks merited the status of a 'system' came under fire, but he held his own. He drove eastwards to Trier and from there he wrote to his wife, saying how well organised the country was with macadamized roads, order and comfort everywhere. He drove down the Mosel and through the Rhine Gorge to Frankfurt, where he found Cambrian strata overlain by red sandstone and limestone with mussel shell fossils. He bought a small carriage there and proceeded down the right bank of the Rhine, collecting organic remains to send back to Lonsdale, before meeting Sedgwick at Bonn. In another letter to his wife, he reported that he had found no

Silurian beds and that he thought the whole region was Devonian. The limestones were all indistinguishable from those at Plymouth and in North Devon and the fossils were of the same classes as those found there – simple ammonites and brachiopods. He advised his wife not to boast too much about his achievements, as he felt that he might have made some errors. In the event this was later shown to be the case. He went on via the Düsseldorf coal-field, expecting the Devonian to pass conformably under it. His intention was to have covered the whole of the right bank of the Rhine before meeting his friend.

When they did make their rendezvous, Sedgwick was delighted with the work Murchison had done and yielded to his persuasion that they should spend the rest of their time together that summer in Germany. By the end of June, they had investigated several valleys in the Harz mountains, in spite of changeable weather. Within the next fortnight, Murchison was able to write to tell his wife that they had covered the Fichtelgebirge, north-east of Bayreuth, where they found no Silurian, only Devonian and Carboniferous deposits, and moved on to Frankfurt. They worked carefully down the Rhine Gorge from Bingen, finding at last, opposite Koblenz, some Silurian rocks with plenty of fossils to identify them. However, they were only able to find small traces of Wenlock strata and none of the Ludlow rocks, so they could not yet establish a connection with the English series. They hoped to find one in the Eifel and the Ardennes.

Murchison was obliged, as one of the Secretaries, to attend that year's meeting of the British Association in Birmingham, so he had to break off his field work in mid-August, leaving Sedgwick on the Meuse. At home, he could not restrain himself from writing to John Phillips and William Whewell to tell them of his success in Germany.

Meanwhile his wife was in the process of selling their house in Eccleston Street and buying for them a mansion, 16 Belgrave Square, not far from Hyde Park Corner. He was to spend the last thirty-two years of his life there and it became famous for their hospitality and as a centre for scientific discussion. It is surprising that a blue plaque commemorating his occupation of this property has not been affixed to it. Writing about a reception he had attended in 1842, John Ruskin, the author and art critic then aged twenty-three, said, 'The old lady at Athlones said that Mr. Murchison had told her there would be above 700. I could not count more than 150 in the rooms at a time – but as they kept rushing in and out, there could not have been many fewer passing through during the two hours I staid. . . . I don't know what fortune Murchison has – but this is coming it rather strong – rooms all pale grey and gold – magnificent cornices – with arabesques like those of Pompeii in colour, furniture all dark crimson damask silk and gold – no wood visible – at least four footmen playing shuttlecock with peoples names up the stairs.'

The Birmingham meeting was not noted for any significant papers, and even that presented by Murchison about his work in Germany was necessarily incomplete. There was a great air of sadness, because William Smith had died, aged seventy, on his way from Scarborough to attend the meeting. He had contracted a chest infection on a field trip, while staying with his friend, George Baker, in Northampton. He had endured a long period of hard times and the infinite value of his work on the identification and mapping of strata was only fully appreciated in the last few years of his life.

As soon as the meeting was over, Murchison crossed the Channel to Boulogne to attend a meeting of the Societé Géologique de France. Charlotte had asked him to look out for some furniture for their new house. On 12 September he wrote to her: 'Having been out daily from half-past five till dark, I have had no time for "furniture" thoughts. It so happens that owing to my having more knowledge of the older rocks than other geologists here, I have been obliged to become a sort of cicerone [guide for antiquities] and orator, and yesterday evening in the great library, the Mayor of Boulogne and many French present, I delivered myself of an hour of Silurianism, and explained the relation of the old rocks of this country. The effect of my discourse was to destroy the coal-boring mania in rocks of Silurian age. They have a poor little coal-field here which lies low in the Carboniferous Limestone group, and this being immediately recumbent on my Silurian schists and shales, they have (their little upper concerns being about done up) been poking at great expense, and with the money of unfortunate shareholders, into my Stygian abysses. The "actions" or shares fell 50 per cent, by my speech, and, notwithstanding that I told unpleasant truths, I was warmly applauded. I should have been off today, but I was so pressed on all sides to remain that the departure was postponed till tomorrow, when I proceed by Calais.'

In fact the official report of the meeting did not show that his views on the impossibility of finding coal in the older rocks were fully accepted.

Murchison took only two days to reach Bonn. He was accompanied by M. de Verneuil, Vice-President of the Societé Géologique de France, who had a good knowledge of fossils found in older rocks in Britain and on the Continent. He met Sedgwick, who had just returned from a further expedition up the Rhine. He was still unhappy about a number of important geological points, but his partner hoped they would be able to clarify much from their investigations of the volcanic areas of the Eifel. From the small town of Lutzerach he wrote, 'I have been a lazy correspondent, but a most active workman. The days are short and though up daily at five (by candle-light) we are soon benighted. Yet, with all, since I wrote we have done a great deal. From Coblenz we journeyed by the river to Limburg on the Lahn, and thence passed over the Westerwald, a high basaltic region, to Dillenberg, where we had a famous excursion on foot, headed by a little broad-shouldered clever Prussian Bergmeister, who, booted and spurred, led the way (pipe in mouth and hammer in hand), followed by S., de Verneuil, and myself and an English miner. We got many additional fossils. . . . At Limburg, de Verneuil took leave of us to run through the Eifel quickly to Paris. He is an excellent companion, and of a charming temper, never making a difficulty, and a thoroughly gentlemanlike Frenchman.'

Murchison and Sedgwick carried on working in the Eifel, facing a few problems

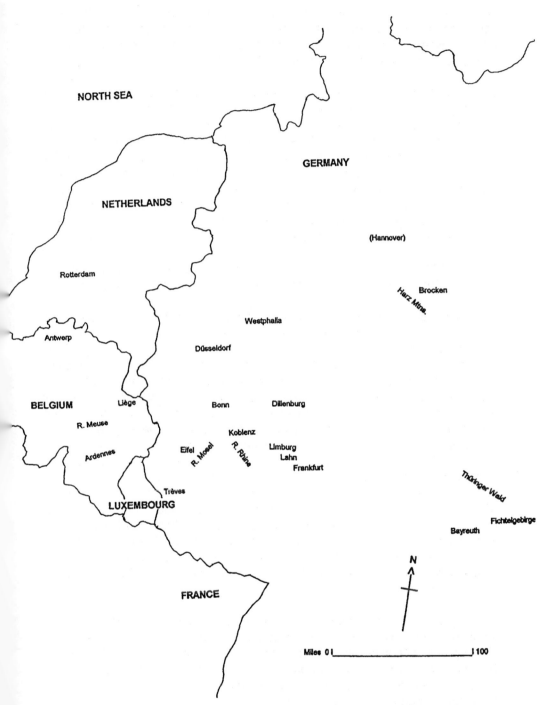

NORTH SEA

GERMANY

NETHERLANDS

(Hannover)

Rotterdam

Brocken

Harz Mtns.

Westphalia

Antwerp

Düsseldorf

BELGIUM   Liège   Bonn   Dillenburg

R. Meuse

Koblenz

Ardennes   Eifel   Limburg   Lahn

R. Mosel   R. Rhine

Frankfurt

Trèves

Thüringer Wald

LUXEMBOURG

Fichtelgebirge

Bayreuth

N

FRANCE

Miles 0 |_____| 100

Some of the places in Belgium and Germany visited by Murchison they could not solve. Eventually the rapidly-shortening days told them they had done enough for this season and they took a small boat down the Mosel to Koblenz, where they caught a steamer to Düsseldorf. They spent a few days in Westphalia, then returned to England via Rotterdam.

Soon after reaching home, Murchison sent a detailed account of their autumn's work to John Phillips. It was clear that he was not entirely confident about their findings and he and Sedgwick did not agree on some points. However, they had brought back a large number of fossils for detailed examination and comparison with those they had found in Devon and Cornwall. While Sedgwick remained at Cambridge, Murchison carried out that work, assisted by Lonsdale, Sowerby and Phillips. Some at least of his conclusions had to be rejected, when the fossil evidence was clarified. He wrote to Sedgwick in December, telling him in detail of his findings, and suggesting that they write a joint memoir on the right bank of the Rhine, comparing the structure with that of the Harz and Fichtelgebirge.

In May 1840, they presented to the Geological Society a paper *On the Classification and Distribution of the Older Rocks of North Germany, etc.*

Three months earlier, Murchison had sent a letter to John Phillips, saying, 'I thank you for Austen's list, as (if to be depended on) it adds one or two clenching fossils to a list already too strong to admit of any doubt as to the identity of the uppermost Grauwacke system of the Continent and the "Devonian" as defined by Sedgwick and myself. I have arrived at this conclusion for many months, and only waited the coming to town of my colleague to open the campaign. Now that he has been here, and that we are all agreed, the course is clear, and we shall soon give a grand memoir to show that the uppermost Grauwacke of both banks of the Rhine, as well as the three members of Dumont's Terrain anthraxifère (supposed by him to be Silurian), as well as the major part of the Harz and of the Fichtelgebirge, are true Devonian, passing up into Carboniferous strata, and reposing on Silurian. . . . I am now highly delighted in having insisted on the "Old Red" as a system, and on my prophecy of what it would turn out in fossils. I too, however, have made my little mistakes, and I will thank you to allow me to amend some words in my communication at Birmingham. Again in returning by Boulogne I gave a field lecture, and, supposing that de Verneuil, Dumont, and others were right in Silurianizing these tracts, I chimed in with the error without looking for fossils.

'I am going to Paris in ten days to read a memoir on the Boulonnais, all the fossils of which have been sent to me, and they clearly Devonianize it. . . . We propose our triple subdivision of Devonian, Silurian, and Cambrian for Europe. Buckland has given currency to our views in his speech, and Greenough has closely imitated our reform of Devon and Cornwall. So at last all is settled as to the great boundaries.'

While in Paris, Murchison enjoyed dinners at the embassy, soirées and evenings at the opera. He was entertained by a number of leading geologists of the city, including Brongniart and Élie de Beaumont, and returned their hospitality by giving a dinner at the "Rocher de Cancale".

He wrote again to Charlotte, saying, 'Today I had de Verneuil with me from nine to one, when we adjourned to M. de Meyendorf's, who starts tomorrow night for Petersburg, and with whom we arranged a Russian campaign for June, July, and August. It is agreed (if I do not change my mind) that I sail for Petersburg the 25th May, de Verneuil coming to meet me some days before. The advantages are too great to be lost, both as respects the Russian factotum and administrator, and de Verneuil.'

Chapter Seven
Journeys into Russia

From what he had learned in Paris and from many other sources, Murchison realised that large tracts of north-eastern Europe consisted of old but undisturbed rocks. There would not be the difficulties he and Sedgwick had had in tracing the strata through widespread distortion in the English West Country. He felt that he might well be able to show that Silurian, Devonian and Carboniferous strata went right across the World. There were reports by G.F, Fischer de Waldheim, C.H. Pander, E.I. von Eichwald and others of large numbers of fossils to prove it. The British Ambassador in St. Petersburg, W.T.H.F. Strangways had, back in 1822 in his *An Outline of the Geology of Russia*, given a description of the rocks in the environs of that city, the oldest in which the remains of organic life had been discovered. He had produced the first sketch of a geological map, but had not determined the true succession of the strata of which the north of Russia was almost exclusively composed. Von Buch had been sent a number of fossils and had relayed to Murchison his opinion that the Palaeozoic deposits in the area were essentially the same as in the Silurian levels in England and Wales. There were few or no igneous rocks.

Imperial Government authority was obtained through the good offices of Baron de Brunnow, His Imperial Majesty's representative at the Court of London, who had strongly recommended the project to the Czar.

Murchison set off therefore with de Verneuil enthusiastically in May 1840 and went straight to Berlin. They had already learned much from von Buch and Humboldt, who had travelled right across Russia to the Chinese border. Murchison wrote to Charlotte, 'The morning with Ehrenberg was arranged by Humboldt, who accompanied us, and I never in my life enjoyed two or three hours more intensely. To have the wonders of the infusorial creation clearly explained by the discoverer himself, and the whole illuminated by the flashes, episodes, and general views of "Der Humboldt," was enough to stir up every sympathy of a naturalist. We little know, at least we do not know enough, in England of Ehrenberg's immense knowledge. He is not merely a microscopic but a great philosophic observer. Humboldt places him in a rank above Cuvier, on account of the superior soundness and accuracy of his discoveries. . . Tell Sedgwick that I am super-saturated with proofs of the correctness of our views, and that I shall be certain to bring home much grist to our common mill. Also from Berlin, Murchison wrote to Whewell, suggesting that perhaps the following year, instead of a meeting of the British Association, there should be arranged an international congress of men of all sciences. He proposed that Frankfurt, easily accessible from England, France and Italy, would be a good choice of venue and that Humboldt would make an excellent Chairman. The idea was not in fact pursued for many years.

Murchison and de Verneuil also met other eminent geologists, including Baron Alexander von Meyendorff, who persuaded them to join him on an official government-sponsored expedition into northern Russia. They were joined by two naturalists, Count von Keyserling and Professor Blasius. The party was accompanied by a young Russian officer, Lieutenant Koksharoff, who later gave excellent service to his country's geology and mineralogy. However, Professor Blasius fell ill and could not take part in the tour. After only three weeks, Murchison's reluctance at not being in sole control of the party led to him, Verneuil and Koksharoff going their own way at a more convenient pace to their research.

They spent two months moving steadily across the great lake country to Archangel and the White Sea, assessing the mineral wealth, particularly the prospect of finding coal. They found that the rocks were of greater age than coal-bearing strata and therefore there would be none. They worked their way up the River Dvina and its tributary the Vaga to Vologda, going south-eastwards to Nijnii Novgorod and then back via the Volga valley to Moscow. Finally, having covered some 4000 kilometres, they returned north-westwards to St. Petersburg. They had hired a light carriage and driver, with a team of six horses pulling it at a great pace. Murchison later described their transport, 'With four ardent little steeds in hand, all abreast at the wheel, and two before, conducted by a breechless boy who is threatened with death if his horse backs or falls, your bearded Jehu rattles down a slope at a headlong pace, and whirling you over a broken wooden bridge with the noise of thunder, he charges the opposite bank in singing "Go along, my little beauties – fly on, from mount to mount, from vale to vale, - 'tis you that pull the silver gentleman" – (their delicate mode of suggesting a good tip); "'tis you, my dears, shall have fine pastures."'

This rapid progress did not interfere with geological observation, as the ground was so thickly covered with clay or sand that none of the underlying rocks could be seen. There were few creature comforts, the group having to find shelter for the night sleeping on the floor of a peasant's shack. Murchison held the peasantry in high esteem, finding them patient, good-natured, courteous resourceful and cheerful. He remembered long afterwards the quality of the tea offered to them after long days of travel. Any food available in the country was of pretty poor quality, so they picked up provisions wherever possible. 'We dined on our portable soup, with an egg or two, followed by the inside of our roast beef, the exterior being by this time (therm. 80°) in a greenish mouldy state.' They fared better in large towns; at Archangel for example the Governor and the English and French Consuls offered assistance and hospitality.

They were able to complete their geological explorations quite quickly, because the regional structure was simple and widespread and only a small number of traverses were sufficient. 'Three causes impede geological researches in Northern Russia: 1st, The flatness and unbroken surface of the country; 2d, The thick cover of drift and alluvium; and, 3dly, More than anything, the suspicion of the peasants, who never would give information, inasmuch that they believe that you are in search of something by which they may be taxed or oppressed by some order of the Government, or its employés.'

Nevertheless, they did gain useful knowledge from the people, particularly about where they might view appropriate sections. At Usting they met the man who had supervised the sinking of a 325-metre shaft in frozen soil at Yakutsk. Initially he had encountered twenty metres of alluvium, the rest being in hard grey limestone, with strata of shale and coal. Putting all their information together, the group were able to establish an ascending series of Silurian, Old Red Sandstone and Carboniferous deposits, not hardened or distorted as in Britain, but flat and only partly consolidated. The crystalline rocks looked young, but they were able to recognise characteristic fossils, which enabled them to determine their true relative age. The chief physical relationship of these Palaeozoic rocks of the northern and central provinces was established beyond doubt.

Most importantly they found Old Red Sandstone fishes in the same strata as Devonian marine shells, clearly linking the two, a proof of Murchison and Sedgwick's contention that the rocks of north-east Scotland (where Hugh Miller had found the fishes) were contemporary with those of Devonshire. Before he left he received a formal request from the Russian authorities to continue his investigations the following year and they promised their support.

Murchison returned home in time for the 1840 meeting of the British Association, held in September in Glasgow, where he was able to report his remarkable discovery. He presented the first geological sketch map of the regions. He was still General Secretary, and so had many duties, minor in themselves but combining to form a considerable workload. He formally proposed the international congress of science he had suggested earlier to Whewell.

Sedgwick did not attend and Murchison wrote a report of the meeting to him, part of which read, 'Agassiz's arrival was very opportune, for he confirmed the identification of the Russian and Scottish fishes. I also resolved to pull out Hugh Miller of Cromarty, and other Scotsmen of the north, and on the last day I gave an exposé of all that you and myself did in the beginning of this foray, and held up our sections and our Dipteri. Agassiz followed, and ended by naming the curious new winged creature Pterichthys Milleri.'

After the meeting, Roderick and Charlotte enjoyed some fine hospitality in Scotland, before returning to London. Roderick much enjoyed a cigar or pipe, and during the winter of 1840-41 he proposed the foundation of a new club which would allow the free use of tobacco. It would be called 'The Smokers' or 'The Raleigh'. He pointed out that many clubs in London insisted that smoking only be allowed in some cheerless attic. The suggestion did not receive very much support and was dropped.

Murchison turned back immediately to his interest in Russian geology. He wrote an article for the *Quarterly Review* entitled 'Tours in the Russian Provinces'. He also prepared a memoir with Sedgwick on the continental Devonian rocks, and drew up an account of his Russian sortie for the Geological Society. In view of the support he had been promised by the Russians, he now determined to strike right into the heart of the country and survey the Ural Mountains. This would involve a much more prolonged absence from England than before and he felt he should resign his position with the British Association. He also had obligations to the Geological Society, but getting wind of his plans his colleagues there voted him into the chair, so that he enjoyed prestige and status.

Two days before leaving for Russia, Murchison wrote to Sedgwick, 'To cleanse an Augean stable filled with Rhenish, German, and Russian fossils, and to leave the home of the British Association clean swept and all in order, has been no light work for the last fortnight. To make the map for our memoir gave me no small trouble, but now all is done, and the whole concern is ready to go to press, if the Council does not turn crotchety and puzzle-headed. If they do, we must publish elsewhere without loss of time, for the data are good. . . . I am off the day after tomorrow. . . . God bless you. Go to Plymouth [the venue for the 1841 meeting of the British Association] and fight my battles. It is now your turn.'

Murchison, accompanied by de Verneuil, whom he had grown to like very much, set off for St Petersburg. He knew that his friend's wide knowledge of early fossils was going to be most useful and would supplement perfectly his own forte of identifying geological structures. They routed first to Paris, where Murchison sounded out the opinions of the local geologists in respect of the work he and Sedgwick had done in the Rhineland and Devonshire. He was able to advise Sedgwick by letter that their memoir was eagerly awaited and there was general acceptance of their findings.

On their way to Berlin, Murchison and de Verneuil were threatened with arrest as they entered Prussian territory, on a charge of issuing false notes (which they had unwittingly obtained in Paris). Von Humboldt vouched for them and saved them from embarrassment. In the capital they acquired such information as there was about Russian geology and went on to St. Petersburg, arriving on 30 April.

The city was then the capital of Russia and the Czar's eldest son and heir was about to marry. There was much celebration and Murchison realised that not only would the proceedings be diverting, but they would also present him the opportunity of meeting senior government officials, from whom he hoped to receive official support during his survey. Through the British Embassy he obtained a much-coveted invitation to the Imperial Palace and wrote to his wife, 'The last few days have given us pleasant dinners, at [the British Ambassador] Lord Clanricarde's, at the French Ambassador's, at General Tcheffkine's [Chief of the Imperial School of Mines], where we settled our line of march, at the Minister of Finance's, Count Cancrine, and, yesterday, at Prince Butera's. The last was the most sumptuous of all these feeds, many Circassian lacqueys, and mushrooms in every dish. From General Kisseleff, the Minister of the Imperial Domains, I had a history of the successive denudations of the wood of each region of Russia, and how each denudation had proceeded from south to north. Herodotus describes the regions bordering on Turkey, now grassy steppe, as dense forests. This being for centuries the great line of march of Tartars and Easterns towards Europe, was cleared first; secondly, a middle region, half wood, half arable, as at Moscow, etc.; thirdly, the present forest region, all in the north.

'The event which charmed me was the great Court ball of Wednesday, on the occasion of the marriage, to which we were invited by his Majesty's order. The entrances to the wonderful Winter Palace are so numerous that you are not surprised when you perceive how a thousand star-and-gartered eminences and well-dressed women have all within an hour found their way into the "Salle Blanche." The whole of this exquisite palace being re-built and re-gilt, it is now in full beauty, and the blaze of light, the elegance of the candelabras, and the masses of gold, quite rivet attention. We have no notion of lighting, and I now understand the criticism of the foreigners who attended our Coronation.

'We waited for our presentation, which took place in about half an hour, when the Emperor came up to Lord Clanricarde, and asked for me, saying to me, "You have travelled a great deal in our country, and intend to do so again." On my thanking his Majesty for the kindness of my reception, he cut me short by saying, "C'est à vous que nous devons nos remerciments profonds de venir parmi nous pour nous éclaircir et de nous être si utile. Je vous prie d'accepter mon personnel,' etc. He then asked if that was not my companion near me, and De Verneuil had his talk; but my excellent friend being short-sighted, had mistaken the Emperor, so that when his Majesty left us, De V. turned to me coolly and said, "Eh bien! C'est un homme très agréable que ce Grand Duc." "Mais c'est l'Empereur, mon cher!"

'It was however in the advanced part of the evening that I really became intimate with the Czar. I had glided through all the apartments, and was seated in converse with Count Stroganoff, when the Emperor appeared, and we were all on foot. He selected me, and leaning against a pilaster began a regular conversation, asking me my opinion on various parts of the country. After I had told him where I had been, he said, "Great traveller as I am, you have already seen large tracts of my country which I have never visited." He then got me to open out on my own hobby, and put me quite at home; I ventured on my first endeavour at explanation, by stating how dearly I was interested in the structure of a country the whole northern region of which was made up of strata which I had spent so many years in classifying and arranging in other parts of Europe; how their vast scale in Russia had surprised me, and how they offered evidences which were wanting in the western countries. We then talked of coal, and I ventured on a geological lecture in order to explain where coal would not be found, the uses of our science, etc. I ushered it in by saying that I was certain that his Majesty liked to know the truth, and my honest opinion, and he instantly said, "Surtout, parlez franchement." Having given him the Silurian reasons against any coal deposits worthy of the name in any of the very ancient rocks on which his metropolis was situated, and a general view of the A B C, to all of which he listened most attentively, I then comforted him about the great coal-field of the Donetz, in Southern Russia, to which I was destined to go. "Coal," I said, "was to be looked for in the south, and not in the north, which seemed a providential arrangement, as the forests were still plentiful in the latter, but annihilated in the former tracts. "Ah!" said he, "but how we have wasted our forests! What disorder and irregularity has existed! It is high time to put a stop to such practices, or God knows what would have been the state of the Empire, even under the reign of my son!" I then offered a few words in favour of the Crown peasants of the north, against whom the wood-cutting remark was directed, and spoke of their intelligence, honesty, and the absence of all great crimes, and how it astonished us to travel through so wide a space, sleeping with our doors open, and in lofts or where we could, without being robbed, and in tracts where no soldiers or police existed. "Oh!" added he, "we are not however so savage as to allow such things."

'After asking what was to be the length of our next tour, and what we hoped to find out and see, he desired me to express every wish to his officers, and all my wants should be supplied.

'He inquired about my former career, in what arms I had served, where and when, whether I was married, whether my wife ever came with me. On my saying that the day was when you were always at my side, and sketched and worked for me, he added, "C'est ainsi avec ma femme, mais hélas sa santé ne le permet plus, elle a eu quinze couches [fifteen confinements!]." Thus he chatted away, and talked of his children, and the happiness of his social circle.

'On my saying that I had served in infantry, cavalry, and staff in Portugal, Spain, and Sicily, his Majesty evidently took to me, for he said that his doctrine always had been that the army was the best school for every profession, and he was right glad to see that it made a good geologist. I then expressed how strong a desire I had to see the Russian army, adding that I had been out at six in the morning in the Champ de Mars, and had already seen his Majesty working some regiments of cavalry. "What!" said he, "talk of that morning drill; we were all dirty and not fit to be seen: to-morrow you shall see us better." And then calling General Benhendorff, "Donnez un bon cheval à M. Murchison pour la Grande Parade." He then added, 'Mais c'est à Moscou que vous deviez nous voir parmi nos enfants – c'est ainsi que l'Impératrice et moi nous appelons nos Russes."

'He talked with favour of his good English friends, and how well they had always served him. "Alas!" said he, "we have just lost two in the space of a few days, and on Friday we bury Admiral ---------, an excellent officer and a very brave man, whom I greatly regret."

'Two days had passed, and amidst my thousand occupations I had forgotten the Emperor's words. On Friday morning, when in my dressing gown, á la Russe, at breakfast, the son of old Mrs. Wilson, our landlady, rushed in exclaiming, "La, mother, only think of it! At eight o'clock the Emperor came in a single drosky to the English Church, and had to wait I know not how long before the parson came, and then he went through all the ceremony." The old Admiral, being a Protestant, was buried in a vault under the English Church. I then bemoaned my want of tact in not having had my uniform on and ready at the church to meet the great man who thus honoured the memory of my countryman.'

During the following week, Murchison was distracted from geology by court life and courtiers. He attended a ball given by the newly-married Czarewitch. However, he made time to deal with the preparations for his expedition, which was planned with the help of General Tcheffkine.

The Russian put forward Count von Keyserling, a particularly observant geologist, to accompany the explorers, together with Lieutenant Koksharof who would help smooth their way. The plan was to make a series of traverses of the vast central and southern provinces and to examine as well as possible the Ural Mountains. The party would split up and come together again to compare notes, with the hope that the work of two summers might be condensed into one.

They were at last ready and set out for Moscow, with the intention of examining the outcrops of limestone and thin seams of coal to the south of the city. The Emperor had invited them to see him amongst his true Russians, so they returned to Moscow. They drove to the Kremlin, where they were found a place on a high balcony, to watch the Czar present his heir-apparent to his people. Below them was a crowd of at least 20,000 Muscovites milling round him in adulation.

****

Saying farewell to Moscow, they began a five-month journey, which, with diversions, would extend to some 14,000 miles, passing through Vladimir and the vast cupiferous region east of Kazan and around Perm and on into the Ural Mountains.

The first part of the journey as far as Kazan provided little of geological interest, but here they were fêted and banqueted by the Vice-Governor, who insisted on showing them the collections at the university, even though the local professors had already offered to do so. Farther east, they encountered more of the same rocks, consisting of endless red sandstones and marls. Murchison did not fully understand them at this stage, but later came to identify a new division, the Permian, which he named after the extensive province of Permia. (In due course this was seen to include well-known sediments in Germany and the Magnesian Limestone in the north of England). They passed through the town of Perm, which was, in the next century, appropriately, but entirely coincidentally, renamed Molotov, meaning 'Man of the Hammer'. It has since returned to its original identity.

Murchison noted in his journal that they overtook a group of about a hundred and fifty men and women, manacled and closely guarded, being marched into exile. 'Thank God that in England we have the sea for our high-road to banishment; for such scenes are very harassing,' he wrote.

The ascent towards the Urals was very gradual and it was difficult to say exactly when they entered the mountain region. Although the peaks were around 5,000 feet (1550 metres) above sea level, the bases were on a high plain and the hills were not very impressive. Murchison likened them to the North Downs of Surrey. He would not have had any idea of orogenies resulting from tectonic plate movement. We know now that the Urals mark the collision point of two landmasses at the beginning of the formation of Pangaea about 250 million years ago. Eventually the travellers reached the gold-mining town of Ekaterinburg (now Sverdlovsk), where they found comfortable accommodation in an inn.

The vast plains to the west had horizontal strata, which masked those beneath them and the only natural sections were river valleys, which had cut down into them. However, the Urals provided the opportunity to look at the outcrops of strata that might have been exposed by the formation of the mountains, to establish their thickness and fossil content. The group split into two pairs and spent several weeks researching parallel tracts, occasionally meeting up at the chief mining establishments to compare their findings. In this way they ascertained the general structure of the mountains and were able to compare the main masses of rocks with those they had found elsewhere in Europe.

The four explorers were hindered by the total lack of any decent maps. Murchison wrote, 'Were I Emperor of Russia, I would make verily at least one thousand of my lazy officers work for their laced coats, and produce me a good map, or they should study physical geography in Eastern Siberia. Excepting General Tcheffkine and a few, very few, I never met with any man who knew how to handle a map. It is really an affair of an hour to get a governor to make his way upon a map along a well-beaten road. I never shall forget my surprise last year at Nijnii Novgorod, when the Government House was ransacked for a map, upon which my line of march to the south of Moscow was to be traced. At length what came forth from this centre of Russian wealth and commerce, in the very fair of Nijnii, and in the Government House? – A district map of Schoubert's which I have so anathematised? - No, but one of the little three-rouble maps which the common traveller buys, with simply the names of the chief places and small towns! The same occurred at Kostroma, where the Governor had no other.

'If such be the case in the heart of Russia, how are we to expect that the best-informed natives here in the Urals should have any idea of their broken and diversified region? Russia must produce geographers before she can expect to have geologists. The cost of a single regiment of cavalry would effect this great national work; and would that the Emperor could be led to see the desirableness and efficacy for all good measures of internal improvement! I never yet heard a Russian speak of any place as being east, west, north, or south of such a point, but merely as so many versts [one verst was slightly more than a kilometre] from this or that town. Ask him in what direction and he is dumb. First he will say it is to the right or to the left, according as he may have travelled; and it is only by a serious cross-examination, which would puzzle a barrister of the northern circuit, that you can guess at something like the fact. But alas! After fancying myself informed, how wide have I found nature from their mark! Here, for example, you will find people disputing as to whether a leading place, such as Stataoust, is to the east or west of the Ural; and as for the roads, they trust to their clever peasants, stout horses, and ever-resisting tarantasse.'

The lack of reliable maps hindered the geological research but was not allowed to prevent the party from moving on, even in the remotest areas. Another extract from Murchison's journal reads, 'A route from the Zavod [mining station] of Chrestovodsvisgensk across the Ural chain to the valley of the Is, on the eastern watershed, was now to be undertaken, as arranged in our programme. But this was no slight affair, inasmuch as no party had travelled by this old and abandoned corduroy road through the forests and sloughs for many years, yet, by sending peasants across, arrangements were made.

'At 3 a.m., 2d July, I roused the whole party, and at $\frac{1}{4}$ past four we were in march from the Zavod, being a party of twenty cavaliers of most grotesque and varied outline. The President of the Geological Society need not describe himself. The Vice-President of the Geological Society of France sported his long blue Spanish cloak, and a broad-brimmed, round-topped, Moscow grey hat, which, on the back of a Wouvermann's grey horse, formed an essential item in the motley group. Herr Graube, the Master of the Mint, who led us, had his long boots above his knees, and large furred coloshes, with his little German cap. Von Keyserling, in his green cap and jacket, bestrode a gallant brown, and his servant, Juan the Venerable, turned out on a Russian saddle in a long black cloak, on a white Cossack-like beast. The Ispravnick of the district, who honoured us, was a sort of sub-military-looking figure, with spectacles and Life-guard boots, superadded to a black shooting-jacket. The German doctor of the Zavod, a most obliging man, was mounted on a capital iron-grey, with high action. Lastly came our two Russian officers, Karspinski and Koksharoff, both of whom were knocked up by our rapid ride of yesterday. The former, dreading the result, today had strapped a large pillow on his Russia-leather red and yellow demi-peak saddle. Our bearded fellows were perhaps the best for the painter, with their caftans, double-coned hats, and long boots; one armed with an axe behind; another with de Verneuil's gun in hand; a third with long Turkish pipes; and others astride of animals carrying sacks, bags and beds.

'Our start was somewhat cheerless as to weather, for the day looked lowering; and in a few minutes we were in the interminable boggy forests which fringe the flanks of the Ural. It was soon evident that all haste was in vain. The sloughs exceeded all that my imagination had conjured up. The road was a sort of bridle road, not to be described to English understanding, for it consisted in most parts, and for ten or twenty versts [seven to fourteen miles] of planks and round trees, most of them rotten and breaking, placed over the quagmires here and there, the track along which seemed hopeless, but for the dexterity of a Russian horse. If the plank broke and his leg went in up to the hock, he pulled it leisurely out, whilst with the other he was fighting his way up the rounded slippery single plank which remained. If his tread on one end brought the other up in his face, he would gently and evenly move on till the equilibrium was established, and he gained another safe footing. Add to this, massive trees, including the noble Pinus cembra and others, lying across the road, immense roots branching in all directions, sedge and long grass up to the horse's belly, and you may have some idea of a bridle road in the Ural.'

The group had to concentrate on picking their way along such a difficult path, which left little time to observe the geology, but occasionally they could climb out of the forested area and catch a glimpse of some of the mountain peaks. At the Katchkanar, in the North Ural, the terrain was described as 'rough splintered crags, shooting high over the damp sombre forests, and nourishing in their crevices and amid their slopes a bright and luxuriant vegetation which recalled that of some Swiss valley. From this peak they could look on one side over the far rolling sea of dark pine, with here and there a snow-streaked summit rising island-like out of it; on the other side lay the vast plains of Siberia, with the level featureless surface, and to the eye at least with the boundless horizon of a great sea.'

Near Stataoust the party was able to climb to the watershed between Europe and Asia. 'Clambering up to the summit, and with one leg on either continent, we sang "God save the Emperor." In this sequestered spot, however, neither officers nor workmen knew the present national air, which I had heard at St. Petersburg and Moscow, but began to chant our old "God save the King," which they had sung since the time of Peter the Great. I then hummed this new air, and this music of Levoff was thus first given out in the western borders of Siberia.'

The team took advantage of the natural sections provided by the course of streams and rivers, some of which had been modified with dams and waterfalls or diverted into lateral reservoirs by the local miners. Murchison wrote in his journal, 'Descending the river Issetz in canoes, between rocky banks of micaceous schists and granite, we came to the mill of Paulken, where the miller offered us tea, observing that his first love was God and the Emperor, the next strangers; for he had travelled in Russia, and knew the value of hospitality. The descent of this river is quite unique, for the water traveller must quit his canoe at every one of the hundred mill-races. There are upwards of two hundred of these mill-dams between Ekaterinburg and Kamensk. At every one of these, one's goods, chattels, and self must go out and in, and his canoe be shoved over the rough roots, sticks, and blocks (often held together by large blocks of stones), and dropped some eight or fifteen feet as the case may be. No ordinary traveller can execute this journey without great loss of time and patience. For us the authorities were so active that at each stoppage a multitude was waiting to get us through. The sub-officer put every "starosta" in play, and our descent was a regular press. "Stupai, pikarea, poshol!" and on we went (at what cost it matters not in this land), carrying with us the inmates of one village till we reached the next. No one who has not descended this Siberian river would believe how much comfort and industry appear on its banks. No mill, numerous as they were, was without six or more little carts before it. A dense population lives all along the Issetz. Good white large churches rise up here and there, and everywhere the cottages are nice and clean.'

Von Keyserling and de Verneuil had gone off to make independent observations and the party met up again at a mining station on the Serebrianska, a tributary of the Tchussovaya, which flows westwards from the Urals into the Permian lowlands. Murchison's journal had the following entry: 'The descent of the Serebrianska was one of the most memorable days of my life. The distance to be accomplished by this winding stream was seventy versts, or nearly fifty English miles. When I went to rest, the bed of the river was almost quite dry, with not water enough to drown a rat, and yet we were to effect the miracle of floating down in a six-oared boat. When I awoke a furious stream was rushing down, and the natives were beginning to get canoes. The good commandant [M. Moskvin], having the Imperial order that I was to descend by water, had let off an upper lake [the Zavod], and thus made a river in a fine dry sunny day!

'The waters having been let off for us, and the river bed filled, we effected our embarkation amid three cheers. The river was muddy, and had rocks hidden, with very sharp curves of the stream. With a hundred groundings and stoppages, we got tired of our big boat of honour, and took to the canoes. These answered well for a while, but trusting to shoot through some stakes and nets (myself on my back at the head of the canoe), we (i.e. de Verneuil and myself) were capsized in a strong current. I saved my notebook (see the stains), but my cloak, bag, pipe, etc., went floating down. A curious scene followed, after we had scrambled out to the shore. The other canoe shot by and picked up our floating apparatus. Fortunately this letting off the waters had brought down some natives to catch fish, and they had a fire, by which we dried ourselves, whilst their large wolf-dogs lay around us. When we re-embarked, we shot several ducks (Merjanier), and here and there found limestones and shales striking to the N.N.W. Some of the limestones were charged with Devonian fossils.

'After this, evening began to fall. Saddles, anticlinals and synclinals arose in magnificent masses on the rocky banks, but our boat-bottom was soon knocked

View from, the summit of the Katchkanar,
North Ural, looking northwards.
(from *Russia in Europe*, vol.1, p. 392)

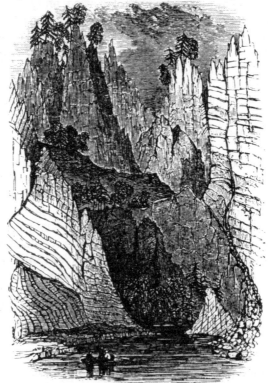

Gorge of the Tchussovaya, west flank of Ural.
Contorted Devonian and Carboniferous rocks.
(from *Russia in Europe,* vol. 1, p. 386)

to pieces by grounding at least a hundred times, and whisking round as in a waltz at each shock. It now filled so rapidly that we had just enough time to escape. We had then a fine evening scene. We landed on shingle, and got into the forest, not having seen a house or hut for fifty miles. The dense wildness of the scene, the jungle and intricacy of a Russian forest, can never be forgotten. We had to cross fallen trees and branches, and to force through underwood up to our necks.

'After our various night evolutions, sometimes by land and sometimes by water, we finally reached our "derevna" (Ust Serebrianska) at two a.m., wet up to the middle, by walking through moist jungle and meadow. Our men were very amphibia, and required no food. They had been half the day in that stream, pulling, hauling, shoving, and shouting, and never eating or drinking. We had to awake the chief peasant's family, and were soon in a fine hot room, with children sleeping all about.

'I awoke with the bright sun, after three hours' rest, and pulling my shoes out of the oven, and my dried clothes from the various long poles, proceeded after a warm tea to embark on the Tschussovaya, into which the Serebrianska flows. The Tschussovaya being a much larger river, we had no difficulty in boating down it, and we had a most instructive and exciting day, as we passed in the deep gorges of Devonian and Carboniferous limestone, here thrown up in vertical beds to form peaks, then coiled over even like ropes in a storm, or broken in every direction. Making many sections, with many memoranda, the 17th June was finished.

'On the following day we worked away down the river in the same great leaky boat as before, the boatmen singing their carols, and abusing the Ispravniks and proprietors who force them to drink bad "vodki" or whisky by their monopoly. Other songs were gentle, plaintive love ditties, so unlike what our coarse country fellows would sing. With no stimulants, getting but black bread, and working in wet clothes, for they were continually in the river shoving the boat on, they sang in rhymes, one of which as translated by Koksharoff was:-

> "My love she lives on the banks of a rapid stream,
> And when she goes to the garden to pull a rose, she thinks of me."

'Another of these ditties began – "Mary, come back from the bower." A third was a comic song, quizzing a soldier who got into a house when tipsy. A fourth was a jollification of peasants in a drinking-shop, to beat the maker of bad brandy, with a famous loud refrain in which all the boatmen joined heartily.'

The strata around the Zavod had been crystalline in character, convoluted and dislocated. They were flinty, fissile schists, often of purple plum colours, with courses of quartzite and metamorphosed sandstone, occasionally highly ferriferous and frequently repeated by flexure. Forty versts lower down, the grauwacke schists folded under the first limestone the party observed, and shortly afterwards they encountered other Silurian limestones. Another two versts took them past strong-bedded black limestones, with fossils indicating that they were of similar age to strata in south Devonshire and the Eifel.

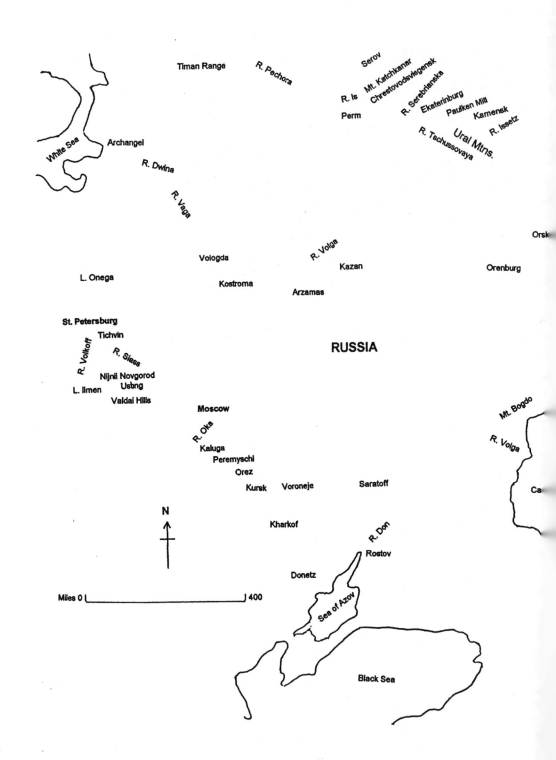

Some of the locations in Russia visited by Murchison in 1840 and 1841

When the adventurers found themselves in mining stations, they were met with great hospitality, with dinners and expensive wines provided in their honour. The post was, not surprisingly, irregular, and contact with home was almost non-existent, as they were moving from place to place. Nevertheless, his wife and friends in England were often in Murchison's thoughts.

They had crossed and recrossed the range on seven different parallels between latitudes 60° and 54° N, from Serov to Orsk, one half of the party breaking off to examine the Asian side and the other the European.

The Imperial document they carried with them ensured hospitable treatment and Murchison remembered for the rest of his life the kindness he experienced from the Russian people. Nevertheless, the travellers had to steel themselves for some pretty uncomfortable quarters and sometimes indifferent food.

The expedition was now to turn its attention to the coalfields north of the Black Sea. En route they passed through Orenburg, where Murchison took the opportunity to enjoy the hospitality of General Perovski, the town's Governor, who was at that time living in great comfort in his country quarters on the north-eastern edge of the Steppe. The General showed him a much better map than he had so far seen, and this tempted him to take one more look at the geology of the Urals. The team recrossed the mountains in their central part and collated their work on the northern and southern sections. Finally, they had to leave the pleasant countryside of the Ural foothills and face the 600-mile monotonous journey south-westwards to the Sea of Azov.

To the south of the Urals, they came into the steppe country – 'wide, monotonous, featureless plateaux, the withered grassy surface undulating to the south and west, whilst to the east all is boundless even. Not a glimpse of what may be called the Ural mountains. The country becomes more decidedly southern; or, in other words, bare, barren, and bad. Dried dung, piled up, is now used in place of wood, and the Kirgiz and Kalmuck faces appear under the military uniform in very poor villages. The road now quits the very low eminences on which the station is placed, defended by men of all arms, including Cossacks, and passes along the wide sea of the Steppe. Low bushes of a sort of Myrica are mixed with a little culture of oats and corn. The very road was grassy, and we galloped by the first armed mounted archer Bashkirs I had seen, with a stout double bow, and twenty heavy arrows. They are used in protecting the conveyance of goods.'

The Bashkir had no sympathy with the geologists in their search for mammoth and other fossils found in the gold deposits and old alluvia of the region, saying, 'Take our gold if you will, but leave us, for God's sake, the bones of our ancestors!' However, the explorers obviously trusted in their honesty, allowing them to go for bread into cupboards in which their money was lying openly. The food available was barely tolerable to the westerners, a staple being 'koumis', a preparation of mare's milk, but apparently Murchison became fond of it and thrived upon it.

Although they had found granite and crystalline rocks, there was no evidence of surface volcanic activity. Having looked at river channels, mining operations and every other source of information, they had been able to identify Silurian, Devonian and Carboniferous strata. They had worked from dawn till dusk, and sometimes into the night. Murchison was fond of quoting a M. Boubée. He said of him, 'This geologist used to maintain that a good deal of geological work could be done as well by night as by day. Rocks had three well-marked sounds under the hammer – Piff, Paff, and Puff! The first of these indicated the hard crystalline rocks, the second the sandstones, and the third the clays!'

Count von Keyserling had peeled off across the Kirgiz Steppe to Astrakhan, visiting the isolated Mount Bogdo, while the others followed the banks of the Volga, tracing the relationship of Carboniferous, Jurassic, Cretaceous and Tertiary deposits. As they went they explored the limits of the ancient sea of which the Caspian was then a shrunken remnant, (it is now even smaller). They went on down the Don to Rostov and the Sea of Azov, to examine the peculiar Tertiary limestone of the southern steppe and reach the coalfields of Donetz (now Doneck).

They found these to be not true 'coal-measures' but to consist of seams in Carboniferous Limestone. They were quite workable and had been mined for many years, but there were a lot of folds and faults in the rocks. Our present knowledge suggests that these were a result of the inexorable northward movement of Africa against southern Europe, which today causes volcanic eruptions in Italy and earthquakes in Cyprus and Turkey. The coal was found to die out on old crystalline rocks to the west, and to pass under Cretaceous and Tertiary deposits in the north and east.

They spent a month exploring the Carboniferous region around Donetz (Doneck). Finally they turned north, one party returning to Moscow and St. Petersburg via Kharkof (Char'kov), Kursk and Orez (Or'ol), the other following the valley of the Don to Voroneje (Voronež).

On their way north to Moscow, they came across some anomalous features in the surface deposits. Murchison wrote in his journal, 'The surface of Russia affords some puzzling problems. In passing from south to north you first meet with the tract of the northern drift, the materials of which become more and more numerous at every ten versts. Still the old rule (applied by me last year) answers perfectly, viz., the diluvia are three-fourths derived from the subjacent rocks, so as largely and loosely to indicate the zone of country you are traversing, provided you have the key to the subsoils of Russia. Thus, whilst the loose stuff was all yellow in the country composed of yellow Devonians, so to-day, viz., from Lichvin to Kaluga, you are immersed either in ferruginous, or reddish, or white sands. The latter prevail in great quantity in the horrible tracts north and south of

Peremyschl – a most wretched town, - and their presence is well explained by the destruction of the yellow and white sands of the Carboniferous Limestone; for, with exception of the section opposite to Peremyschl, and one or two rare localities, the valley of the Oka is here denuded to a width of several versts, which space is flooded in spring-time. This is one of the numerous cases which realize in modern times (viz., in spring floods) the geologist's idea (mine at least) of the condition of the earth's surface during the intermediate period, viz., shortly after emersion from the sea, when the mammoth had left his bones sticking in the mud.

'The drifting and excavation are explicable as in other places. The vast spaces denuded and broken up in the most horizontal districts explain perfectly the vast masses of local detritus in the northern governments, and their transport for 150 versts southwards.

'But how explain the Tchornaia-zem which overlaps the diluvium of the north, and is also spread over vast regions of the centre and south of Russia, sometimes in river valleys, sometimes on slopes, sometimes on high plateaux, and is always of precisely the same composition, without a trace of true pebbles, or, in short, of any extra ingredient? What colours the black loam? If it be of vegetable origin, whole forests of mighty extent must have been destroyed to produce it. But how destroyed? In all other superficial deposits, whether in bog, in mud, or in the youngest tertiaries, we find traces of the trees, branches, grasses, etc., but not a vestige have we in the Tchornoi-zem. All is black, uniform, finely levigated [reduced to fine, smooth] paste, sometimes highly tenacious, and very much so when not worked into with the plough, for after labour it works into a fine black mould. In this virgin state it is seldom to be seen, for 90 to 100 parts of all that is good in soil, from the Ural to the swamps of Poland, is already in culture. The specimens I selected, however, had evidently never been touched by plough or man; they were taken from the precipitous sides of the Oka, just after a subsidence of the cliffs which exposed the section, the lowest deposit of which is the iron sand which covers such large tracts in Vladimir, and many governments, and overlaps the truncated and denuded edges of the Devonian limestone in these parts. Perhaps it is Tertiary, but only perhaps, for we have similar ironstones under the chalk at Kursk, and similar limestones over the lower Jura shales at Saratoff.

'If the drift was, as I believe it to be, a great submarine operation, then we are to suppose that the Tchornaia-zem is the result of a great change of a pre-existing terrestrial surface? To believe in this seems to me very difficult, and for this reason, that no imaginable destructive sub-aërial agency could produce a general widespread and uniform condition. By what conceivable sub-aërial agency can this very thick black cerate have been spread out as with a mighty trowel, and fashioned to the surface over millions of square miles? If forests were destroyed to furnish it, how were they so triturated [ground to fine powder] and reduced to this black cement, that no chemist could invent apparatus to produce

105

such results, even in a crucible?

'I end, therefore, in believing that this black earth is the last covering of mud and slime which was left by the retirement of the Liassic sea, and was to a great extent derived from the wearing away of the shales of the Jurassic strata.

'If such are some of the difficulties of the Tchornaia-zem, what are we to say of the great sub-jacent masses of clay and sand of South Russia? In this way we have not a pebble of transport, nothing but a sort of clay or loam, which might well pass for "loess" [unconsolidated, wind-deposited sediment composed largely of silt-sized quartz particles]. If so, and if "loess" was produced as Lyell thinks, then all south and central Russia was one vast pond, in which all was tranquil during two epochs – 1st, that of the so-called drift, with mammoths; 2d, that of the black earth.'

The party had split up to make several different traverses of the country and joined each other in Moscow at the beginning of October. Murchison spent several days 'in condensing thoughts, comparing notes, examining von Keyserling and Koksharoff, consulting with de Verneuil and all the party, and preparing two general sections, a Tableau Générale, the map, and the report of fourteen pages to Count Cancrine [Minister of Finance, after whom the mineral cancrinite (an aluminium-silicate) had been named in 1839] on the results of the "Expédition Géologique." Also a letter was concocted to old Professor Fischer, for publication in the Bulletin de Moscou and the German periodicals, giving a slight sketch of our doings, and in which I first suggested the term Permian.'

Murchison described his last few days in Russia, 'Having travelled 20,000 versts [over 14,000 miles] in the distant provinces without losing a pin, we were twice robbed between Novgorod and Moscow of our beds and things behind the carriage. One trunk only was left in the hinder parts, and this was viced on; but besides this security, I resolved to guard it from the station where we detected our losses, and so letting down the head of the calèche, I laid de Verneuil's double-barrelled gun over the rear, and determined to bag the first thief who approached; and in this form we reached Madam Wilson's house. Besides several interviews with the old minister, Count Cancrine (who was much gratified with my report, of which he had prepared a digest for the Emperor), and a dinner at his house, and the same at Tcheffkine's, we were occupied in looking after more than twenty cases of fossils, which had arrived from our distant parts, and were deposited in the magazine of the School of Mines.

'All our reports and work being delivered in, official letters were received announcing the Second Class St. Anne in diamonds for myself, and a plain cross for de Verneuil, as a mark of the Emperor's approbation of our labours.

'We were to sail in the Nikolai steamer on Saturday the 24th, and Friday was fixed by the Emperor for seeing us – a great compliment, as it was His Majesty's working day with his ministers. On these occasions Nicholas uses no ceremony. After thanking us for taking so much pains about the Ural Mountains, and after asking if I thought the gold alluvia were likely to last much longer, he desired me to open out and explain the rolls of drawing and paper under my arm. This I did secundum artem [according to my skill]. He was serious when he was receiving his lesson about the productive and non-productive tracts of coal, and the rationale thereof, and laughing when he saw the Productus Cancrini and the Goniatites Tcheffkini inscribed upon the roll, he asked, "Quel espèce de produit est celui-là de mon ami le Comte?" "And so you have seen General Perovski? He is my good and dear friend. I hope you were pleased with him?" I had then to sing the praises, which I naturally did con amore, of the frank and gallant soldier who had been so truly kind, and also so very useful to us.

'When our geological talk was over, and he had asked us about our health, our travels, and many special points, I broached my desire to revisit Russia in 1843, with my work in hand, and on that occasion to explore the Altai [a mountain range on the borders of Russia, Mongolia and China]. "Come when you will," was his reply, "I shall always rejoice to see you, and to afford you a hearty welcome; and be assured that I am most particularly grateful for all your exertions to impart knowledge amongst us whilst you are studying the natural history of our country." And then with as hearty an "au revoir," and as warm a shaking of hands as ever took place between the oldest familiar friends, we took our leave.

'Such is Nicholas. Let those who criticise him look into his noble and frank countenance, and then let them try to tell me he is a tyrant. No; utter ignorance of the nature of the man has led to this most unjust notion. Nicholas is above all deceit, and squares his conduct on more noble principles than that of any potentate of modern times. He disdains subterfuge, and is transparent as to all his emotions. Hence if ill-served (knowing perfectly what duty is) he does not suppress his feelings. He is sometimes quick in his anger, but like all such generous souls, his confidence in his friends is unbounded. Firm and unchanging in his resolves as an Emperor of Russia must be, if he desires to reign, his entire aim is to ameliorate every institution which he can touch. But alas! So bound up is everything in Russia by forms, customs, and prejudices, that he supposes the autocrat powerful for all good, and capable of making every conceivable reform, would find himself most egregiously mistaken. The nobles and their privileges meet him here, the different bureaucracies there. Here the Minister of the State Demesnes places a veto upon some great projected change; there the Minister of the Finances tells him such a thing cannot be, or, in other words, cannot be paid for.'

Murchison's farewells were reciprocated with heartiest congratulations and good wishes, looking forward to his speedy return. He reached the mouth of the Humber on 1 November, 1841, completing his Russian journal with the words: 'Seven months and seven days have now elapsed since I left my home on a fine day in the end of March, and I hail Old England with a shining sun again after having travelled through space equal to the diameter of the earth. The Kirgiz, the Kalmuck, and the Bashkir excitements are now to give way to plain English comforts, of which I have neither tasted nor sought since I bade adieu to them.'

Over the two years, Murchison had collected twenty crates of fossils and now invited several palaeontologists to study them - Richard Owen at the Royal College of Surgeons, Louis Agassiz of Neuchâtel, William Lonsdale, the Curator of the Geological Society's Museum for the corals, and John Morris the apothecary for the plants. He had asked de Verneuil to deal with his specialities, the molluscs and the brachiopods, and undertook himself to deal with the trilobites.

Murchison's extensive notes were mainly geological and later turned into his great 1213-page work *The Geology of Russia in Europe and the Ural Mountains,* co-authored by de Verneuil and von Keyserling and published in 1845. They had ensured that John Murray would publish it by securing an agreement with the Russian government that they would buy 100 copies at £7 each.

Archibald Geikie sums up Murchison's Russian campaign thus: 'The ample record which is given in the great work by his colleagues and himself has made the general scientific results long familiar to geologists. The geological structure of the Russian provinces was now for the first time broadly sketched out and mapped so as to bring the rocks of one half of the European continent into family relationship with those of the other half. Nor were the benefits conferred only on the country in which the long and arduous journey had been made. New light was thrown on questions of general geological import, such as the structure of mountains, the physical geography of the times of the Old Red Sandstone, the classification of the Devonian and Old Red Sandstone rocks of Western Europe, the history of the earlier part of the Carboniferous period, the true order and relations of the red rocks lying between the Coal-measures and the base of the Jurassic series, the former extension of that ancient sea of which the modern Caspian and Sea of Aral are but the diminishing fragments, the southern extension of the ice-borne boulders carried during the Ice Age from Finland and the north far into the low plains of Europe, the occurrence of gold and its distribution in the old alluvia of rivers. The campaign indeed proved to be most fruitful in its issues. It raised Murchison to the same place with regard to the geology of Russia that Pallas [a German naturalist who spent six years (1768-74) exploring the Russian interior] fills in its botany. It opened out a new field for research, and paved the way for the good work which has since been done in Russia by other and later observers.

'On Murchison himself its influence was profound. It gave breadth to his method of dealing with palaeozoic rocks; it increased his aptitude in applying the evidence of fossils to determine questions of geological chronology, and it strengthened his confidence in his Silurian and Devonian work, and in the principles on which that work had been based. Bringing him too into constant and intimate association with foreigners and foreign ways of life and thought, the

Russian campaign increased in a high degree his sympathy and respect for men and things abroad, removed from him much, if not all, of that insularity of feeling of which his countrymen are so often accused, and made him more than ever the considerate friend and courteous host of all scientific brethren whose lot brought them to this country, no matter from what quarter of the globe they might come.

'Whether the influences of this bold and skilfully conducted journey were altogether beneficial may be matter for doubt. In the course of a few months the geological structure of a vast empire embracing the greater part of Europe had been sketched out – a feat to which there had probably been no parallel in the annals of geological exploration. The success of the campaign and the applause which that success brought from all quarters, were so great that a more than usually well-balanced nature might well have felt the strain too severe to keep its equipoise. From this time forward characteristics which may be traced in the foregoing narrative became more strongly developed in Murchison's character. In his letters and in his published writings his own labours fill a larger and larger space. His friends could trace an increasing impatience of opposition or contradiction in scientific matters, a growing tendency to discover in the work of other fellow-labourers a want of due recognition on their part of what had been done by him, a habit, which became more and more confirmed, of speaking of the researches of his contemporaries, specially of younger men, in a sort of patronizing or condescending way. He had hitherto been, as it were, one of the captains of a regiment; he now felt himself entitled to assume the authority of a general of division. To many men who did not know him, or who knew him only slightly, this tendency assumed an air of arrogance, and was resented as an unwarranted assumption of superiority. But they who knew Murchison well, and had occasion to see him in many different lights, will doubtless admit that these feelings were in large measure those of manner, and at the most lay openly on the surface of his character. You saw some of them at once, almost before you saw anything else. Hence it was natural enough that casual intercourse with him should give the impression of a man altogether wrapt up in his own work and fame. Yet underneath those outer and rather forbidding peculiarities lay a generous and sympathetic nature which inspired many an act of unsolicited and unexpected kindness, and which was known to refuse to be alienated even after the deepest ingratitude. The success of the Russian researches probably quickened into undue prominence some of the less pleasing features in Murchison's character, but they in no way lessened the measure of kindly interest and sympathy which, in spite of the way he often chose to show them, were those of a true friend.'

In a letter to the President of the Society of Naturalists of Moscow, quoted in the *Philosophical Magazine* of December, 1841, Murchison wrote: 'Our principal objects this year were, - 1st. To study the order of superposition, the relations and geographical distribution of the other and superior sedimentary rocks in the central and southern parts of the empire. 2nd. To examine the Ural Mountains, and to observe the manner in which that chain rises from beneath the horizontal formations of Russia. 3rd. To explore the carboniferous region of the Donetz, and the adjacent rocks on the Sea of Azof.

'Our last year's survey had pretty nearly determined the limits of the great tract of carboniferous limestone of the North of Russia. On this occasion we have added to its upper part that remarkable mass of rock which forms the peninsula of the Volga near Samara, and which, clearly exposed in lofty, vertical cliffs, and charged with myriads of the curious fossils Fusilina, constitutes one of the striking features of Russian geology.

'The carboniferous system is surmounted, to the east of the Volga, by a vast series of beds of marls, schists, limestones, sandstones and conglomerates, to which I propose to give the name of "Permian System," because, although this series represents as a whole, the lower new red sandstone (Rohte todte liegende) and the magnesian limestone or Zechstein, yet it cannot be classed exactly (whether by the succession of the strata or their contents) with either of the German or British subdivisions of this age. Moreover the British lithological term of lower new red sandstone, is as inapplicable to the great masses of marls, white and yellow limestones, and gray copper grits, as the name of old red sandstone was found to be in reference to the schistose black rocks of Devonshire.

'To this "Permian System" we refer the chief deposits of gypsum of Arzamas, of Kazan, and of the rivers Piana, Kama and Oufa, and of the environs of Orenbourg; we also place it in the saline sources of Solikamsk and Sergiefsk, and the rock salt of Iletsk and other localities in the government of Orenbourg, as well as all the copper mines and the large accumulations of plants and petrified wood, of which you have given a list in the "Bulletin" of your Society (anno 1840). Of the fossils of this system, some undescribed species of Producti might seem to connect the Permian with the carboniferous æra; and other shells, together with fishes and Saurians, link it on more closely to the period of the Zechstein, whilst its peculiar plants appear to constitute a Flora of a type intermediate between the epochs of the new red sandstone or "trias" and the coal-measures. Hence it is that I have ventured to consider this series as worthy of being regarded as a System.'

In his 1843 Presidential Address to the Geological Society, Murchison said:

'Permian System of Rocks. – On its eastern frontier, far removed from the tract to which allusion has been made, the uppermost member of the carboniferous limestones of Northern and Central Russia, distinguished by the presence of multitudes of the foraminifera Fusilina, is succeeded by the most widely spread of the Russian systems; to which, from its occupying of the whole of the ancient kingdom of Permia, we have assigned the name of Permian. You have been told, that this vast group is composed of limestones, marls, great masses of gypsum, rock salt and repeated alternations of cupriferous strata; and that it contains a flora and a fauna, of characters intermediate between those of the Carboniferous and Triassic periods. The shells are, to a great extent, those of our Magnesian Limestone or Zechstein; and, like the conglomerate of that deposit near Bristol, the Permian rocks are distinguished by the presence of Thecodont Saurians ["tooth-in-socket" reptiles, ancestral to the dinosaurs]. The interest attached to these vast deposits, which have been spread out on the western flanks of the Ural Mountains, is increased by the inferences which have been drawn, that springs and currents holding much copper in solution must have flowed from the edges of that highly mineralised and metamorphic chain, while the Permian strata were accumulating. But the great value of having worked out a fuller and richer type of a group of strata between the Carboniferous and Triassic epochs than any which exist in Western Europe, will be found in the fossil shells, the plates of which are already far advanced; for, with some species hitherto known in the Zechstein of Germany and Magnesian Limestone of England, we shall publish others which are identical with or analogous to forms that occur in rocks occupying the same position in North America.

'In America, indeed, as in Russia, these beds had been compared with every deposit, from the coal to the Keuper inclusive, whilst in our work they will be shewn to have no connection with the New Red Sandstone or Triassic group, but to occupy a definite position, truly intermediate between that system and the carboniferous. At the same time it is manifest, that although they overlie and are, as they ought to be, very distinct from the Carboniferous system, yet they contain some species of shells which occur in that division. Thus it will be made evident, that after all there now remains scarcely any real difference of opinion on this head between Mr. Phillips and myself (to which I alluded last year); for I learn from him, that in England the analogy between the fossils of the Magnesian and Mountain Limestone obtains to a far greater extent than could be supposed from any published catalogues. I trust, therefore, that the ensuing year will not be without its fruits in the production of new works on the shells of the Magnesian Limestone of our own country; I am glad to have it in my power to inform you, that Mr. King, the Curator of the Natural History Society of Newcastle-on-Tyne, is preparing some excellent materials for this purpose.

'A better acquaintance with the Permian fossils, particularly the prevalent Mollusca, induces me, notwithstanding the arguments I employed last year, to infer that this deposit, so naturally connected through its characteristic fossils with the Carboniferous strata, must be classed with the Palæozoic rocks. (My companions, M. de Verneuil and Count Keyserling, have long entertained the same views as Mr. Phillips on this point). The physical structure of Russia is also greatly in favour of this view; for, in large portions of that country, there is an entire absence of the great rupture between the Carboniferous rocks and the Magnesian Limestone, which is so prevalent in the British Isles. The examination of rocks of this age in North America leads to the same opinion; viz. that the Permian deposits must be viewed as the fourth or uppermost stage of the Palæozoic series, notwithstanding the occurrence of Thecodont Saurians.'

Roderick Murchison in 1836, aged 44
(lithograph by W. Drummond)
© Copyright The British Museum

Chapter Eight
Permian Rocks in Britain

Murchison still found time to enjoy the hospitality of landed friends. He shot game birds at Beaudesert (Leighton Buzzard), looked at the geology of Cannock Chase, addressed the Midland Geological Society at the home of Lord Dartmouth and gave five after-dinner speeches to a convention of ironmasters.

Back in London, Murchison took up his duties as President of the Geological Society with a much-enhanced reputation. He was able to entertain handsomely in his new home at 16 Belgrave Square, bought largely with his wife's inheritance. He also had to spend a great deal of time on the preparation of his forthcoming book *The Geology of Russia in Europe and the Ural Mountains*, which he would co-author with de Verneuil and von Keyserling. It was put together when his colleagues visited England in 1842, but publication was delayed while von Keyserling explored in the following summer the almost untrodden regions of north-east Russia around the River Petchora and the previously-unknown Timan Range, largely north of the tree-line. As Murchison came across anomalies, he took short trips to Scandinavia, France, Germany, Poland and Russia to gain evidence to verify his ideas on the true order and classification of the older fossiliferous rocks of Europe and their relationship with those of the British Isles and Russia. He was particularly interested in the equivalent of the Permian System.

The propositions in his earlier book, *The Silurian System*, published in 1839, were becoming more and more accepted across Europe. At the same time a sad estrangement between himself and Sedgwick, previously the closest of friends, began to develop. In February 1842, Murchison, gave a long and detailed presidential address to the Geological Society. The report of it in the Society's Proceedings runs to forty pages. In the previous ten years a great deal had been achieved, in particular in the identification of the older rocks, and Murchison could reasonably claim that much of this was down to his own strenuous efforts. He said, 'The perpetuity of a name affixed to any group of rocks through his original research is the highest distinction to which any working geologist can aspire – it is in truth his monument.' However, others complained that he was 'too omnivorous of fame, grasping at what does not belong to him.' By this they did not suggest resentment of his seeking of fame, but that he was stealing the monuments of others. In 1836, John Phillips had placed the Magnesian Limestone of Yorkshire in the Palaeozoic, but Murchison had dated it later. The angry Phillips suggested, 'It is a sort of précis on a passage of Scripture which may be falsely rendered: Let others praise thee; (if) not – (praise) thyself.' Knell (2000) observes that 'Phillips knew the risks of being a "plainspoken friend" to Murchison "among so many flatterers": he might advance (perhaps) & he might check (perhaps) my power of being useful to science.'

Murchison naturally referred to his adoption of the term 'Silurian', saying that he was proud to restore the name in view of the boast of the Roman General Ostorius, who conquered Caractacus and claimed to have wiped out the British Silures. The use of geographical terminology was appropriate, as no zoological boundary between the Cambrian and the Silurian systems had been detected. He was able to speak of the extension of the Silurian System in Europe, Africa, America, Australia and the South Seas. In other hands, the Geological Survey was progressing in South Wales and trying to delineate the boundary between the Cambrian and the Silurian. He mentioned the bone-cased fishes discovered in the Old Red Sandstone by Hugh Miller and the remarkable announcement by Christian Ehrenberg, a German naturalist, that he had found fossils of still-living species in Cretaceous rocks. He presented to Leopold von Buch the Society's Wollaston Medal (of which the first recipient, in 1831, had been William Smith).

After the meeting, Murchison wrote to Sedgwick, 'The anniversary went off gloriously, though I say so. The morning discourse was well received, and in truth I put a deal of powder and shot into it, foreign and domestic, and took so much pains as to stop my original work on Russia. . . . [I write] as well as a man can whose first soirée begins to-night with probably 200 or 300 people coming! The morning room was full, and I read for two hours without losing a man. I entered at length into the Silurian and "Palæozoic" question. . . . I defended the temporary division set up between your lower slaty rocks and my superior groups on the ground of positive observation of infraposition, and if in the end (as I now firmly believe) no suite of organic remains will be found, even in the lowest depths, which differs on the whole from the Silurian types, why then we prove the curious law that in the earliest inhabited seas of our planet the same forms were long continued.

'I took care to show that any other plan than that which we adopted would have led to fatal errors, such as "Système Hercynien" and other hypotheses, and that now all must come right, to whatever extent (and the extent can probably never be defined) the base of the Lower Silurian zoological type may be extended.'

Murchison took a major part in the commissioning of a bust of George Greenough, the Society's first Chairman and now, thirty-five years later, still an active and vociferous member. The sculpture was to grace the Society's rooms in Somerset House.

The Provincial Government of Canada was anxious to have a geological survey of their territory. They asked through the British Government for the opinion of the Geological Society as to the suitability for the job of William Logan, born in

Canada but educated at Edinburgh University. He had made a map of the coal basin of South Wales, which was incorporated into the Geological Survey. Murchison was familiar with his work and had used some of it in his Silurian map, so he was pleased highly to recommend him for the post. Logan was appointed as the first Director of the Geological Survey of Canada, a position he held for twenty-seven years. He was knighted in 1856.

In the early summer of 1842, plans that the team in Russia had made in the previous year began to come to fruition. Count von Keyserling came over to join Murchison in making a careful examination of the best sections of the older rocks of Britain. They began in the Isle of Wight and then worked westwards through Cheltenham and the Malverns, turning north into Silurian country and on into Adam Sedgwick's domain in North Wales. In the environs of Snowdon they found some of the fossils illustrated in *The Silurian System* and were thus able to extend Murchison's series much further north than before. They then cut across the Pennines and northwards to Durham, where they compared the rocks and fossils with those they had found in Permia. Underneath them were coal-measures, which also provided considerable interest. They continued northwards into Scotland to look at the Old Red Sandstone emerging from under the coal. It reminded them of what they had seen in Russia.

Turning for home, they passed through Carlisle and the Lake District, the Carboniferous Limestones of Yorkshire and Derbyshire and the Staffordshire coalfields, before again reaching the Malverns. They still could not find a dividing line between the Silurian and the Cambrian deposits, either mineralogically or zoologically. Sedgwick had agreed that no distinct assemblage of fossils had been found to belong to the Cambrian series.

Meanwhile, the Geological Survey was carefully mapping the Welsh strata. De la Beche wrote to Murchison, 'Touching the Silurian system, heaven knows where it is to end northwards in this land! It goes in great rolls, and no mistake, a long way beyond the Caermarthen (Ordnance map) sheet. No want of fossils; in fact, organics and sections all going to prove the same thing. The cleavage no doubt is abominable, but by very careful hunting of all the natural sections, and giving lots of time to it, the affair has at last come out clear enough. . . . It would be a long story to go further into the old story hereabouts; that your Silurian system must have a jolly extension at our hands over the rocks of this land seems certain.'

Andrew Ramsay, for whom Murchison had secured a lucrative post in the Geological Survey two years previously, had also been hard at work in Wales. He reported to Murchison in August, 'I have gradually gone over the whole of the ci-devant Cambrians between St. David's and Llandovery, and I can clearly show, particularly since I came here [Plumsant], that all your rocks, under a somewhat different form, spread over the surface of the land at least as far as Cardigan. . . . I should much like to show you some of the evidences of this Cambrian revolution.'

The Society's Museum Curator, William Lonsdale, who had given fourteen years of invaluable service, had failing health and felt he wanted to retire. Murchison was prominent in promoting a testimonial to him. In gratitude for his untiring work in the palaeontological and other fields, the Society presented him with a silver cup and the sum of £600 subscribed by its members. His place was taken by Edward Forbes. As a naturalist, Forbes had joined the crew of the *Beacon*, under Captain Graves, to undertake a survey of parts of Asia Minor, and had shown how a study of the history of existing species of animals could assist in the solution of geological problems. He had recently been appointed Professor of Botany at King's College, London. He joined the Geological Survey and was able to work out the natural history of Silurian and Tertiary deposits. He became an intimate friend of Murchison, De La Beche, Ramsay and others.

The winter of 1842-3 was a busy one for Murchison. He entertained widely and lavishly at his mansion in Belgravia, inviting men of letters, politics, science and art, and making personal friends of many of them. He also, of course, discharged his duties as President of the Geological Society, from which he was due to retire the following February. He prepared his address, which would pay particular attention to the impending changes in Cambrian and Silurian nomenclature.

He wrote to Sedgwick in October, 'On the 1st of next month I go to press with the work on Russia, which with amplifications and emendations is composed of the memoir referred to you last year, and two which I have read since on other parts of Muscovy and on the Ural Mountains. The country is described in ascending order, and I therefore must cast my Silurian at once into type, with a preamble on "Palæozoic rocks," which shall render my views intelligible to the Russians, for whom the work is hereafter to be translated. In doing this I necessarily give a little sketch of our own operations in the British Isles and in the Rhenish Provinces, and then go on to show how Russia completes the proofs desired, and confirms our views. Now in effecting this to my satisfaction, I wish to have your own authority to speak out concerning the Cambrian rocks zoologically considered. You know as well as myself that on those parts of the Continent which we have seen together, there is but one type of fossil remains beneath an unquestionable Devonian zone, and that we have called Silurian. The same is still more clearly exhibited in Russia in the limestones, sandstone, and shale, which lie beneath true Old Red Sandstone, filled both with fishes of Scotland and shells of Devon. The Silurian rocks of Russia, Gothland, and Sweden rest at once on the crystalline slates of the north. The same succession has been recently established (zoologically) in Brittany by Verneuil and d'Archiac this summer, though there they have inferior slaty rocks without fossils unconformable to Caradoc sandstone. Whilst these enquiries have been deciding the zoological succession on the Continent, and extending it even into Asia, our own region at home has been silent. I was rejoiced therefore when I knew you had been again into North Wales, and that you had taken young Salter [son-in-law of James Sowerby] with you, because you could then make up your mind to put your oracle out, without having it trumpeted forth by others.

'In the meantime, besides what Mr. Maclauchlan stated in respect to Pembrokeshire, De la Beche and his workmen assure me, that the whole of that tract is nothing more than Caradoc sandstone and Llandeilo flag, or Lower Silurian, folded over and over in troughs, and exceedingly altered by intrusive rocks and changed by crystallization and cleavage. They contend also that the very same identical fossils, in the very same strata as those which I have described and figured as Lower Silurian at Noeth Grüg, north of Llandovery (and only a few miles from the Old Red escarpment), are repeated over and over, up to the sea coast at Cardigan, and to the north of it. To this I cannot say nay, because in my work I have described descending passages into what I certainly conceived, without perhaps sufficient examination, to be a great inferior slaty mass, and in which I never observed the fossils in question. If their position is true it would be in vain to contend for Cambrian rocks in South Wales, and certainly not as identified by organic remains, though I am certain there are inferior slaty grauwackes at St. David's, like those of the Longmynd in Salop, which are much older than my fossil Silurian – and of this you know I have decisive proofs in Salop, where the Caradoc sandstone rests on the edges of the Longmynd. [Here Geikie notes, "This happened to be a blunder on Murchison's part; he was right as regarded the unconformability, but wrong in the position which he had assigned in the Silurian System to the overlying strata. These are what we now [1875] term Upper Llandovery (that is, at the base of the Upper Silurian series), and not Caradoc."]

'But the question is, If there are no rocks containing fossils differing from those published as Lower Silurian in South Wales, are there such in North Wales, where limestones appear in the oldest slaty masses, and the whole is expanded and broken up by the anticlinals you have so well described? As to Bala, you know that its examination will do nothing in establishing a distinction, and fortunately I have said so very distinctly in my Silurian System, and have asked the question, To what extent will the Orthidae and Leptaenae in question be found to descend into the Cambrian rocks, and if they really constitute the Protozoic type?

'I mention this now because I understand from Lonsdale that Mr. [Daniel] Sharpe is going to read a paper at the second meeting of the Geological Society, in which he is to show that the Bala limestone is nothing more than a calcareous course in the middle of the Caradoc sandstone. I do not see how he is to do this stratigraphically, but as I never made the transverse section but once, and in your company, I do not pretend to be armed with sufficient proofs that the limestone is inferior to the slaty flagstones on the eastern side of the mountain in which Asaphus Buchii and Silurian Orthidae occur; and on this point, by way of parenthesis, I should like to be furnished with your view, in order that I may keep the "Sharp" fellow in his place, should he transgress bounds.

'But to come to the question: If Bala is zoologically Lower Silurian (and that you have yourself now stated in your Letters to Wordsworth), if Coniston Water Head and Ambleside (at the latter place Keyserling and myself convinced ourselves of the same) is the same thing, and if no older rock is known to contain fossils in Cumberland, it follows, that the only fossil type which remains to be appealed to is that of the Snowdon slates. In our recent visit, Keyserling and myself collected a good many fossils both on the north and on the west flanks of that mountain, and my friend, who is a very good conchologist, came to the conclusion on the spot, that the prevalent and abundant forms are two or three species of Orthis (flabellulum and alternata) well known in Lower Silurian and Caradoc, with a rare new form of Leptaena; and Sowerby, who has since seen our lot, writes to me to the same effect, and tells me that Salter's determinations with you came to the same results.

'Now I have no intention whatever of writing upon this point, except in my exordium on Palæozoics touching Russia, where I have to treat of them over an area as large as all our Europe together. On that occasion, and also in taking leave of the geologists on the 17th of February, I must deliver my opinion. Your Wordsworth letter is before me, and is a meet subject for my comment, but I wish to have something from you touching North Wales. If this is not done, De la Beche and Co, advancing from South Wales, will have the credit with the public of correcting you. But if you now say that the slaty region to the north-west of the Silurian rocks was left undefined as to fossils, on account of your never having examined the forms you so long ago collected (and take any line you please, either to contend or not for great thickness of the lowest fossiliferous strata) then I shall be at ease, and know how to use your authority as well as my own.

'The triple zoological division of the Palæozoic rocks (exclusive of the Magnesian Limestone) is now so very generally proved to the very eastern extremities of Europe, that it is well that we who have been the agents in first enunciating it should not be frightened and driven out of our fairly won views because the Cambrian tailpiece was not finished off. For my own part, I am as convinced as it is possible to be, that we have now thoroughly ascertained not only the Palæozoic, but, as I ventured long ago to call it, the Protozoic type, and that that is no other than the striking orthidian [species of brachiopod] Lower Silurian group, which, first rising up on the flanks of old Caradoc, is extended to any thickness you please to contend for. In this last respect, however, you must have the fear of De la Beche and his trigonometrical forces before your eyes, who, whilst they give 12,000 or 15,000 feet thickness to the South Welsh coal-field, are cutting down our older rocks at a terrible rate.'

Murchison was clearly anxious to have Sedgwick's blessing on his proposed change to the Silurian base-line. He wrote a postscript to the letter: 'In the part which specially refers to what I have been writing to you about, I should, in case you will authorise me, propose to write something such as follows:- After asking "if no efforts had been recently made to determine the point if there were or not a group of older fossils than the Lower Silurian, and some paragraphs relating thereto," I go on to say, "Judging from our infraposition, great thickness, and distinct lithological characters, it was presumed (when the Cambrian system was so named) that these greatly developed inferior slaty rocks would be found to contain a class of organic remains peculiar to themselves, the more so as the few forms then discovered in them seemed to differ from the Lower Silurian types. Subsequent researches have, however, decided otherwise. In the slaty region of the north-west of England, of which by hard labours he so long ago rendered himself the master, Professor Sedgwick has now satisfied himself that the lowest organic remains which can be traced are no others than those published as Lower Silurian, whilst in revisiting the mountains of Cambria and Snowdon, whose framework he was the first to explain, he has come to similar conclusions respecting the oldest fossiliferous tracts of North Wales."

'"In the meantime, through the labours of the Ordnance Survey," etc. Then Mr. Sharpe et hoc genus omne [and all of his kind].

'This is the form in which I should wish to place the case, both because it is in my mind quite true, and also because, as I have said in my letter, I wish you to speak in your own place.'

Sedgwick did not at the time object to any of this, while making comments on other parts of the proofs, which he returned saying: 'The papers are excellent, and use my hints as you think right. . . . I have looked over the slips and made marks. . . . I did look over the peroration. It is very good.' However, in a letter to William Wordsworth he said, 'I smiled when I read this *strange passage*; but I did not think it worthwhile formally to contradict it; in omission and commission it is a virtual mis-statement of the facts.' Murchison had demonstrated the greatest care towards him, yet now he made this unfair comment. The 'strange passage' to which he referred (quoted and italicised by Sedgwick himself) was: 'We were both aware that the Bala limestone fossils agreed with the Lower Silurian; but depending on Professor Sedgwick's conviction that there were other and inferior masses, also fossiliferous, we both clung to the hope that such strata, when thoroughly explored, would offer a sufficiency of new forms to characterize an inferior system.'

Sedgwick's remarks on this passage were: 'When the author states "that we both clung to the hope that the Cambrian group would offer a sufficiency of new forms to characterize an inferior system," I can only reply, that the hope to which he clung was not derived from anything I had ever said or written; and that I had not, in 1842 and 1843, the shadow of a hope that any new system of animal life, any group of new forms 'marking an inferior system,' would be found among the Lower Cambrian groups. I had constantly expressed, and repeatedly published, a directly contrary opinion.'

After their autumn expedition of 1842, Sedgwick had written to Murchison, 'To my knowledge of the sections I added nothing last autumn, but I hoped to make out distinct fossil groups, indicating a descending series, and marking the successive descending calcareous junks. But, as I told you, I failed.' In February 1843, just before the Society's anniversary meeting he replied to Murchison's request for information, 'In regard to North Wales you know my general views. I stated last year (see the abstracts) that on unpacking my Welsh fossils I could not discover any trace of a lower zoological system than that indicated in your Lower Silurian types. I did however expect to find certain definite groups indicating a succession in the ascending steps of a vast section (certainly many thousand feet thick), and my hope was last September to prove this point, but I failed utterly, as I told you before, and at present I really know no such definite groups.'

Archibald Geikie says, 'In the beginning of his paper Mr. Sharpe stated that the view of the infraposition of the so-called Cambrian rocks of Sedgwick to the Lower Silurian of Murchison was adopted by the latter geologist on the authority of the former. In long subsequent years, Sedgwick bitterly complained that this was a mis-statement, which Murchison never corrected, but, on the contrary, proceeded to profit by, though he had abundant opportunity of rectifying it in this address. And the inference drawn is, that Murchison was guilty of disingenuous conduct unworthy of a gentleman, still more of a friend. But so far from regarding it as a mis-statement, Murchison himself repeats it in this very address. He says that he steadily relied on Sedgwick's original opinion, that great masses of the slaty rocks of North Wales lay below the Silurian rocks. His respect for Sedgwick's opinion was profound, and that opinion he believed to have been all along in favour of the infraposition of all the so-called Cambrian rocks. This belief, as we have already seen, was commonly held by geologists, and, if a mistake, Sedgwick never did anything to set it right until he found some of his Cambrian formations claimed as Silurian, when he maintained that he had never made any error in his work, except in being misled by his friend. The charge of unfair conduct on Murchison's part was utterly unfounded. Nothing could have been more candid than the way in which he acted in this matter. Equally groundless was the accusation that he had "stolen a march" upon Sedgwick, unless we are to be told that under such conduct we must include making our victim privy beforehand to the theft, and submitting for his approval the plan by which he is to be cozened. Yet Sedgwick asserted that the first intimation he had of Murchison's claim over the Upper Cambrian rocks as Lower Silurian was obtained, accidentally, some years after the seizure had been made!'

Many years later, Murchison wrote, 'That address embodied all my matured views on the classification of the older rocks, and particularly as to the unity of the Silurian System and the impossibility of manufacturing a fossiliferous Cambrian system separate from the well-recognised Lower Silurian types. Von Buch, Humboldt, and all the foreign geologists, as well as my colleagues in the work in Russia, saw the necessity of this. I therefore openly proclaimed my conviction that the masses of hard and slaty rocks of Wales to the west of my Silurian map and sections, and which were supposed to be Cambrian, before

Tarradale in 2002

Nursted House, Buriton in 2002

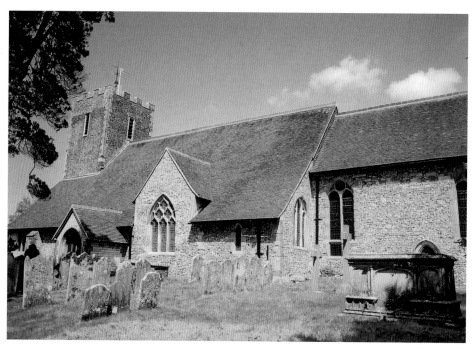

St. Mary's, Buriton

21 Galgate, Barnard Castle

Blue plaque on 21 Galgate, Barnard Castle

Trericket Mill, near Builth Wells

Waterfall in Sgithwen Brook, Trericket Mill

Possible site of 'Cavansham Ferry', River Wye

Hiro Rocks, River Wye

Murchison's Mansion, 16 Belgrave Square, London

Murchison family tomb, churchyard of St. Nicholas, Bathampton

IN MEMORY OF

SIR RODERICK IMPEY MURCHISON BART. K.C.B. F.R.S.&c.

C.C.St ANNE AND St STANISLAUS OF RUSSIA,

FOREIGN MEMBER OF THE ACADEMY OF SCIENCES &c.&c.;

DIRECTOR GENERAL OF THE GEOLOGICAL SURVEY OF THE UNITED KINGDOM,

AND FOR MANY YEARS PRESIDENT OF THE ROYAL GEOGRAPHICAL SOCIETY;

AUTHOR OF THE SILURIAN SYSTEM AND RUSSIA AND THE URAL MOUNTAINS.

BORN 1792.   DIED 1871.

HIS REMAINS, TOGETHER WITH THOSE OF HIS WIFE,

CHARLOTTE, DAUGHTER OF GENERAL HUGONIN,

ARE INTERRED IN THE BROMPTON CEMETERY, LONDON.

Memorial plaque, church of St. Nicholas, Bathampton

Up Park, near South Harting, West Sussex

Memorial near Kyle of Lochalsh, erected by Murchison to his Great Grand-uncle

Murchison's tomb in Brompton Cemetery, West London

Diamond-studded gold snuff box presented to
Murchison by Czar Alexander II in 1866
©The Natural History Museum, London.

their order and contents were elaborated by the surveyors and Sir H. De la Beche, were simply folds and repetitions of the already classified Silurian rocks of Shropshire, Hereford, Radnor, etc. It is from this date that I considered my classification to be established on the broad European scale.'

****

A matter which presented itself for Murchison to deal with this winter was the possible purchase of the island of Staffa. It seemed most appropriate that, as it was likely to come on the market, the Geological Society should acquire it as a monument to the progress of science. It is interesting today to note that Geikie says, 'It is needless to say that this project never took shape. There is little sympathy in Britain with any such fanciful notions regarding the acquirement of places of great natural interest by the State or learned societies for the good of the country and in the cause of scientific progress. Fortunately that fairy isle is too small and too barren to warrant the cost of protecting walls and notices to trespassers, and its wonders are of too solid and enduring a nature to be liable to effacement by the ruthless curiosity of the British tourist.' The National Trust was founded in 1895, twenty years after this was written!

Murchison's 1843 Presidential Address to the Society covered eighty-seven closely-printed pages and ranged not only on the subject which had occupied him so fully in recent months, but also over the general progress of geology all over the World. He presented the Wollaston Medal to two foreign geologists, Élie de Beaumont and Pierre Dufrénoy. There was praise for the work of Captain (later General) Portlock, Director of Operations of the Geological Survey in Ireland, and of Richard Griffith (knighted in 1858), who had in 1838 published the first complete geological map of Ireland. Murchison handed over the Presidency to Henry Warburton.

130

Chapter Nine
Eastern Europe and Scandinavia

Murchison had, some three years earlier, been asked by the Society for the Diffusion of Useful Knowledge to produce a small geological map of England and Wales and he wrote to Sedgwick, asking him to mark on it, from his knowledge, the igneous areas and those that consisted only of 'pure slates without fossils'. In thanking him a few days later for doing so, he was able to tell him that he had heard from the Belgian geologist d'Omalius d'Halloy that he was going to publish a new edition of a book he had written, now adopting their classification of the Carboniferous, Devonian and Silurian strata.

Now that he had relinquished his duties in London, Murchison felt he must revisit Russia and her neighbouring countries to confirm some of his findings. For the first time in many years, Mrs. Murchison accompanied her husband, with the intention of staying in a central location, while he made some of the more distant and energetic forays in his researches. They left for Paris in April, 1843, where he met Élie de Beaumont, who heard with disbelief Murchison's pronouncement that there existed in Bavaria a continuous stratum of Carbonaceous Limestone lying conformably over Devonian deposits. They had always been on friendly terms, but Murchison felt he had offended him, though de Verneuil and others were probably in the same position.

Whilst in Paris, Murchison dined with the Prime Minister, François Guizot, and the next day was presented to Louis Philippe, the elected 'Citizen King', to whom he gave a copy of his *Silurian System*. Louis showed a great interest in Murchison's maps, though he professed an ignorance of geology. He recalled that in Norway 'I was one day standing on the sea-shore, and gazing at a ship in the offing, when an old pastor of the country, eighty years of age, who was near me, exclaimed, "You only look at the sea, sir, but you do not see what is under your feet!" On doing so, I found that I was standing on gravel and seashells, a little above high-water mark. The old clergyman then continued:- "When I was young the sea washed these shells, but now it never reaches them; and so you see we believe that our land is rising!" The King added, 'From that moment I conceived that the earth is always swelling out as a balloon when it is being inflated; but pardon me if my theory is foolish and untenable!' Modern measurement confirms that Scandinavia is indeed rising, but the reason is an isostatic anomaly – the whole area was frozen over to great depth during the recent Ice Age and the removal of the weight on melting has allowed the ground to recover its earlier level above the sea.

A few days later, Murchison received a large gold medal from the King, with his head on one side and 'À M. Murchison, de la part du Roi' on the other.

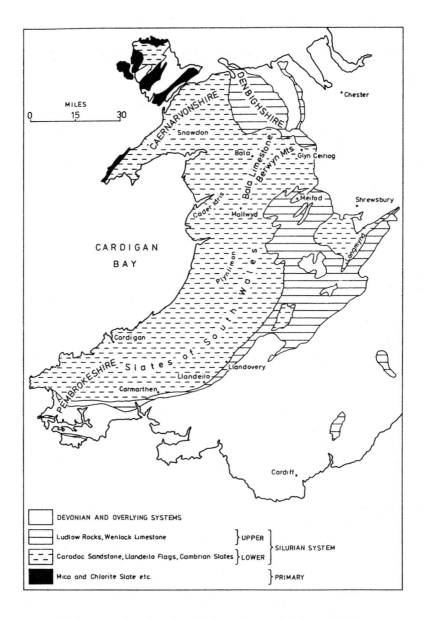

MILES

0   15   30

•Chester

CAERNARVONSHIRE

DENBIGHSHIRE

Snowdon

Bala

Bala Limestone

Berwyn Mts

Glyn Ceiriog

Cader Idris

Mallwyd

Meifod

Shrewsbury

CARDIGAN
BAY

Plynlimon

South Wales

Longmynd

Cardigan

Slates of

PEMBROKESHIRE

Llandeilo

Llandovery

Carmarthen

Cardiff.

DEVONIAN AND OVERLYING SYSTEMS

Ludlow Rocks, Wenlock Limestone } UPPER }

} SILURIAN SYSTEM

Caradoc Sandstone, Llandeilo Flags, Cambrian Slates } LOWER }

Mica and Chlorite Slate etc. } PRIMARY

Part of Murchison's map for the Society for the Diffusion
of Useful Knowledge,1843. Note the extension of the
Lower Silurian to cover most of Wales.

From Paris Roderick and his wife travelled across to the Rhineland, where Charlotte stayed at Baden and he went via Karlsruhe to Heidelberg, to visit Professor von Leonhard's museum. Murchison called him 'Igneous to the backbone, for he even believed that rock-salt, gypsum, and haematitic iron were produced by intense heat and fusion; he admitted, but could not explain, the difficulty I had had in examining the Ural Mountains, viz., why the iron-ore which is in contact with eruptive rocks is the most magnetic? On another count his disbelief in the metamorphism of great mountain masses of gneiss and mica-schist was founded solely on his own minute researches, in which he had never seen igneous effects extend more than a few feet or yards into sedimentary strata beyond the point of contact.'

Murchison went on to Berlin to talk to geologists there about Poland and the Carpathian Mountains in the south, for this was unknown country to him. He visited von Humboldt in Potsdam to show him a sketch of his *Geological Map of Russia in Europe and the Ural Mountains*. Fourteen years earlier, the explorer and naturalist had visited Central Asia with Christian Ehrenberg and the mineralogist, Gustav Rose, examining the strata which produced gold and platinum and making magnetic observations, so he was able to put forward useful comments on various points.

Von Humboldt had told the King of Prussia that Murchison was coming to Potsdam and he had asked that he come to the Royal Palace. The King had recently been to London and had there been admitted an Ordinary Fellow of the Royal and Geological Societies. They had a pleasant discussion about the building of the Houses of Parliament, and Nelson's Monument in Trafalgar Square, then turned to Murchison's travels in Russia.

Later von Humboldt told him he had come across a reference to the gradual uprising of the Continent in the *Timaeus* of Plato, written some 2,200 years earlier, and Murchison relayed Louis Philippe's anecdote from his visit to Norway.

On this trip (in 1843) a railway is mentioned for the first time. Where one had been built, it presumably made a world of difference to Murchison's comfort and speed of travel.

Murchison went on to Warsaw with the intention of gathering as much information as he could from museums, professors, Bergmeister and every other available source. He was able to persuade Professor Zeuschner of Cracow to accompany him to the Carpathians, which saved him a great deal of time and yielded a wealth of information. Geikie comments, 'Getting out of the plains into the valleys and ravines of the Tatra range of the Carpathians, he and his companion had sometimes to wade knee-deep in snow. They made many traverses of the rocks with the view of comparing the structure of the country with that of the Ural chain. Amid the heaps of detritus in some of the valleys, he speculates on the former presence of glaciers, but regards the grand source of all the gravel and waste as traceable not to any superficial action, but to the upheaval of the solid nucleus of crystalline rocks through the secondary formations at the time of the birth of the Carpathians! In such observations as these we see how completely the early lessons of waste, taught him by the valleys of the Auvergne, had been forgotten, and how thoroughly he had identified himself with the cataclysmic school of geologists.'

On his way back, Murchison routed through Cracow (Kraków) to Breslau (Wroclaw), then turned south-westwards into the Sudetengebirge to make a section of the range. He crossed the plain of northern Bohemia to Prague, where he met Joachim Barrande, who had been tutor to the Duc de Bordeaux. He had taken up studies in natural history and had first seen Murchison's *Silurian System* on a trip to Vienna. He had noticed the great similarity between fossils he had found in Bohemia and those in the book, made further research and discovered hundreds more. He published a classic work, *Système Silurien de Bohème.* Murchison was to have much discussion and correspondence with him, and in 1865 he wrote, 'I have had of course long and continued intercourse with this gifted and excellent man for the last twenty-two years, and every year I have learned to admire and esteem him more and more.'

Striking north to Dresden, Murchison enjoyed a few days' study of his old interests, art and art criticism, before going on to Berlin. Here he collected a number of letters, the most pleasing of which was from Count Cancrine, officially advising him that the Czar had presented him with a huge Siberian aventurine vase, four feet high and six feet in circumference and originating from Kolyvan on the frontier with China. It was of solid polished mid-grey chalcedonic quartz with strong reddish-orange streaks. It weighed about two tons. On its porphyry baluster-type pedestal was inscribed:

GRATIA IMPERATORIS TOTIUS ROSSIÆ
RODERICO MURCHISON
GEOLOGIÆ ROSSIÆ EXPLORATORI
MDCCCXLIII

Engraved in Russian on its steel plate stand was:

TO THE GEOLOGIST MURCHISON
IN TESTIMONY OF ITS PARTICULAR ESTEEM.
THE ADMINISTRATION OF MINES
OF RUSSIA

The vase was displayed prominently at 16 Belgrave Square and bequeathed to the Jermyn Street Museum of Practical Geology in 1872. It was passed in 1985 to the Natural History Museum, South Kensington, where it is now in store. Because it was so difficult to find such a large block and to polish such hard material, only one other similar vase was made – that presented to von Humboldt.

Murchison caught the train to Leipzig and then struck south-westwards into the Thüringerwald. Further westward he stopped at the Reichelsdorf mines, where a rather naïve Bergmeister was consistently taken in by fake fossils supplied to him by his miners. His collection had become notorious in the district, but he sold it to Murchison for eleven thalers.

At the end of July, Roderick was again united with Charlotte at Baden. They set off homewards immediately, in order to be in time for the meeting of the British Association in Cork. There had been political unrest in the south of Ireland that summer and the question of security at Cork was raised. The original proposal had been to hold the meeting in York, but the General Committee voted for southern Ireland. The arrangements for the meeting had been poorly executed and only a few members had arrived from afar. Murchison said of it, 'That which we hoped would prove to be a south of Ireland meeting, turned out to be a mere city of Cork concern. It was desperately uphill work, and the few of us who had any position were obliged to swell ourselves out and speechify, and jollify, and make the best of a very untoward thing. We were never so near shipwreck as at this Cork meeting. For myself I was so imbued with our desire to go to York that I was constantly putting in that word instead of Cork.'

Murchison had not been to Cork since he had sailed from there to Portugal in Sir Arthur Wellesley's expedition. He now took the opportunity to investigate the older rocks of south-west Ireland and spent several weeks working from Bantry Bay round to the mouth of the Shannon.

An unexpected visit to London by the Czar in May delayed Murchison in town, as he wished to see the Emperor again, because he had shown him so much courtesy and friendship. He was not ready to leave until the beginning of July and had to be back for the meeting of the British Association in York in September. This left him somewhat short of time, but he determined to visit Scandinavia, where abundant Silurian fossils had been found. His intention was to co-ordinate the Palaeozoic rocks of Scandinavia with those he had found in Russia, and through Baron Berzelius and Professors Keilhau and Lovén he obtained access to every appropriate museum collection. He wanted to identify the prominent features of the Great Scandinavian Drift, which covered large areas of the surface of Norway, Sweden, Germany and Russia. He felt that his book on Russia would not be complete without such a survey and it was unfortunate that illness prevented de Verneuil from joining him.

He wrote to a friend in Norway: 'My dear Professor Forchhammer, - I have resolved to visit Christiania [Oslo] at the meeting of the Scandinavian philosophers under Hansteen and his conjoint Presidents. I was for some time undecided about it, as I wished to get my great work on Russia finished, but finding that this is impossible before the early part of the winter on account of various delays which must always occur in extensive scientific publications, I have resolved to take flight for Hamburg and Copenhagen in the first days of July, and hope to find you still at home, that we may go on to Christiania together.

'My intention is further to traverse the country from Christiania to Stockholm, and to return by the isles of the Baltic. By this hasty visit and *your instructions* hope to render my map, which embraces a good part of Sweden, somewhat more perfect. At all events I shall see the source of all my old friends, the erratic blocks, and look at some Silurian relations in situ.'

En route, he stayed a few days in Copenhagen, where he paid his respects to King Kristian VIII, who he found had some knowledge of geology, met the scientific men of the city and indulged in some art-criticism of the bas-reliefs of Bertel Thorvaldsen. In Christiania he attended the meeting; three-quarters of those present were medical men. Murchison was proposed as President of the geological section, but, as he had no knowledge of the language he felt himself unsuitable and was delighted when von Buch was elected. On the evening of the second day, after a formal dinner attended by Ministers of State, Bishops and the Consuls of France, England and Russia, the geologists climbed to the top of the valley to the north of the town to look at *serpulae* [kinds of marine worm inhabiting beautifully coloured tortuous calcareous tubes often massed together] of existing species on the surface of the rock.

Moving on from Christiania, Murchison went first to Gothenburg, where he met Professor Lovén, who accompanied him for most of his stay in Sweden. At Stockholm he was presented to the Royal Family and spent several evenings with Jöns Jacob Berzelius, Emeritus Professor of Chemistry at the Royal Caroline Medico-Chirurgical Institute, in whose house he met some of the best scientific minds in the capital. During the day he looked for examples of the striated and polished rocks, which had now been universally accepted as the result of the passage of ice. He records in his journal the size and extent of huge ridges which run across the country, like the gravel eskers of Ireland (long ridges of cross-bedded deposits laid down by glacial meltwater) and the kames of Scotland (mounds of bedded sand and gravel with collapsed edges resulting from the melting of stagnant ice). On the way up the Baltic, Murchison left the steamer at every port of call to study the rocks and their striations and grooving. In mainland Sweden he discovered early Silurian rocks immediately above primeval gneiss, a conjunction that had not before been found. This satisfied him that his Silurian rocks did indeed contain the earliest traces of life on Earth.

Part of Murchison's plans for this trip was another visit to St. Petersburg, partly to meet von Keyserling again, to update himself on any new data for the geological map of Russia. He had undertaken to convey to Czar Nicholas a gold medal struck to commemorate his recent visit to England. It had been executed by Leonard Wyon of the Royal Mint and inscribed NICOLAUS I TOTIUS RUSSIAE IMPERATOR REGINAE BRITANNIARUM VICTORIAE AMICUS ET HOSPES 1844. Imagine his embarrassment when, on arrival at the palace he found the medal had been stolen! It was later found by the Police in a jeweller's shop.

Whilst in St. Petersburg, he took the opportunity to examine some of the nearby strata. He started to put together the first outlines of a geological map, which, because of his rather superficial and partial examination of the region was very general in content, though nevertheless useful in indicating where useful minerals might be found (and where they would not). In particular the search for coal was significant, but the authorities were also interested in finding the best building stone and limestone for new edifices and public works. They needed to know the best routeing for new railways. Throughout, Murchison remarked on the cheerful co-operation of the local people, whose watchword was 'mōjna' – literally 'it is possible' but perhaps the equivalent of the naval 'ay, ay, sir'.

Murchison returned home via Berlin, where he dined with the Royal Family and met von Humboldt again, obtaining yet more detail for his Russian map. He was back in London in the second half of September. He was very pleased with his tour of Scandinavia, for he had found something which had eluded him in Russia, the old platform of metamorphosed rocks on which the Silurian strata rested. He had seen fossils from the older rocks in numerous museums and learned more of the actions of ice. He had gained from von Keyserling details of the geology of the largely unexplored wilds of north-eastern Russia, which he had explored well beyond the tree-line to the shores of the icy sea. He had met men of science from Denmark, Norway and Sweden, and been presented to four crowned heads of Europe.

He put the finishing touches to his book, *The Geology of Russia in Europe and the Ural Mountains*, the cost of which, with delays and corrections, had trebled from the original estimate. It was finally published in the summer of 1845. Geikie's assessment was that it was a magnificent work. 'It extended to two massive volumes, the conjoint labour of Murchison, von Keyserling, and de Verneuil. The first volume was written by Murchison from his own notes and those of his colleagues; the second, treating of fossils, was the work of de Verneuil [in French, 511 pages and 46 plates]. In the first volume [702 pages and 5 plates], a *résumé* is given of what was known of palaeozoic geology in Europe and America up to the date of publication. The successive geological formations of the great Russian plains are described, and then follows a detailed account of the structure of the Ural chain. The last chapters, among the most readable and generally interesting of the whole, treat of the more recent deposits, the formation of the Aralo-Caspian basin, the gravels and drifts so widely spread over the low grounds, the range of the Scandinavian boulders, and the extent and origin of the "black earth," and later alluvia. In short the volume presented for the first time a clear outline of the geology of more than half of the Continent, and crowned the work which had been in progress ever since Murchison's earliest observations of the transition rocks on the banks of the Wye, by combining on one broad canvas a picture of the whole succession of the palaeozoic rocks of Europe.'

The entire book was translated into Russian by Major Alexander Osersky and Part I into German by Gustav von Leonard. Plate VI of the English edition of Volume I has been described as the finest hand-coloured geological map ever produced.

Though Murchison was responsible for co-ordinating all the work that went into the book, he openly shared the honour with his co-authors. It was dedicated to 'His Imperial Majesty, Nicholas I, Emperor of all the Russians' who had taken a lively interest in its production and completion. The dedication reads:

Sire,
The recent auspicious Visit of Your Imperial Majesty to my August Sovereign, and your cordial reception by my countrymen, have augmented my just pride in the privilege so graciously accorded to me, of dedicating to Your Imperial Majesty this Work, description of the Geological Structure of a large portion of Your Mighty Empire.
This privilege enables me to express the warmest gratitude of my fellow travellers and myself for the kindness with which Your Imperial Majesty has been pleased to sanction and approve researches carried on under Your own auspices, and also to record our lasting acknowledgement of the unbounded hospitality of Your generous and loyal people.
With sentiments of profound admiration of Your Imperial Majesty's great qualities as a Sovereign, with unfeigned respect for Your domestic virtues and with sincere thanks for the honours You have deigned to confer on us. I subscribe myself
Sire,
Your Imperial Majesty's
Most devoted and most grateful Servant
Roderick Impey Murchison
Belgrave Square, London, May 1, 1845.

From being totally ignorant of science and scientific methods twenty years earlier, Murchison had acquired a position amongst the greatest geologists of Europe. There was still more research to do, but from this point he tended slowly to turn more towards an interest in the development of geographical knowledge.

The Geographical Society had been founded in 1830 out of the Raleigh Travellers' Club, of which Murchison was a member. It was designed to foster the progress of geographical research by collecting and publishing travel reports, by forming a good reference library, especially of maps and charts, by keeping illustrations of the best kinds of instruments for exploration in different climates, by assisting potential explorers with information and advice, and by corresponding with other geographical and scientific societies and interested individuals. From a slow start it went from strength to strength, as we shall see. Whilst still deeply involved in the preparation of his great work, Murchison had written an elaborate address to them and was elected President, a post he subsequently held for seventeen annual terms, right up to his death. His Anniversary Addresses to the Society averaged 30,000 words. He became an earnest and influential promoter of geographical enterprise. There had grown up a particular interest in exploration of the polar regions and at the 1838 meeting of the British Association in Newcastle, a series of resolutions had been passed strongly urging the Government to fit out an expedition to Antarctica primarily to carry out important observations on terrestrial magnetism.   James Clark Ross had long experience of survey work in high latitudes and in 1831 had located the Magnetic North Pole.   Later he made a magnetic survey of the British Isles.   He was thus well suited to lead a four-year expedition to the southern continent, and set of with the *Erebus* and the *Terror* in 1839.   He was knighted on his return, having brought back a harvest of scientific information.

The two ships were not idle for long and were taken by Sir John Franklin on an attempt to find the Northwest Passage.   When he failed to return, numerous relief expeditions were sent and Murchison took a deeply sympathetic and personal interest in the tragedy.   It was twenty-two years before the whole story was uncovered and proof was found that Franklin had indeed found the Passage but been trapped by thick ice in the Victoria Strait.

Murchison had actively promoted the aims of the Society and it could count many distinguished names amongst its members.   Over the years it grew to become a very significant organisation and received a royal charter in 1859.

The 1845 meeting of the British Association was held at Cambridge under the Presidency of Sir John Herschel.   Murchison was able to exhibit an early copy of *Russia and the Ural Mountains* and he was again elected President for the following year's meeting to be held at Southampton.   The authors, having dedicated their work to Czar Nicholas, determined to travel to St. Petersburg to present him with a copy personally.   They were cordially welcomed and invited to dinners and receptions.   On the eve of their departure Murchison was honoured as a Knight Grand Cross of Stanislaus and de Verneuil received a Second Cross of St. Anne (the same award as had been given to Murchison back in 1841).

On their way home they took the opportunity of examining the ice-worn rocks of the Baltic coast.   Murchison believed they had been affected by icebergs, but de Verneuil felt strongly that the agents were glaciers.   Louis Agassiz, Professor of Natural History at the University of Neuchâtel, had recently shocked the geological world by talking of whole continents being covered in ice, the first suggestion of an Ice Age.   On reaching Stockholm, the two travellers found widespread fresh evidence of his theory.   They made a tour of southern Sweden observing the effects of ice but primarily to make sections of the Silurian deposits.   On returning to the capital, they were met and welcomed by Jöns Berzelius and other scientists and they were presented at Court.

They experienced some violent storms and prolonged their tour by stopping in the island of Gotland.   Going on to the southern tip of the country they met at Lund Professor Nilsson, a well-known archaeologist, who submitted them to a long discourse on craniology.   Murchison recorded in his journal, 'Nilsson asks, as the greatest favour, the cranium of a Highlander. I have promised him mine when I die. He looked at it with special affection as coming so near his Phoenician type.'

They crossed the strait to Copenhagen, where they renewed some friendships and were entertained by the king, whom they found to be an unpretending but interested student of natural history. Murchiston assessed him as 'happier in a museum than governing a kingdom'. On reaching Paris, he heard that his wife was in Tours, indisposed with a recurrence of malaria. By the time he reached her, she was well enough to move to Paris, where they stayed for several weeks.

There were official objections in Britain to the wearing of Russian orders. However, while he was in St. Petersburg, Murchison had been in communication with certain dignitaries as to his being given a scientific post in the Russian service that might circumvent these rules. It was suggested that he be 'Inspecteur des Explorations Géologique de l'Empire' with the rank of Privy Councillor. Before he left Paris, he heard that the project was to be carried out in a different form. He was appointed by the Emperor of Russia an 'Effective Member of the Imperial Academy of Sciences, with all the rights, privileges, and rank attached to that office in the Imperial service'. This gave him a position in the Russian service intermediate between those of a Colonel and a Major-General. Shortly afterwards the *London Gazette* announced that the Queen had granted him the privilege of wearing the Russian orders.

While Charlotte slowly recovered from her illness, Roderick joined heated argument in the Societé Géologique de France on the subject of glaciers versus icebergs being the cause of striations on rocks in Scandinavia and elsewhere. Because of their proximity to the Alps, most Frenchmen favoured glaciers, but he stuck to his own preference for ice-floes, which opinion he held for some years to come, before he conceded that there was merit in both theories. They were able to return to London in time for Christmas and Roderick was kept busy writing up his experiences of the effects of ice and of Silurian rocks in Scandinavia.

Geikie does not mention direct correspondence to Murchison from the Prime Minister's office, but quotes the following letter, sent to his old friend at Oxford, datelined Whitehall, February 5, 1846:

'My dear Dr. Buckland,

You will be glad to hear that yesterday, on our own spontaneous idea of Mr. Murchison's claims to a mark of favour from his own Sovereign, Sir James Graham [the Home Secretary], with my entire concurrence, wrote to the Queen, advising Her Majesty to confer the honour of knighthood on Mr. Murchison at the first levée. The value of the distinction will be that it was unsolicited and unprompted, and that it is intended as a recognition by the Queen of Mr. Murchison's services in the great cause of science and human knowledge.

Most truly yours,

ROBERT PEEL.'

Geikie states that it had been entirely unexpected and Murchison accepted amid warm congratulations from his friends and associates. In fact manuscript letters in the British Library show that, five years earlier on the Tory government of Robert Peel succeeding the Whigs in 1841, Murchison had written to the Prime Minister asking for a baronetcy, citing his Russian honours, his achievements in geology and his active support for the Tory cause in Durham in 1818! He also pointed out that he was heir to his uncle, whose baronetcy would die with him. Peel replied that he felt that honours had already been too lavishly dispensed by the previous government.

It was particularly pleasing that Sir Henry De la Beche had also recently been knighted, showing that the valuable work of British geologists at home and abroad was appreciated and recognised by their own Government. Sir John Herschel had been raised to the baronetcy in 1838 and Murchison wrote to him saying that he had been minded to refuse a knighthood but now felt it would be impertinent to decline Peel's 'unsolicited and unprompted' offer. Sir Roderick was inundated by social invitations, which interrupted his work, but by the beginning of April he had prepared his account of the Scandinavian icebergs for the Geological Society and two months later was able to present a memoir on the Silurian rocks.

Under the presidency of Leonard Horner, the Society's programme of evening meetings continued successfully and younger blood was attracted to it. In 1846 the Society honoured William Lonsdale with its greatest gift, the Wollaston Medal. Dr. William Hyde Wollaston had made his name in scientific research and had invested £1,000 in 3% bonds so that, after his death, the Geological Society 'should apply the dividends in promoting researches concerning the mineral structure of the earth, or in rewarding those by whom such researches should hereafter be made; or in such manner as should appear to the Council of the said Society for the time being, conducive to the interests of the Society in particular, or the science of geology in general.' The Society had had made a series of gold medals, the first recipient of which, in 1831, had been William Smith.

Adam Sedgwick was always welcome and many came to listen to his papers on the older rocks of Cumberland and North Wales. He had spent part of the autumns of 1842 and 1843 trying to find fossil evidence of a different fauna in his Cambrian rocks from that in Murchison's Silurian series, but he had failed. He could not find a geological division between the two. However, he was able to show that the rocks of the Upper Silurian did not graduate down to the Lower series but rested on them unconformably, that is a long period of time had elapsed between the two deposits, during which the lower ones had been folded and eroded. There were very few species of fauna from the earlier period which survived into the later one. He therefore believed that the vast lower series of Cambrian rocks should now be united with what had been called the Lower Silurian and he gave the group the name Protozoic. He acknowledged an upper series, bounded above by the Old Red Sandstone. He had also looked at the ancient volcanic activity in North Wales and recognised that some of the eruptions had occurred at the same time as the submarine rocks had been deposited, and some had been thrust later into cracks in the overlying strata.

John Phillips, at least, had considered the idea that the Cambrian should be extended upwards, rather than the Silurian downwards, and had written to Murchison on the subject. In his reply, he said, 'I cannot read the paragraph which follows in your note without being hurt by the *possibility* to which you allude of the Cambrian going up to the Wenlock Shale. As a matter of fact, unquestionably it does. But what is Cambrian? Why, as De la Beche has shown in South Wales, nothing but Lower Silurian? Now, bear in mind, that my two clear and distinct types, Upper and Lower Silurian, were proposed to geologists, and, being laid before them, they were asked to see how far the lower type would go down. This is repeatedly put to them in my book.'

Sedgwick did not pursue his researches further and the fossils he had collected remained in their packing-cases. He therefore had little right to make the claims he did some years later. Meanwhile Sir Roderick was energetically working on rocks in which he believed he had found a distinct fauna, and established their relationship with the deposits above them. He had called them Silurian and was naturally loath to alter his classification unless and until it could be shown that some other type of life had occurred earlier.

In March 1845, Sedgwick had written a paper on the geology of Cumberland, which indirectly opposed Murchison's classification. He cited erroneous sections, in which the Llandeilo flags had been incorrectly placed and put them in with the Caradoc beds. He proposed that the older rocks be divided into three levels, namely Cambrian, Middle Lower Silurian, including the Llandeilo, Caradoc and Wenlock, and Upper Silurian. Murchison wrote to him, 'I did not read your memoir until about a month ago, when my attention was called to it both by letters from Élie de Beaumont and by a visit from de Verneuil. I at once saw either that I must defend the position taken up in the opening chapters of the work on Russia . . . or allow geologists to think that the shot you have fired in the eleventh hour was effective in breaking up all my entrenchments. If we had fully co-operated as coadjutors to produce one work in Wales and the adjacent parts of England as in the Alps and Scotland, there is every probability that when we found (as we must soon have done) that you had no fossil type essentially differing from the Lower Silurian, the whole of that stage might have been merged in the term Cambrian. . . I can see no shade of a reason for changing my classification of Upper and Lower. The very limits between them I would select tomorrow if I had to begin afresh. . . I shall express in public, as strongly as I do in private, my real grief in being compelled, for the first time in our career, to hold any material geological opinion at variance with your own, and shall announce that if you could produce a group of peculiar fossils, I would at once subscribe to your views. . . .Be assured that nothing of late years has annoyed me so seriously as to be compelled to make this defence of the views which I have elaborately worked out, and the classification which I had established after much toil and travel.'

In 1846, Sir Roderick went back to Durham to visit his old school and recall his tearaway days there. On his return to London he played host to several important foreign scientists coming over to attend the meeting of the British Association at Southampton. These included Hans Christian Oersted, the Danish physicist, and his compatriot Professor Forchhammer, Christian Friedrich Schönbein, the German Professor of Chemistry at Basle, Matteucci from Italy and Retzius from Sweden. In order to improve the prestige of the meeting, he secured several well-known men as Vice-Presidents, including the Duke of Wellington, Lord Palmerston, the Foreign Minister, and the Speaker, Mr. Lefevre, besides Herschel and Whewell. He was also able to persuade Prince Albert to attend and was impressed with his knowledge and interest, especially in mathematics.

A persistent critic of the British Association had been *The Times* newspaper, only deigning to print the pedantic pronouncements of its members if inserted as advertisements. Sir Roderick resented this deeply, remarking, 'Notwithstanding all my efforts and those of my associates, the meeting was held up to ridicule in *The Times*. But I was nothing cowed, and, at the public dinner at Southampton, I declaimed against such ribald vulgarity and ignorance, saying I was ashamed my eminent foreign friends should go away with the impression that *The Times* in its vituperation of science represented my country, and I vehemently declared that *tempora mutabuntur* [they might change in time].' In fact, after 1845 the 'top people's paper' published an average of more than two pieces from Murchison every year – some sixty-one items altogether. In most cases these were letters by way of announcing to the public information generated for the Royal Geographical Society. These covered such things as Lieutenant Pim's proposed journey across Russia to the north-eastern coast of Siberia and beyond, to search for, and if possible rescue, Franklin's missing expedition to find the North-West Passage; the exploration by John Speke and James Grant of the sources of the Nile; the prospect of finding coal between the Permian rocks and the Old Red Sandstone; and above all the welfare and progress of David Livingstone in his exploration of the Zambezi and central African lakes.

In the early summer of 1847, Murchison took a trip to Cambridge to look at the fossil collection in the Woodwardian Museum, which had recently been rearranged under Sedgwick's supervision, but it did not inspire him with any new interest in British geology. He went over to Paris, where he met von Buch, who persuaded him to join a party going to attend a meeting of the Scienziati Italiani in Venice. Lady Murchison had not fully recovered from her bout of malaria in Tours and they resolved to let the house in Belgrave Square and go abroad for at least a year, first visiting the eastern Alps then going on to winter in Rome. It was thirty years since their cultural tour and now they had a new interest.

Lady Murchison travelled to Bad Homburg, near Frankfurt-am-Main, to await her husband, who had first to attend a ceremony at Cambridge, at which he and Sedgwick were made Honorary Masters of Art. They were installed by Prince Albert in the presence of Her Majesty Queen Victoria. They were to have been made Doctors of Laws (LL.D.), but this honour was reserved for Lords and Privy Councillors.

Sir Roderick made all haste to join his wife in Germany. They then took a month to reach Venice, going through Bohemia to Vienna and then zig-zagging through the Alps to see geological sections. In the Austrian capital they enjoyed meeting again de Verneuil, von Keyserling and Barrande, who had an outstanding collection of rocks and fossils from the Silurian of Bohemia.

Murchison and de Verneuil left Vienna by train, to visit at Vöslau, a small town on the eastern flank of the Austrian Alps, Dr. Ami Boué, now in semi-retirement. He had spent his life establishing the geology of Europe, from the Highlands of Scotland to western Turkey. From there they struck south-westwards, crossing the Styrian Alps by the Semmering Pass, observing exposures of the rocks where road construction was under way. They often left their coach to take steep short cuts, while their coachman nursed his horses up the longer but more gentle slopes. They were able to make close observations of the rock structures and gained some valuable knowledge. They rejoined Lady Murchison in Innsbrück, where they also met Leopold von Buch, who was now some seventy-three years old, yet still sprightly and determined to drive himself physically. He was to accompany them to Venice, where a scientific assembly had been arranged, taking in more Alpine geology on the way.

While Lady Murchison went on to await them at Bolzano, de Verneuil, von Buch and her husband set off on foot. Von Buch was very slow and, despite his protestations, Sir Roderick was obliged to strike on ahead to St. Lorenzch, to arrange for a carriage to pick him up on his arrival and carry him the last two miles on to Brunecken, where they were to spend the night. Von Buch, like Murchison, did not believe in the theory that the huge boulders they encountered had been moved to their present position by glaciers, which were now only visible in the distance. Murchison was a disciple of the doctrine of convulsion and cataclysm. In the moraines and scattered boulders he could only see the work of powerful torrents set in motion by cataclysmic upheavals, to which he also attributed the formation of the Alps. However, some of von Buch's beliefs were even too unrealistic for him – the Austrian believed that the granite blocks atop the Jura Mountains were shot across the valley of Geneva like cannon-balls and the rounded and scratched boulders that we now call *roches moutonnées* were not caused by ice, but were the result of concentric exfoliations of crystalline rocks.

They went on to Venice, where preparations for the conference were in full swing. It covered all aspects of science and agriculture and the meetings were timed in such a way that delegates could attend many different factions, should they so wish. Sir Roderick gave a lecture, mostly to Australians, on the similarities of their mountain ranges with the Urals and suggested that gold might well be found in the colony. After the meeting, de Verneuil, von Buch and Murchison joined a party of eleven geologists spending a fortnight in the Venetian Alps looking at the rocks and comparing ideas.

Sir Roderick collected his wife from Padua and they set off for Rome, via Bologna, Florence, Pisa, Siena and Viterbo, recalling their journey thirty years previously, but now taking an interest in the geology. Mixed in with his enduring regard for art are details in his journal of rock exposures he encountered, as though he meant to write later an exhaustive memoir on the subject.

It was 1847 and already the discontent in Italy which would lead to revolution across Europe the following year was stirring. Murchison was no politician but could not help but be affected by what was going on around him.   Geology and art were displaced in his journal by shrewd observation of the situation. In Florence he wrote, 'People who know the Florentines tell me that all this vox populi will subside with the first tramontano, or cooling north-west wind, but I put little faith in their sayings. An enormous change has been made in the whole framework of Italian society, of the ultimate effects of which I am by no means certain. I cannot see the mighty assemblages of singers in the streets, nor their enthusiasm, the crowds of drunken people in the low cafés, and the complete licence which they are taking, without a fear that the revolutionists, that is, root and branch fellows, will work something of their own out of it, and will shake, if they do not eventually upset, the throne of their benevolent sovereign, the Grand Duke.'

When he reached the ancient capital, he noted, 'Rome is fallen away from what I left it thirty years ago, and a single walk round my old haunts led me to see that in beggary, filth, and decay, she is more pre-eminent than ever. What a singular fatuity in those who govern to expect to produce effectual reforms, when all is as rotten at the core as the mouldering antiques, whose foundations are daily giving away under the old edifices! A truly efficient reform would be to retrench one-half of the overgrown charges for cardinals and priests, employ the poor, and reanimate this land of the dead.

'Oh for an Oliver Cromwell to drive this ermined vermin from the world, or, at all events, to subordinate them to a good civil government! Yet here, forsooth, it is that we hear of the *risorgimento dell' Italia*, and such nonsense, amidst squalor and rags, and with a hundred beggars at the side of every carriage. When is the day of retribution to come? Not, I apprehend, for many a day. There is no intelligent middle class. I expect, however, scenes of great disorder and tumult, followed by a good deal of highway robbery, and the revival of the good old times of the brigands.

'How is improvement to be combined with the conservation of the Papacy? How is the spiritual power of the Pope to be untouched? How is His Holiness to be left in undisturbed possession of the influence he wields over all Catholics, foreign and domestic, whilst in his own States, the laws, internal government, trade, commerce, etc., are to be administered by civilians? That this separation will be attempted sooner or later no one can doubt, now that His Holiness has put arms into the hands of many thousand citizens, two-thirds of whom will seek for such an adjustment, and will eventually compel it.'

However, his love of geology had superseded his interest in art to such an extent, that, a few days after his arrival in Rome, he says of himself, 'A visit to the Vatican revived some of my foregone pleasures; and glorious bright gleams over all the Campagna and the distant snowy mountains, with sea glittering at Ostia. These and the finest sunsets from the Pincian are not enough for the unhorsed geological knight. For here, in truth, I find myself a fish out of water, an animal without belongings, and deprived of the conditions in which I have lived for some years past, viz., a set of men with pursuits entirely akin to my own. The other avocations of the sight-seer in the Eternal City are forced on me, *faute de mieux,* and I endeavour with these, and visits to the studios of the Tenerani and Gibson, to occupy the mind, but in vain. These are only *scherzi.*

'My geological notebooks of the summer lie undigested, and I lack the courage and stimulus in this city of indolence to work them up into something. In short, that something on the Alps and Apennines would be too general and desultory, and too little decisive to satisfy me. I feel this, and must desist at present from the endeavour. I wished to be in Sicily and doing something, but the troubles stopped me; and now I find I might have gone there and explored the mountains before the snow fell. I look daily to the Apennines with a wish to be there, but their backbone is a mass of snow, and I should only do things by halves until I can make clear transverse sections of the whole chain. I may, however, make a run to Tivoli and the Sabine Farm of Horace, and compare the rocks with the version given of them by Ponzi. But this is fragmentary work, and unworthy of me. Often do I wish that the long quarantine of winter were passed, and that I was once more at work with my hammer, and out of the gulf-stream of English sight-seers and 'Syntaxes' in search of the picturesque. And yet I have joined an English club here, where Lord L----, gouty and unable to stand on his legs, talks of his shooting pigeons and larks from his carriage, whilst a lot of young dandies are betting on their horses and their performances in red coats. As a climax, I am just going out with Canino [Charles Bonaparte] mounted on one of his nags to view the throw-off at Magnonella on the road to Civita Vecchia.'

Sir Roderick thus found the winter somewhat tedious, but as soon as spring arrived, he set out for Naples to have another look at the volcanic activity in the area. Meanwhile revolution was in the air right across Europe and Naples became a dangerous place for a foreigner. He commented, 'If I croaked about the prospect of the Italians in their new condition, and foresaw in the establishment of civic guards the germ of the overthrow of all monarchical government, how forcibly is this conviction driven home now that the French Republic is re-established by the zealous co-operation of the National Guards of Paris! This is what I have foreseen for years. I have always said that in the formation of the National Guards, France had established a body of janissaries who would change dynasty and government at their will and pleasure.

146

'If the detestable law of the division of property, which deprives an industrious individual of the power of establishing a family, and forbids the preservation of an old lineage were to be applied to England, then should we proud islanders become in a trice Yankees, and with the addition of National Guards our ruin would be complete. I now begin to think that Tocqueville [French political scientist, author of *De la démocratie en Amérique*] was right in his view of the rapid spread of democracy.'

Sir Roderick witnessed widespread demonstrations in the streets of Rome, and despaired that there was little geology to be done. However, he did take a short ride with a friend to look at the succession of the Tertiary and volcanic rocks on the right bank of the Tiber. He also went on several rambles in the area, the geological aspects of which were, in due course, reported to the Geological Society in London. He wanted to explore the Apennines and the Adriatic coast, but the political situation in the country was likely to make it hazardous. So he turned north to have another look at the Alps.

The carriage was stopped at the gates of Rome for the 'citizens' to check that Lady Murchison was not a Cardinal in disguise! Sir Roderick's journal contains here comments on politics, scenery, art and antiquities, as well as geology. He spent some four months in the Alps, making traverse after traverse and drawing sections across most of the range. He rested briefly at Vevey, on Lake Geneva, with Lady Charlotte's distant Swiss relations. He attended the Swiss Scientific Congress over three days at Soleure, south west of Schaffhausen, meeting the local geologists, with some of whom he afterwards explored the glacier valleys of the Oberland. He then turned his attention to the area to the east of Lake Constance, before journeying west-wards to Basle and down the Rhine to Bonn, where by chance he met von Buch again. He was none the worse for his exertions in the Alps and was now studying the Chalk and Nummulitic Limestones (formed from a genus of larger foraminifera, marine micro-organisms of the late Palaeocene and middle Tertiary periods). The couple finally reached London on 23 September, 1848, after some fourteen months' absence.

A marble bust of Sir Roderick was made that year by Richard Westmacott, RA. It was presented to the Geological Society by Lady Murchison in 1853 and stands next to one of Adam Sedgwick at the top of the eastern staircase in the Society's apartments in Burlington House, Piccadilly.

Murchison now worked on his notes to produce a paper for the Geological Society entitled *On the Geological Structure of the Alps, Apennines, and Carpathians*, generally considered to be the best of all his original memoirs. It occupies 155 pages of volume 5 (1849) of the *Quarterly Journal of the Geological Society*. By including the Carpathians, which he had explored a year earlier, he hoped to prove a transition from Secondary to Tertiary rocks and to show how widely the deposits of the Eocene Age extended across southern Europe. As far as his studies of the Alps were concerned, he had had two main objects in mind, firstly to get to understand the structure of the Alps, and secondly to try to resolve the argument as to whether the polished and striated rocks resulted from the action of icebergs or from glaciers that had been very much more extensive than they were then. He believed in the theory that the convulsive upheavals that caused the formation of the mountains had set off sudden rushes of water carrying stones and other debris, including large blocks of floating ice. In spite of being in the heart of glacier country, he could not accept that it was they which had gouged and rounded the rocks. He reasoned that, if the glaciers had extended so far down, then all the plains of northern Europe must have been covered in ice, which he found inconceivable! This, of course, turned out to be have been the case, and later in his life he reluctantly at least partially acknowledged it. He had been with a champion of the glacier theory, de Charpentier, to see the famous blocks of Monthey. The Swiss had shown the spread of huge erratic blocks over the plains of his country and along the slopes of the Jura, which he was convinced could only have been carried out by glaciers. He explained how the highest erratics had been stranded by melting ice and others had been deposited at progressively lower levels as the glaciers receded. Murchison considered him ingenious but remained unconvinced!

In his paper he included some good sections and much fossil evidence to show that there were enormous masses of early Tertiary strata in the Alps and southern Europe. He was able to show that the hard, greenish sandstones and schists of the mountain ridges flanking the Alps were of the same geological age as the soft clays and sands of north-west France and south-east England. He acknowledged the help of many geologist friends with a local understanding of these rocks, but nevertheless it was a supreme effort to co-ordinate it all. He received a letter of appreciation from von Buch in only slightly unidiomatic but extremely imaginative English, 'Your admirable paper on the Alps has been my companion during my rambles last summer in Switzerland. Every day when I took forth my breviary I could not help to repeat "Je vous admire". Such a genius of sound and extensive combination, the very test of an eminent geologist, was never before; such talent of exposition will always be a very rare and admirable gift. You do approach the Nature to lift up her veil with due reverence and attention to her, and then she speaks to you graciously. Others come hastily with spurs and boots and gross hands to draw the veil, as it was a curtain, and they discover behind not the flying nature, but a phantom they have constructed themselves.'

Sir Roderick's exertions in the Alps, or possibly his intense work on the production of his paper, had, for the first time, made him significantly unwell. Lady Charlotte was also not in the best of health, so they spent the summer of 1849 in Buxton and other spas and in visiting friends. He found this enforced search for rest and rehabilitation extremely frustrating. 'How dull, tame, and insufferable,' he said, 'is the west midland geology after Alpine frolics! And what a gloomy and sepulchral air has every English watering-place after the baths of the Continent!'

In anticipation of returning good health, he wrote in July to John Phillips, Professor of Geology at Oxford, 'This watershed of England is perhaps the best place during the cholera-plagues, and I wanted good air and quiet. I hope to be as sound as a geologist ought to be in the summer, and then think of excursionizing a little before the Birmingham meeting, and I wish to consult you about this trip. My present notion is to join Ramsay, if he is, as I suppose, somewhere in North Wales, there to learn, as well as I can, the progress that has been made since the bygone days of Silurianism. I really wish to bring myself up to the existing state of knowledge in those beloved regions, and a few mountain walks will, I trust, complete my cure. Inter alia, I shall take a glance certainly at your Malvernia, of which you have rendered every corner so attractive.'

However, a few weeks later he was obliged to write to Ramsay, 'I never wrote a letter with more repugnance than when I inform you that I cannot join you at the foot of Snowdon. In truth I am (I regret to say) quite unfitted for any geological excursion on account of health and nerves. I have been more ailing this year than in any previous one, and I have not regained what I expected at Buxton.

'This is the first summer in my life in which I have been fairly obliged to strike work, and the very thought of it adds to my depression. Hoping, however, that I may be in better plight when the Birmingham meeting comes off, I trust to meeting you there, and who knows that later in the autumn I may not accomplish what I have failed to do now under your kind and instructive auspices.'

He was indeed fit enough to attend the meeting of the British Association in September and, because its venue was close to Silurian territory, he led an excursion there. Tickets were offered to the residents of Dudley and the vicinity, and *The Illustrated London News* reported that nearly 15,000 people took advantage of the offer. The group entered the Dudley Caverns, which had been illuminated by candles by their owner, Lord Ward, and Murchison gave them a lecture on the submarine formation of the rock. He wore for the occasion a high-crowned green Tyrolean hat and a shepherd's plaid scarf. He then took them to the top of the Wren's Nest, where he was enthroned by the Bishop of Oxford, to everyone's amusement, as 'King of Siluria'.

The Wren's Nest has two bands of solid Wenlock limestone separated by shale. The caverns are not natural, but derive from extensive quarrying. The upper stratum is 8·64 metres and the lower 12·88 metres thick. The outcrop is elliptical in shape, with the east face sloping at 60° and the west at 45°. At the time of Murchison's 'open day', visitors were allowed to view an open-air thirty-foot seam of coal, which was being quarried rather than mined, as it was in nearby pits. Some of the limestone is impure and has not been removed, otherwise the Wren's Nest would by now have disappeared. It is presently part of a National Nature Reserve.

Notice boards by several of the gates state: 'The dramatic limestone outcrop of the Wren's Nest, or "Wrenner" as it is known locally, has towered above Dudley for many thousands of years. Formed some 420 million years ago in a warm shallow sea, the rocks are rich in fossils of marine creatures, including the "Dudley Bug", a trilobite which appeared on the town's coat of arms. Past quarrying has created the awesome Seven Caverns and exposed the spectacular Ripple Beds, both of which can be seen from purpose-built viewing platforms. Today the Wren's Nest is one of England's foremost geological National Nature Reserves, owned and managed by Dudley Metropolitan Borough Council in association with English Nature, for the benefit of thousands of visitors from all over the world.'

No geological hammers are allowed, but there are several screes from which fossils can be collected by the observant. The Reserve is the best part of a mile from north to south and a quarter of a mile from east to west. It is overseen by a small team of helpful wardens.

Anthony Brook (2001) says, 'In later life, Sir Roderick Murchison revelled in recalling the circumstances in which he was proclaimed "King of Siluria". This event is so powerfully iconographic that cynicism arises as to its actuality. Was Murchison really proclaimed "King of Siluria"? Or was it more a case of the invention of tradition, whereby colourful stories gain legitimacy over time and turn into myth and legend? It supposedly took place in September 1849, after publication of *The Silurian System* (1839) but before the first edition of the wider-ranging and more populist Siluria appeared in 1854. There are only two contemporary reports, providing reliable eye-witness accounts, and two retrospective reviews published decades later, in the quest for the origin of this potent pronouncement.

Reporting on the BAAS Excursion on Saturday 15 September 1849, as part of its Annual Conference, *The Literary Gazette* related a week later (22 September, 691-92) that the principal feature of the afternoon had been an impromptu address by Sir Roderick Murchison on the circumjacent geology from the Wren's Nest, the highest eminence in the Dudley Hills. Murchison considered these hills to be miniature replicas of the grander phenomena to westwards, across the Severn, in the heartland of courageous Caractacus, King of the Silures. The belligerence of this Celtic chieftain "was caught up by the Bishop of Oxford, who, in calling on the surrounding groups to give three hearty cheers, proclaimed Sir Roderick, in his eloquent manner Silurian King". This grandiloquent gesture was also extensively reported in the principal illustrated weekly news journal of the day, *The Illustrated London News* (22 Sept., 201) which, after Murchison had delivered his field oration, concluded thus: "Sir Roderick was much applauded, and the Bishop of Oxford jocosely remarked that he thought the assemblage had better proceed, at once, to install the great geologist as Silurian monarch".

'Many years later, in his *Life of Sir Roderick I. Murchison* (1875), Geikie wrote that Murchison led the crowd to the top of the Wren's Nest, "where amid much merriment and with general approbation, he was enthroned by the Bishop of

Oxford as 'King of Siluria' (Vol. II, 103). Even later still, in 1891, *The Midland Naturalist* wished to remove any misapprehension by ascertaining the facts of the matter (14 [1891], 268). It stated that "in proposing a vote of thanks [to Murchison for his discourse], the Bishop of Oxford said that, although Caractacus was an old king of part of the Silurian region, yet Sir Roderick had extended the Silurian domain almost illimitably, and it was only just and proper that, there, upon a Silurian region, he should be acknowledged the modern King of Siluria." It then proceeds to gild the lily, forty-two years after the event, by continuing: "the Bishop then called upon all those present to repeat after him, three times 'Hail – King of Siluria'. The vast assembly thrice responded, with stentorian voices and most hearty hurrahs, and ever afterwards, Sir Roderick was proud to be acknowledged King of Siluria.'"

'Curiously, contemporary reports do not specify the designation King of Siluria – only retrospective accounts written many years later recording events decades earlier. The 1891 reminiscence is particularly florid and baroque, but it could well have happened that way. Murchison certainly felt it had and, thereafter, made everyone fully aware of it. Indeed, this was the regal title by which he was addressed in a letter from a French geologist two months later. This grandiloquent soubriquet, which only served to feed his gargantuan ego, stuck fast, particularly in the popular imagination, as it so perfectly matched his vainglorious and pompous character. Murchison as ruler of an expansive rock realm seemed only just and proper for one of the natural leaders of the geologically-minded multitude. *Sensu stricto*, Murchison should have been hailed as "King of the Silures", but at least Siluria gave him a crisp title for his next book!'

In spite of the apparent improvement in Sir Roderick's health, Geikie reports, 'Immediately after the meeting we find him at Brighton drinking mineral waters, and noting each disordered symptom about him, with the treatment recommended, as if he had been all his life a confirmed valetudinarian. A man whose chief subjects of thought at the time would seem to have been the miseries of "suppressed gout," "ill-arranged bile," "stomach attacks," "vertigo," and "bad nights," with the relative effects of "bismuth pills," "blue pill," and "cordial rhubarb;" and who, after trying in vain the virtues of "Carlsbad waters," "resumed tippling the waters at the Ems tap" – such a man could hardly be expected to produce any coherent mental work. A day's shooting now and then was tried, particularly in that old haunt, the pheasant-covers of Up Park, but with no good effects. "What a weathercock," he writes, "is a bothered stomach, affected as mine is, through every pore of the skin, and how unnerved is the stout man of yesterday! It is freedom from these ailments which is the basis of the success of great public men – an iron stomach, the skin of a pachyderm, and no nerves, forming the *sine quâ non* of a Duke of Wellington."'

In his brighter moments, he began to prepare a memoir on the 'pseudo-volcanic' rocks of Italy and to consider the production of a general geological map of Europe. At this time, he was greatly cheered by the announcement that the Royal Society had unanimously awarded him the Copley Medal 'for the eminent services he has rendered to geological science during many years of active observation in several parts of Europe, and especially for the establishment of that classification of the older Palaeozoic deposits, designated the Silurian system, as set forth in the two works entitled *The Silurian System founded on Geological Researches in England,* and *The Geology of Russia and the Ural Mountains.*' The granting of the honour had been strongly urged by his old friend, Sedgwick.

In early 1850, Sir Roderick was appointed Vice-President of the Royal Society and wrote to Sedgwick, urging him, if his health allowed, to attend his lecture on 6 February on the 'pseudo-volcanic' rocks of central Italy and expressing his astonishment at not being able to understand the latest developments and phraseology of chemistry.

The Prime Minister, Lord John Russell, announced that the Government would grant £1000 per annum to the Royal Society, for the advancement of science. Murchison was instrumental in seeing that the money was spent according to the principles of the British Association, which he felt had come into being because of the 'lethargy and want of general spirit' of the Royal Society.

As the summer wore on, the health of both Sir Roderick and his wife took a turn for the worse and they decided to winter on the Continent, moving first to Vichy, where his old enthusiasm for exploring rocks took over and he prepared two more papers for the Geological Society – *The Slaty Rocks of Sichon shown to be of Carboniferous Age* and *On the Origin of the Mineral Springs of Vichy.*

From Vichy he went out, with Le Coq of Clermont, to have another look at the igneous rocks of the Auvergne, which he had last visited twenty-two years before in the company of Charles Lyell. His recent excursions among the extinct volcanoes of Italy had rekindled his interest in them. He remained convinced that the valleys could not have been cut down by 'such a puny stream as the Dordogne', and that the nature of the terrain was the result of violent upheaval at a point where the surface was torn by radiating faults.

Murchison had a life-long belief in convulsionism, that the distortions had occurred in the distant past and were not reflected in the processes he observed in the current era, quite the opposite of Hutton's 'the present is the key to the past'. Of his creed he said, 'The crust and outline of the earth are full of evidences that many of the ruptures and overthrows of the strata, as well as great denudations, could not even in millions of years have been produced by agencies like these of our times.

'Let it not be supposed, that we who hold to the proofs of more powerful causation in ancient periods, do not fully admit that the former physical agencies were of the same nature as those which now prevail. We simply assert on the countless evidences of fracture, dislocation, metamorphism, and inversion of the strata, and also on that of vast and clean-sweep denudations, that these agencies were from time to time infinitely more energetic than in existing nature, - in other words, that the metamorphisms and oscillations of the terrestrial crust, including the uprise of sea bottoms, and the sweeping out of debris, were paroxysmal in comparison with the movements of our own era. We further maintain that no amount of time (of which no true geologist was ever parsimonious when recording the history of bygone accumulations of sediment, or of the different races of animals they contain) will enable us to account for the signs of many great breaks and convulsions which are visible in every mountain-chain, and which the miner encounters in all underground workings.'

He had by chance discovered that the rocks of the Forez, south-east of Vichy, contained fossils which corresponded with the Carboniferous Limestone of England. They had previously been assigned by French geologists on purely mineral evidence to an earlier period. He appreciated the significance of this, in that it corroborated what he and Sedgwick had said many years before, that some at least of the Continental coalfields had been laid down after the older Carboniferous rocks had been fractured and upheaved. He was delighted to be able to report this to the British Association at its 1850 meeting in Edinburgh.

At this meeting he was elected President of the Geology and Geography section and he strongly recommended that Hugh Miller be appointed as joint Secretary with James Nicol, Professor of Natural History at Aberdeen University. He was particularly proud to be President in his native country and to work with Miller, a fellow Scot and author of *The Old Red Sandstone.*

After the meeting, Murchison and Sedgwick set out together for the last time, firstly to undertake some sightseeing and socialising in the central Highlands, but also to make some geological observations. To this end, they climbed Ben Lomond on their way to Inveraray and on into the Highlands. With his greater experience, he was able to see that the rocks were not just primeval crust, but were metamorphosed sand, gravel and mud, possibly of Silurian age. He was later to draw on his notes, when he came to establish their structure.

After he left the Highlands, Murchison invited Professor Nicol to join him on an expedition down the Clyde to Girvan (opposite Ailsa Craig), where they worked for a week. With the help of fossils found by Sandy Maccallum of Girvan, they investigated the shelly sandstones of the area. They found numerous examples of *Calymene blumenbachii,* a species of trilobite, which was also reported in the lower rocks of North Wales.

Writing to Hugh Miller, Murchison said, ' As far as my researches go, they teach me that whilst the Silurian rocks occupy so very large a portion of the south of Scotland, they are far from being very thick. Their apparent enormous development is due to countless flexures. . . Unquestionably there is no top or bottom to the series in the southernmost of the Scottish Silurians. I look, therefore, for the top and bottom of my system as it is now expanded in an European sense in the Highlands of Scotland; and so, after all my labours and peregrinations, I think

COAL UNDER THE PERMIAN ROCKS.

TO THE EDITOR OF THE TIMES.

Sir,—In the otherwise correct and lively account of the proceedings of the excursionists of the British Association at Dudley on Thursday last your reporter has made a mistake, quite excusable in any one who is not a geologist, but which must be corrected. In his account of the short address which I delivered in the Dudley caverns the word "old" is introduced in conjunction with that of Permian sandstone; while geologists well know that the old red sandstone underlies, and the Permian sandstone overlies, the coal.

In illustrating the structure of the district one of my chief objects was to do away with an erroneous impression received by some of the audience at Professor Jukes's able lecture in Birmingham, by their confusing this Permian red sandstone (the lower new red sandstone of former years) with the new red sandstone or trias. Now, these deposits are of very distinct age, the elder being the youngest of all the palæozoic rocks; the other, or the trias, the base of the secondary or mesozoic deposits.

Professor Jukes stated clearly that coal may be found at no great depth beneath the Permian sandstone where it is in contiguity to coal-fields a fact which I had seen satisfactorily developed near Birmingham 27 years ago, and which I have more recently seen verified in Nottinghamshire, where coal of fine quality has been won under the magnesian limestone, another member of the Permian group. In regard to the new red sandstone or trias remote from such coal-fields, and overlying Permian rocks, Professor Jukes very properly indicated the vast depths at which coal measures could possibly be reached, even if they should extend to such districts.

I must say that your reporter has done full justice to the very agreeable day which we enjoyed at Dudley, and I only beg to add that at the banquet prepared for us, and at which 400 persons sat down, under the presidency of the accomplished Mayor, Mr. Frederick Smith, we offered our heartiest thanks to the Earl of Dudley for the illumination of his great caverns. Your obedient servant,

RODERICK I. MURCHISON.

16, Belgrave-square Sept. 16

One of many letters from Murchison written to *The Times* – this one published on 18 September, 1849 of returning to work at home, and ending my days where I began them.'

James Hutton, John Playfair and Sir James Hall had established that the uplands of Scotland, south of the Clyde/Forth valley, had been heavily folded by early movements of the Earth's crust. They had placed them in the vaguely-defined 'Transition' series. Later Sedgwick had compared their mineralisation with that of his discoveries in the Lake District and Wales. Now John Carrick Moore and Professor Nicol had found fossils which clearly placed them in the Silurian system, and Murchison was able to show that they corresponded with his Llandeilo and Caradoc formations and to read to the Geological Society the following February (1851) a memoir entitled *On the Silurian Rocks of the South of Scotland.*

Meanwhile Murchison set to thinking more about the problem of what caused the loose jumble of boulders, gravel and sand known as 'drift'. During the winter, he scoured the Weald and the North and South Downs, gaining evidence, as he saw it, of his débâcle theory (that the drift had been carried into its present position by sudden torrents of water caused by violent upheaval of the Earth's crust). There were protests from the followers of James Hutton's uniformitarianism theory, but Murchison could just not see how vast tracts of Europe could have been covered in ice. In March, he gave an evening lecture to the Royal Institution entitled *On the former Changes of the Alps,* citing the stupendous overthrow of the rocks as proof of his theory. In a letter to a friend, J.P. Martin, he explains that, as far as the drift is concerned, he is thinking only of 'the last great geological revolution, in which the mammoths and their allies were specially massacred and destroyed'.

These geological cross-sections were drawn by Murchison for a lecture given in 1852 to the Ludlow Natural History Society. He worked with members of the Society during pioneering field-work to produce his treatise *The Silurian System* and first visited their museum in March 1834. The upper section runs east-west from the Cambrian of Wales through Murchison's Silurian of the Stiperstones and Ludlow Castle to the Carboniferous of Clee Hill; the lower section runs north-south from Bromfield across the Ludlow anticline and into Herefordshire.

Until recently, the sections were in storage. They were conserved in 1994 with generous grant aid and are now displayed in the Norton Geological Gallery of the new Ludlow Museum, Castle Street, Ludlow, Shropshire. © Shropshire County Museum Service 1996.

Chapter Ten
Siluria

Murchison now determined to collect the results of research by geologists all over the World into rocks and fossils of the Silurian age and publish them as a general view of primeval geology. In this he was encouraged by his best friends, Sir Henry De la Beche and other Government geologists. He spent the next three years gathering fresh observations in the field, comparing the exhibits of museums, talking to other observers and reading their published works. He revisited the Welsh border country, working westwards into the principality with Professor Nicol. Starting from Ludlow, they struck north-westwards to Welshpool and through the Berwyns to Bala, where they were joined by A.R. Selwyn. From there they turned south-westwards to Cadair Idris and Barmouth, thence north along the coast to Harlech and through Snowdonia to Anglesey, where they ran the section out to sea. It was logical to continue westwards to Ireland, and this they did.

Murchison's notes and letters comment as much about the destitution caused by famine as about the geology. He wrote, 'I have been looking for many a long day for any base of Siluria in Britain, and until yesterday, between Blackwater and Tallicconer Bridges, I never saw it, as made up of fragments of mica-schist, quartz rock, etc.; in short, of all antecedents. Today we had no reason to hope for a similar base-line. But Griffith's map gave us an outline, and his notes a direct indication of the fossil-beds, i.e. of Silurian, related to primary rock; and in following it, despite of wind and rain, we worked out all our points north and north-west of this comfortable little inn, and the table is now strewed with the relics of the lower fossil group.

'A penny given in alms brings out a colony of beggars. They seem to rise from the earth quicker than mushrooms after a genial shower, and in a country where no man seems to live. In truth, the cabins, such as are left, and the blocks and boulders so resemble each other, that you cannot tell where the people are.

'Galway. – The export is nil, beyond Paddies and the stones that would not feed them.   .   .   . Roofless houses and pompous fat sleek Papist priests are disheartening to see.

'Passed the nick or opening in the mountains where the tradition is that the devil bit a piece out, and flying away with it, found it too heavy, and dropped it at Cashel. If geologists had lived in the old days, they would have defeated these lying inventions, for the hill with the nick is Old Red Sandstone, and the rock of Cashel dark grey Mountain Limestone.

'I have looked at some of the Connemara sections, as well as those of Dublin, Wicklow, Wexford, and Waterford, and bring back to mind all that I saw in former years. . . . The multitude of intrusive granites, and the horrible spread of drift and bog are intolerable obstacles.'

****

As has been mentioned, Murchison had noted, some years previously, the similarity of the structure of the Ural Mountains with those of Australia, and had forecast the discovery of gold there. He was, not unnaturally, keen to have due recognition of his claims, when it was indeed found there. He was therefore moved to write to the Editor of *The Times* thus:

'Dear Sir, - In commenting upon a recent vote of the Legislature of New South Wales, by which Mr. [Edward] Hargreaves was recompensed for having first opened out the gold-fields of that colony, your correspondent at Sydney, after an allusion to the inductions of science, has thus spoken of me: - "Sir R. Murchison pointed out the similarity of the Blue Mountain chain of Australia to that of the Ural in 1844; it was considered a mere speculation, and, as to any practical effect, might as well have been written of the mountains of the moon."

'As my relation to this subject is thus summarily settled, I must, for the credit of the science which I have so long cultivated, state the following facts: - The comparison above alluded to was drawn by me after an exploration of the Ural Mountains and an examination of rock specimens gathered from the whole eastern chain of Australia by my distinguished friend Count Strzelecki. In 1846 I renewed the subject, and applied my views practically by inciting the unemployed Cornish tin-miners to emigrate and dig for gold in Australia. Both of these notices were published (1844 and 1846), the one in the volumes of the Royal Geographical Society, the other in the Transactions of the Royal Geological Society of Cornwall. I have every reason to believe that they are the earliest printed documents relating to Australian gold; and, unquestionably, they were both anterior to the discovery of the Californian gold. Let me further state that they produced results; for in 1847 a Mr. W.T. Smith, of Sydney, acquainted me that he had discovered specimens of gold, and a Mr. Phillips, of Adelaide (equally unknown to me), wrote to me announcing the same fact. It was also in the same year (1847) that the Rev. W.B. Clarke [first discoverer of gold in the alluvium of Macquarie], whose geological labours have thrown so much light on the structure of New South Wales, published his first essay on the subject of gold in the *Sydney Herald*, and referred to my previous comparison with the Ural.

'Seeing, therefore, that I had become a sort of authority upon Australian gold, and that the metal had actually been discovered and could be profitably worked under due regulations, I addressed a letter in 1848 to Her Majesty's Secretary of State for the Colonies, explanatory of my views, urging the desireableness of such a geological survey of the region as would realize auriferous and other mineral products. That letter, written three years before the operations of Mr. Hargreaves, has, through the courtesy of the Duke of Newcastle, been printed among the papers relating to Australian gold presented to both Houses of Parliament, August 16, 1853.

'My scientific friends are indeed well aware that on various occasions between 1844 and 1851 I addressed public meetings on the same important phenomenon; and I should not have sought to encroach on your columns had not my name been associated in your widely-circulated journal with the mountains of the moon, of which, I regret to say, I have no knowledge, whether they be situated in the heart of Africa or in our nearest neighbour of the solar system.

I remain, Sir, yours very faithfully,

RODERICK IMPEY MURCHISON
4 Circus, Bath, *Jan*. 10, 1854.'

Archibald Geikie, who knew him well, wrote some twenty years later: 'In spite of the frequent reference to "science" and "scientific induction" in the course of the controversy, it is not easy even for a partial friend to discover in what way Murchison's share in the finding of gold in Australia could be regarded as in any way scientific, or more than a lucky guess. He had come home full of his doings in the Ural Mountains, and with some rather crude notions as to the mode of occurrence of gold throughout the world.

'One of his favourite, but singularly unphilosophical, notions on this subject was, that gold was the last created metal, and only occurred therefore in the uppermost parts of any formation. Theoretically, according to this doctrine, there could be no profitable gold-mining by sinking shafts into the solid rock. He clung pertinaciously to this notion, until the successful reef-mining of Victoria compelled him to modify it.

'At that time he met Count Strzelecki, and saw his maps and the collection of specimens which he had brought home from Australia. Ready to find analogies with his Urals, Murchison noticed a general similarity of trend in the Australian and Russian mountain ranges. On looking at the specimens, he recognised many fragments of quartz, and when comparing the Australian with the Russian rocks, remarked that as yet (1844) the former had not yielded gold. He knew nothing personally, and very little more by report, of the geological structure of Australia. When, therefore, he advised the unemployed Cornish miners in 1846 to emigrate and dig for gold in Australia, he had absolutely no scientific grounds on which to base his advice. All he knew was that there were crystalline rocks with quartz veins in Australia as in the Urals. But the same might have been said of almost any country on the face of the earth. His advice, however, was, under the circumstances, as good as could have been given, for if the miners found no gold, they at least would be in a colony where other openings for gaining a livelihood presented themselves much more abundantly than at home. They could hardly lose by emigration; they might gain a good deal.

'Even now, with all the experience of gold-mining since 1846, he would be an exceedingly bold geologist who, from the inspection of a few bits of quartz, none of them containing gold, should pronounce on the auriferous nature of the country whence they came. Science has not been able to make so clear the circumstances which have determined the presence or absence of gold in quartz. If the geologist declares that the quartz will prove auriferous, he has no more scientific ground for his assertion than any empiric or miner with a divining-rod. He makes a guess, and if the prognostication should be fulfilled he may talk of his luck, but has no cause to boast of his science.

'When gold had once been actually found, it was natural to desire a thorough examination of the country yielding it. The world was ringing at the time with the newly-discovered marvels of the Californian El Dorado, and no one could tell whether a rival to that region might not be found in Australia. It was at least worth while to explore. In urging this matter upon the Government, therefore, Murchison showed an enlightened desire for the spread of geological knowledge and industrial development. But he did not thereby establish any claim to have foretold on sound scientific grounds the really auriferous character of the Australian rocks.

'Count Strzelecki appears to have been the first to ascertain the actual existence of gold in Australia. But at the request of the colonial authorities the discovery was closely kept secret. The first explorer who proclaimed the probable auriferous riches of Australia on true scientific grounds – that is, by obtaining gold *in situ*, and tracing its parent rocks through the country – was the Rev. W.B. Clarke, M.A., F.G.S., who, originally a clergyman in England, has spent a long and laborious life in working out the geological structure of his adopted country – New South Wales. He found gold in 1841, and exhibited it to numerous members of the Legislature, declaring at the same time his belief in its abundance. While, therefore, geologists in Europe were guessing, he having actually found the precious metal, was tracing its occurrence far and near on the ground. It is only an act of justice to render this acknowledgement, which Murchison himself, through some over-estimate of his own contribution to the question, and probable ignorance of what had really been done by Mr. Clarke, never made.'

****

Murchison, as President of the Geographical Society, had taken a keen interest in the despatch of Franklin's expedition to find the Northwest Passage and in 1845, had wished God-speed to it. No news had been received of its fate, but in the spring of 1851 two half-wrecked ships that could have been the *Erebus* and the *Terror* had been spotted drifting southwards along the shores of Newfoundland. This had caused excitement in England and inspired a new interest in rescuing the survivors, or at least to learn their fate. Now, again President, Sir Roderick followed keenly the proposals to fit out further expeditions. So in the spring of 1852 he prepared his Address to the Society with great care, to include his support for such projects. He also proposed commercial routes across the American Continent and from the Mediterranean to the Persian Gulf.

Touching on the work of Andrew Bain, an amateur geologist in Cape Colony, the geological structure of Africa as suggested by Francis Galton (explorer of unknown territory in South Africa) and the observations of David Livingstone, he suggested that the Palaeozoic uplands of the south of the continent surrounded a large central basin. Deep ravines through the hills carried rivers which flooded from time to time. He forecast that good quality coal would be found on the coastal fringe. He reasoned that fossils found by Bain indicated that the rocks were of great age and being of freshwater creatures showed that the continent had not been submerged for several hundred million years. Evidence from the Sahara and the age of the Atlas Mountains led him to believe that the structure of the north was similar. The mountains of East Africa were at that time thought to be the source of the Nile and he called for their watershed to be explored, together with the upper reaches of the Niger and Gambia Rivers in the west. Four years later it was reported that rich deposits of copper, lead and probably gold could be found in the Niger region.

Murchison became more and more interested in geography and held regular *soirées* to encourage explorers to meet each other and to mingle with men of science, literature and art. Under his leadership the Geographical Society's membership grew and its financial status became sound. He encouraged and assisted the French-born American explorer of West Africa, Paul du Chaillu, and Charles Beke, a scholar of ancient history who mapped 70,000 square miles of Abyssinia and fixed the latitude of over seventy stations.

Sir Roderick had considerable influence with leading politicians of all persuasions. He met them socially at frequent intervals and they considered his conversation rather more interesting than many who knew little else than their pet subject. He was able to pull strings on behalf of many a petitioner, whose cause he espoused. There were several university chairs which became vacant and he quite frequently made recommendations on behalf of his friends to those in power. In 1852, he himself was granted a Doctorate of Civil Law at Oxford.

The combination of his interests in both geology and geography led him to draw the Government's attention to the potential economic wealth of Africa, in particular the occurrence of coal and gold. David Livingstone was not only evangelizing but also reporting to him on stratigraphy, mineral deposits, erratic boulders, the orientation of the mountain ranges and the alignment of the rivers. He mentioned coal outcrops in the Zambezi valley and the possibility of navigation along the river. He had crossed the south of the continent from Angola to Mozambique between 1853 and 1856, and drew, with Murchison's aid, a complete geological section from west to east. This was eventually published in Livingstone's *Missionary Travels and Researches in South Africa* (1857).

Further reports from other sources, including the apparent existence of easy water communications between the headwaters of the Zambezi and the Congo rivers, suggested to Murchison that Britain could benefit from the great mineral wealth in the region. He proposed to the Earl of Clarendon, the Secretary of State for Foreign Affairs, that an offer should be made to the Portuguese colonists to buy the

Zambezi Valley from them, but nothing came of the idea.

****

Geikie (1875, p. 139) now says: 'The Cambro-Silurian fire which had been smouldering for a little, broke out with renewed and unexampled energy in the spring of 1852. Murchison had not been doing or saying anything fresh on the subject of North Wales. Indeed, he had made no material addition to the announcement of his geological addresses of 1842-43 already referred to [in his *Life of Sir Roderick I. Murchison*]. These were *An Outline of the Geological Structure of North Wales* and *On the Older Palaeozoic (Protozoic) Rocks of North Wales.* It was remarkable that in the second paper the terms 'Upper Cambrian' and 'Cambrian' were not used. It is also interesting to note that the term 'Protozoic' was introduced in the sense that Murchison used it, when he said in his *The Silurian System*, 'But the Silurian, though ancient, are not, as before stated, the most ancient fossiliferous strata. They are, in truth, but the upper portion of a succession of early deposits which it may hereafter be found necessary to describe under one comprehensive name. For this purpose I venture to suggest the term 'Protozoic Rocks', thereby to imply the first or lowest formations in which animals or vegetables appear.'

Meanwhile, however, the Geological Survey had been steadily unravelling the structure of North Wales, and had pronounced the rocks there to be in the main only the extension, in folded and contorted masses, of the Lower Silurian formations of Murchison's original Silurian region. The officers of the Survey restricted the term Cambrian to the thick unfossiliferous deposits which, in several areas of North Wales, were seen to form the base on which the fossil-bearing Lower Silurian rocks rested. Sedgwick, however, refused to accept this nomenclature. In a paper read to the Geological Society on 25 February, he gave forcible expression to his dissent, using language with respect to his old comrade, which, though probably far from being meant to offend, was yet felt by the friends of both antagonists to be too personal.

Writing in 1892, J.D. Dana assessed from Sedgwick's paper: 'He states definitely that from 1834 until 1842 he had accepted Murchison's conclusions, including the reference of the Meifod beds to the Caradoc or Silurian, without questioning; but from that time he began to lose his confidence in the stability of the *base-line* of the 'Silurian System'. He adds that Mr. Salter, the palaeontologist, informed him that the Meifod beds were on the same horizon nearly with the Bala beds; and he accepted this conclusion to its full extent, using the words "if the Meifod beds were Caradoc, the Bala beds must also be Caradoc or very nearly on its parallel." Thus the inference of Murchison was adopted and the discrepancy between them deferred. And on the following page he acknowledges that all his papers of which there is any notice in the *Proceedings* or *Journal of the Geological Society* between 1843 and 1846 admit this view as to the Bala beds and certain consequences of it – "mistakes" as he pronounced them six years later, in 1852 (*Q. J. Geol. Soc.* **8**, 153).'

Dana goes on to say: 'The map accompanying the paper [of 1843] as originally prepared, had colors [sic] corresponding to five sets of areas, those of the "Carboniferous Limestone," "Upper Silurian," "Protozoic" Rocks, "Mica and Chlorite Slate," "Porphyritic Rocks;" and here again Cambrian, Upper or Lower, does not appear, the term Protozoic being substituted. The map, as it stands in the Journal of the Geological Society, has in place of simply *Protozoic*, the words "Lower Silurian" (Protozoic)." Sedgwick complains, in his paper of 1852, pages 154, 155, of this change from his manuscript, and attributes it to Mr. Warburton [President of the Geological Society], saying that "the map with its explanations of the colors plainly shows that Mr. Warburton did not comprehend the very drift and object of my paper." "I gave one colour to this whole Protozoic series only because I did not know how to draw a clear continuous line on the map between the upper Protozoic (or lower Silurian) rocks and the lower Protozoic (or lower Cambrian) rocks." "Nor did I ever dream of an incorporation of all the lower Cambrian rocks in the system of Siluria." Sedgwick also says on the same point: "I used the word *Protozoic* to prevent any wrangling about the words Cambrian and Silurian." But this is language he had no disposition to use in 1843, as the paper of 1843 shows.

'Page 155 has a footnote. In it the aspect of the facts is greatly changed. He takes back his charges, saying, "I suspect that, in the explanation of the blank portion of the rough map exhibited in illustration of my paper I had written *Lower Silurian* and *Protozoic*, and that Mr. Warburton, erroneously conceiving the two terms identical, changed the words into Lower Silurian (Protozoic)." "I do not by any means accuse Mr. Warburton of any *intentional* injustice – quite the contrary; for I know that he gave his best efforts to the abstract. But he had undertaken a task for which he was not prepared, inasmuch as he had never well studied any series of rocks like those described in my papers." Sedgwick here uses Protozoic in the Sedgwick sense, not, as above in the Murchison sense. Sedgwick again in 1854, speaks of "the tampering with the names of my reduced map." But these explanations of his should take the harshness out of the sentence, as it was in 1843 to 1846 out of all his words.

'The paper has further interest in its long list of fossils in two tables: I, "Fossils of the Older Palaeozoic (Protozoic) Rocks in North Wales, by J.W. Salter and J. de C. Sowerby," showing their distribution; and II, "Fossils of the Denbigh flagstone and sandstone series."

'Thus, until 1846, no serious divergence of views had been noted by Sedgwick. This is manifested in his paper on the Slate rocks of Cumberland, read before the Geological Society on the 7th and 21st of January, 1846 (Q. J. Geol. Soc., **2**, 106,122), which says, on the last page but one: "Taking the whole view of the case, therefore, as I know it, I would divide the older Palaeozoic rocks of our island into three great groups: 3d, the upper group, *exclusively Upper Silurian*; 2, the middle group, or *Lower Silurian*, including Llandeilo, Caradoc, and perhaps Wenlock; 1, the first group, or *Cambrian*;" differing in this arrangement from Murchison only in the suggestion about the Wenlock. The italics are his own. He adds: "This arrangement does no violence to the Silurian system of Sir R. Murchison, but takes it up in its true place: and I think it enables us to classify the old rocks in such a way as to satisfy the conditions both of the fossil and physical as well as mineralogical development."

'But before the year 1846 closed not only the overlapping of their work was recognised but also the consequences ahead, and divergence of opinion began.

'In December a paper was presented by Sedgwick to the Geological Society on "the Fossiliferous Slates of North Wales, Cumberland, Westmoreland and Lancashire," (Q. J. Geol. Soc. **iii**, 133), which contains a protest against the downward extension of the Silurian so as to include the Cambrian. It is excellent in spirit and fair in argument. Many new facts are given respecting sections of the rocks in South Wales and North Wales, in some of which occur the Lingula flags, and characteristic fossils are mentioned. In describing some South Wales sections, Sedgwick uses the term *Cambro-Silurian* to include, beginning below, (1) "Conglomerates and slates, (2) Lower Llandeilo flags, (3) Slates and grits (Caradoc Sandstone of the Noeth Grug, etc.), (4) Upper Llandeilo flag passing by insensible gradations into Wenlock shale." The Cambrian series is made to include (1) The Festiniog or Tremadoc group; (2) Roofing slates, etc.; (3) the Bala group; and then (4) "the Cambro-Silurian group," comprising "the lower fossiliferous rocks east of the Berwyns between the Dee and the Severn – the Caradoc Sandstone of the typical country of Siluria – and the Llandeilo flags of South Wales, along with certain associated slates, flags, and grits." The extension of the term Silurian down to the Lingula flags, or beyond, is opposed because the beds below the Llandeilo are not part of the Silurian system.'

In a paper of January 1847 Murchison objected to this absorption of the Caradoc sandstone and Llandeilo flags, pointing out that their fossils were Lower Silurian, as he had shown in great detail in his *Silurian System* eight years previously. Since then geologists the World over had accepted the terms 'Upper' and 'Lower Silurian' and they were already in use in memoirs, maps and geological treatises. In February 1852, Sedgwick earnestly presented to the Geological Society his case for the upward extension of the Cambrian to include the Bala beds, the Llandeilo flags and the Caradoc sandstone, although he acknowledged Murchison's 'magnificent series of fossils' from the Llandeilo flagstone. He pointed out some errors in *The Silurian System*, which had been published some fourteen years earlier, and closed with the words:

'I affirm that the name "Silurian," given to the great Cambrian series below the Caradoc Group, is historically unjust. I claim this great series as my own by the undoubted right of conquest; and I continue to give it the name "Cambrian" on the right of priority, and, moreover, as the only name yet given to the series that does not involve a geographical contradiction. The name "Silurian" not merely involves a principle of nomenclature that is at war with the rational logic through which every other Palaeozoic group of England has gained a permanent name, but it also confers the presumed honour of a conquest over the older rocks of Wales on the part of one who barely touched their outskirts and mistook his way as soon as he had passed within them.

'I claim the right of naming the Cambrian rocks because I flinched not from their difficulties, made out their general structure, collected their fossils, and first comprehended their respective relations to the groups above them and below them, in the great and complicated Palaeozoic sections of North Wales. Nor is this all, - I claim the name Cambrian in the sense in which I have used it, as a means of establishing a congruous nomenclature between the Welsh and the Cambrian Mountains, and bringing their respective groups into a rigid geological comparison; for the system on which I have for many years been labouring is not partial and one-sided, but general and for all England.'

Murchison's feelings are told by himself in a letter written to the Woodwardian Professor two days after the reading of the paper: -

"'My dear Sedgwick, - In enclosing you one of my cards for soirées, let me beg of you to prepare the abstract of your paper, so that there should be nothing in it which can be construed into an expression on your part that I had acted unfairly by you. This is the only point which roused my feelings the other night, and made me speak more vehemently than I intended. But I did intend to tell the meeting in reference to that very point (what I forgot to say) that I have over and over urged you to bring all your fossils and complete the subject you had undertaken. It is no fault of *mine* that you did not do this. . . .

"But enough of this. I cannot presume to do more than speak frankly to you; and whilst I daresay you will not change your opinions after nomenclature, I again entreat you to allow nothing to appear in print which can lead the world to suppose that we can quarrel about a name. . . .

"We have done many a stroke of good work together, and if we had waited to describe the whole Principality and the bordering counties of England, the lamentable position in which we now stand would never have occurred. But I am told by [Sir William] Logan [who had discovered animal tracks in Upper Palaeozoic rocks in Nova Scotia] and others that if I had delayed a single year or two in bringing out my Silurian System with all its fossils, the Yankees would have anticipated me. And you well know that Wales, North and South, was not to be puzzled out in less than many years of hard labour.

"I have been grievously pained to be set in antagonism to you, but I can solemnly assure you that I know no possible way by which my present position could be altered without stultifying my original view of the Silurian System as a whole, and my confirmed and extended views respecting it as required from a general survey of the world.

Yours, my dear Sedgwick, most sincerely,

ROD I. MURCHISON.'"

Geikie continues with the story: 'The reading of Sedgwick's paper produced a lengthened debate and some commotion at Somerset House [then the premises of the Geological Society]. But it nevertheless passed the review of the Council, and was printed and published in the Society's *Journal*. When, however, its pungent language, stripped of all the humour and *bonhommie* of oral delivery, came to be calmly read in print, there was a very general expression of sympathy with Murchison. At first the Council decided to cancel the printed part – a curious decision to make when the *Journal* had already been published and circulated over the world. Ultimately Murchison was allowed to write a short historical statement by way of reply, which was placed in the next issue of the *Journal* immediately after Sedgwick's paper.

'It was a most temperate and friendly rejoinder, showing the writer's very earnest desire to keep the peace, and to persuade the world that in spite of appearances, no personal quarrel existed between him and his old friend. Later in the year he again writes to Sedgwick:-

'"Nov. 22, 1852. - . . . . I can safely aver that I did nothing whatever to induce the Government surveyors to adopt the line they have, and I never went into your region until they had quite settled all their nomenclature, except a skirmish to Snowdon in 1842. It has a very bad effect upon the progress of our science to see Sedgwick and Murchison trotted out as controversialists. All our oldest and best friends regret it sincerely, and the more so as there is really nothing in the philosophy of the case on which we differ. We agree in the grand doctrine of a progression of creation, and we both start from the same point, now that the data are as fixed in the British Isles as they are in other countries.

'"Why then can you not state *totidem verbis* [in as many words] that the fossiliferous part of your Cambrian is my Lower Silurian, or if there be this remarkable community of fossils between the upper and lower groups, why not call on your part the lower half, as exhibited in Britain, 'Cambro-Silurian,' a term you once proposed for what really now proves to be the same as Llandeilo? Such an explanation from you would let the world know that there was no philosophical dispute between us. Rely upon it that the more they are examined, the more will these two things be united, and I therefore wish that there should be nothing dissonant in our mutual expressions respecting them. . . .

'"I did not intend to have said a word (when I began) on this topic; nor will I ever write more on it. *Nomine mutator* [with the name changed] the thing remains the same. If you are ever so gouty, as you term yourself, stupified (which I do not accept), when you receive this, you must not quarrel with me for telling you all my thoughts and feelings. I have too sincere a regard for you not to do so, and the matter must now be in your hands."

****

The 1852 meeting of the British Association was held in Belfast, and afterwards

Murchison, de Verneuil and a Russian acquaintance made a brief tour of Ireland, followed by a leisurely journey through Wales.

In 1853, as his script for his new book developed, he found it necessary to revisit Gloucestershire and other sites of his earlier researches, this time using railway cuttings as exposures of the strata. He also undertook a tour of Germany, accompanied by John Morris (later appointed Professor), who had a wide knowledge of fossils. They spent fifty-three days, passing through Westphalia (where they again used new railway cuttings) to Kassel and on via the Thüringerwald to Leipzig, and Bohemia, where they met in Prague Joachim Barrande, highly knowledgeable with regard to the Silurian strata. From there they went north to Berlin to see von Humboldt and others. They looked for fossils in the Devonian rocks to the south and west, until they reached the Rhine again and went home via Belgium and Paris. They presented a joint memoir on their trip to the Geological Society.

Murchison wrote to Sedgwick about his trip, 'The great point of interest for you, as for myself, is to know the final result of all the Rhenish business. As we went thither like Luther and Melanchthon [a German Protestant reformer] (I hope not like Calvin), to reform the old 'greywacke creed,' it is right that we should show to what extent we also erred. Not that any of our sections were erroneous – not that the chief physical masses are not as we placed them; but simply that we were wrong in applying 'Silurian' to that which has proved to be Lower Devonian. On that point I take to myself naturally the greatest blame.

'I have given up an hour or two, though very very busy in condensing all my "foreign affairs," to have this chat with you on things upon which we must have a community of feeling and thought. In looking over our old publications and my old memoranda-books, we seem to be such complete Siamese twins that it does my heart good to turn to them and pass away from all the *irritamenta* about a nomenclature which has led too many persons to think that we were estranged. I will never go on wrangling. What I have done, and said, and published, has never impugned the accuracy of your labours in the field, and I only regret that some expressions that have fallen from you about my mistakes and errors should have appeared harsh to others. Why, there is no geologist alive or dead who has not made plenty of mistakes, and though I have never alluded to those of your omission or commission, other persons have done so. At all events, whatever be the nomenclature adopted, we mean the same thing: our views on the progressive creations, on the true order, on the infinitely greater intensity of former causation – on these and numerous other points we are agreed, and my object in writing to you is to show how well our Devonian views have been eventually worked out upon the Continent.'

To this Sedgwick replied, 'I hope you won't think my last letter ill-tempered. If so, set it down to the fiend Gout. I am delighted with the tone of your letter. It is frank and friendly, as it ought to be, and as your letters used to be. Two or three things helped to set my back up. I know that I am a great procrastinator, partly from temperament, partly from multitudinous engagements that pull hard at me, and chiefly from a condition of health which for months and months together makes writing and sedentary work very very irksome, and almost impossible. Still, though a man is behind time with his rent, he rather grumbles when he finds on coming back to his premises that a neighbour has turned out his furniture, taken possession, and locked the door upon him. This is exactly what you did.'

Geikie takes up the story: 'And then he reopens the question in the wholly groundless belief that his friend had "stolen a march upon him," and in total forgetfulness of the fact, which has already been proved in this narrative, that Murchison actually consulted him and made him privy, by sending both MS and proof-sheets, to all that he was doing and meant to do. Sedgwick's confession as to his own dilatoriness is valuable, for that temperament of his led directly to the whole of the dispeace.'

****

Murchison's uncle, General Sir Alexander Mackenzie, died at Bath on 17 October, 1853, at the age of eighty-three, severing one of Sir Roderick's last links with his days in the Peninsular War. He was buried in the family tomb in the graveyard of the church of St. Nicholas, Bathampton. Sir Alexander left his nephew a considerable sum in his will. Sir Roderick now again solicited a baronetcy from the Prime Minister, Lord Aberdeen, a Tory who had formed a coalition government with the Whigs. Also in that year, Murchison lost his good friend, Leopold von Buch, at the age of seventy-nine.

It was the summer of 1854 before Murchison's book *Siluria* was at last published. It ran to 523 pages and included numerous woodcuts and plates of fossils and was dedicated to Sir Henry De la Beche. It described in detail the rocks and fossils of six Palaeozoic systems of Europe and North America. Since the publication of *The Silurian System* some sixteen years earlier, a great deal had been learned. The number of workers in the field had increased and the field itself had been widened to encompass most of the World. The rocks once classed as 'Transition' and 'greywacke' had been grouped in England into two series, Murchison's Silurian with well-characterised fossils, and Sedgwick's unfossiliferous Cambrian beneath it. In the absence of fossils there was no facility for comparison, but Sedgwick had identified them by their physical and mineral structure. He had in fact collected some fossils, but these had been stored away and when they were eventually identified, they turned out to be Silurian.

J.D. Dana continued the story: 'In 1854, the Cambrian system not having secured the place claimed for it, Sedgwick brought the subject again before the Geological Society. Besides urging his former arguments, he condemned Murchison's work so far as to imply that none of his sections "give a true notion of the geological place of the groups of Caer Caradoc and Llandeilo"; and to speak of the Llandeilo beds, in a note, as "a remarkable fossiliferous group (about the age of the Bala limestone) of which the geological place was entirely mistaken in the published sections of the Silurian System." There were errors in the sections, and that with regard to the May Hill group was a prominent one; but this was sweeping depreciation without new argument; and, in consequence of it, part of the paper was refused publication by the Geological Society.

'The paper appeared in the *Philosophical Magazine* for 1854. It contains no bitter word, or personal remark against Murchison. Sedgwick was profoundly disappointed on finding, when closing up his long labors [sic], that the Cambrian system had no place in the geology of the day. He did not see this to be the logical consequence of the facts so far as then understood. It was to him the disparagement and rejection of his faithful work; and this deeply moved him, even to estrangement from the author of the successful Silurian system.

'Conclusion - The ground about which there was reasonably a disputed claim was that of the Bala of Sedgwick's region and the Llandeilo and Caradoc of Murchison's. Respecting this common field, long priority in the describing and defining of the Llandeilo and Caradoc beds, both geologically and palaeontologically, leaves no question as to Murchison's title. Below this level lie the rocks studied chiefly by Sedgwick; and if a dividing horizon of sufficient geological value had been found to exist, it should have been made the limit between a Cambrian and a Silurian System.

'The claim of a worker to affix a name to a series of rocks first studied by him cannot be disputed. But Science may accept, or not, according as the name is, or is not, needed. In the progress of geology, the time finally was reached, when the name Cambrian was believed to be a necessity, and "Cambrian" and "Silurian" derived thence a right to follow one another in the geological record.

'"To follow one another;" that is, directly, without a suppression of "Silurian" from the name of the lower subdivision by intruding the term "Ordovician," or any other term. For this is virtually appropriating what is claimed, (though not so intended), and does marked injustice to one of the greatest of British geologists. Moreover, such an intruded term commemorates, with harsh emphasis, misjudgements and their consequences, which are better forgotten. Rather let the two names, standing together as in 1835, recall the fifteen years of friendly labors in Cambria and Siluria and the other earlier years of united research.'

STRATIGRAPHICAL CORRELATION TABLE
Compiled by Dr. A.W.A. Rushton and Dr. D.E. White, British Geological Survey

Murchison's classification		Modern classification	
System	Stratigraphical units	Series	System
Old Red Sandstone	Quartzose Conglomerate and Sandstone		Devonian
Old Red Sandstone	Cornstone and Marl	- - - - - -	Devonian
Old Red Sandstone	Tilestone	Přídolí	Silurian
Upper Silurian Rocks	Upper Ludlow Rock (with 'bone bed' on top)	Ludlow	Silurian
Upper Silurian Rocks	Middle Ludlow Rock (or Aymestry Limestone)	Ludlow	Silurian
Upper Silurian Rocks	Lower Ludlow Rock	Ludlow	Silurian
Upper Silurian Rocks	Wenlock Limestone	Wenlock	Silurian
Upper Silurian Rocks	Wenlock Shale	Wenlock	Silurian
Lower Silurian Rocks	Caradoc Sandstone	Llandovery	Silurian
Lower Silurian Rocks	Caradoc Sandstone	Ashgill	Ordovician
Lower Silurian Rocks	Caradoc Sandstone	Caradoc	Ordovician
Lower Silurian Rocks	Llandeilo Flags	Llandeilo	Ordovician
Lower Silurian Rocks	Llandeilo Flags	Llanvirn	Ordovician
Lower Silurian Rocks	Llandeilo Flags	Arenig	Ordovician
Cambrian (of Murchison)		Tremadoc	Ordovician

Notes: Murchison included in his Caradoc Sandstone not only fossils from the Caradoc Series of the modern classification, but also fossils from beds now referred to as the upper part of the Llandovery Series in Shropshire and to the Lower and Upper Llandovery of South Wales. The 'bone bed' at the top of Murchison's classification is now called the Ludlow Bone Bed, the base of which is correlated with the base of the Pridoli Series (formerly Downton Series). For details of the modern international chronostratigraphical classification of the Silurian System, see Holland (1985) and Holland and Bassett (eds.) (1989). Details of local Silurian lithostratigraphical classifications in the British Isles are given in Cocks et al. (1971); for Ordovician sequences, see Williams et al. (1972).

Chapter Eleven
The Cambrian System

The line between the Cambrian and Silurian deposits was rather an arbitrary one, in part drawn by Sedgwick and not based on any natural feature or series of sections. In 1842, Andrew Ramsay found Silurian fossils in the Llandeilo flags and the following day Henry De la Beche made a similar discovery at Llangadoc. These strata had been placed in the Cambrian, but were now indistinguishable from the Lower Silurian. With his wide experience of foreign rocks, Murchison considered that the line was no longer of geological significance and that Cambrian should cease to be used as a zoological classification. Between 1842 and 1846, the Geological Survey found that Murchison's Lower Silurian rocks extended right through South Wales and into the north and concluded that Cambrian and Silurian were two names for the same series of strata. As Silurian was based on fossil evidence as well as mineral characteristics, the nomenclature could be adapted to other countries and was adopted in both the Old World and the New.

The name Cambrian was originally used to describe a vast succession of strata divided into groups by their minerality, which may have been of local significance only. However, Sedgwick had determined their physical succession in North Wales. He had assumed that Murchison's stratigraphical units were all younger than his own and when this assumption was proven wrong, claimed that Sir Roderick had misplaced his groups and that the Lower Silurian rocks were properly part of the Upper Cambrian. Murchison had already described the strata as Silurian and so claimed priority. No change of name was appropriate and all rocks with his Silurian fossils should be classed by that name. This caused growing ill-feeling between them.

A great deal of progress had been made since 1839 in the ordering and grouping of rocks and the enumeration and description of fossils. Murchison had played little part in this, but Sedgwick had done sterling work with some assistance from others, including some younger geologists new to the scene. He had established the general order of succession amongst the older rocks of North Wales. The term Cambrian was now reserved for the (so far as was known then) unfossiliferous strata below the Lower Silurian. In 1846, Sedgwick had given the name Lingula Flags to a zone overlying the Cambrian Bangor Group and containing a large number of *Lingulae* (brachiopods) and *Fucoids* (seaweeds). He also named the zone above these, distinguished by fossils and mineral characteristics, Tremadoc Slate. These were both below Murchison's lowest Llandeilo stratum and contained only a few fossil species. Sedgwick was thus responsible for the establishment and naming of the lowest zones of life so far found in Great Britain.

The basement of Murchison's series, the Llandeilo group, had meanwhile been traced by the Geological Survey over a large part of Wales, and, immediately above that, the Caradoc Sandstone had been identified over a wide area. Sedgwick, by his work in the field, found by fossil evidence that both Murchison and the Geological Survey had classed more than one distinct zone under the name Caradoc. The upper part of this group lay unconformably on the rest in Shropshire and showed Upper Silurian fossil characteristics. It came to be known as the *Pentamerus* (brachiopod) Beds. Murchison had not detected a break in his Silurian rocks and was loath to accept it. He thought of it as a local phenomenon, but it turned out to be general across Shropshire and South Wales.

Since he had published *The Silurian System,* he and Sedgwick had co-operated, with Lonsdale and Sowerby, in establishing the Devonian System. They had also separated out the Permian, between the Carboniferous and the Triassic. Long before, German miners had developed copper ores through the sand and grits of Perm and Orenburg on the western side of the Ural Mountains. The group was characterised by only one type of animal and vegetable life. Neither in Germany nor in Great Britain do the same cumulative proofs exist to establish the independence of the geological system, so it was named after the province of Permia.

Workers in other countries included de Verneuil and Barrande in Europe and James Hall and Dale Owen in America. The Silurian was recognised as comprising the oldest fossiliferous rocks and a vast number of new species was identified. So *The Silurian System* was based almost entirely on Murchison's work, but *Siluria* also included the discoveries of many others.

Following the publication of his book, Murchison had intended to venture into the Continent again, particularly with a view to improving his knowledge of the geology of Germany, but this was delayed and curtailed by the outbreak of the Crimean War, in which Britain and Russia found themselves on opposing sides, and by the death of his brother, who had been Governor of Singapore. In spite of the geological dispute between them, he still considered Sedgwick his greatest friend, and wrote to him: 'Alas! My dear friend, I am in a grievously afflicted state, and quite unequal to much business. My only brother Kenneth, to whom I am sincerely attached, is stricken with death, and cannot survive many hours, or days. His malady (a heart disease) has made frightfully rapid progress in the last few weeks. I am myself bent down by a vile influenza, which has left me weak, and my doctor has ordered me abroad. But for this unfortunate state of affairs I should have been on the Brocken. I had resolved to see again our old ground, and satisfy myself, *in situ,* as to whether there are any fossil-beds older than the lowest Devonian.'

Three days later, he wrote again: 'I had no hope, but certainly was unprepared for the rapid dissolution of my poor brother, who died at half-past four on Tuesday, 1st of August, in my presence. He conversed a little with me even a few minutes before, and he only struggled to live on in hope of seeing his only living sister, Mrs. Hull – but in vain. This is a sad shock for my worn-out nerves, which required a cheerful summer tour, and now I am nailed down by all sorts of business, every act of which reminds me of my loss. We have been loving brothers through life, ever since he came, at five years old, to Durham School, where I, being two years older, had to fight his battles.'

With his indifferent health, Roderick's doctor suggested a trip abroad. This, of course, turned into a geological excursion and he chose to visit the Harz Mountains and the Thüringerwald, this time accompanied by John Morris of Kensington. With the help of fossils collected by local geologists, the two were able to tie up the strata here with those of other parts of Europe. The results were in due course reported to the Geological Society. Murchison's health problems were soon forgotten and he proudly wrote in his journal, 'Walked for three hours, to the summit of the Brocken. Good weather for ascent; thin floating clouds. The old pillar on the summit has gone. Here I write in my sixty-third year, having walked up the 4000 feet as well as I did in 1828 with Sedgwick.'

The pair returned in time to attend the meeting of the British Association in Liverpool at which Murchison was elected President of Section E (Geography and Ethnology), a position he had held at the Ipswich meeting in 1851. It ended with a dinner for three hundred. He was required to make speeches and drink champagne and, not too surprisingly, immediately following the meeting he became ill again, to such a degree that Lady Charlotte was sent for. He repaired to Up Park, but soon became disinterested and returned to London, still in poor health. He now gave up smoking, a habit for which he had previously been well known.

Meanwhile, he had obtained from the Government a grant of £500 a year to establish a public map-office in the Geographical Society's rooms, for general reference.

In the spring of 1855, Sir Henry De la Beche, Director-General of the Geological Survey, died after a period of ill health. He had developed his work, so that it became recognised as part of the Ordnance Survey. He had conceived the idea of creating a national school of geological and mineralogical science and had over the last twenty years amassed a collection of economically valuable mineral substances – anything with industrial importance. He had suggested that this Museum of Economic Geology should be put under the management of the Office of Works, Woods and Forests, and the idea had received a favourable response from the Government, with special interest expressed by Sir Robert Peel. It was eventually housed in Jermyn Street and became a school of applied science. As well as the Museum's collections of rocks, minerals and fossils, chemical and metallurgical laboratories were set up. A Mining Record Office was established, to preserve mining plans and information regarding collieries and quarries.

The School of Mines, the Metropolitan School of Science applied to the Arts and the Museum had been formally opened by Prince Albert in November 1851. It had been extremely well run by De la Beche, and now the search was on to find an adequate successor. It was necessary to appoint someone who would have a clear understanding of the Government's requirements and who would be the head of a Government educational establishment for the diffusion of science generally, as applied to productive industry.

Murchison wrote to John Phillips, 'When poor De la Beche was gone, very old and valued geological friends (not of the Survey) urged me to look to the place as the man who, by his labours in British fields, and his application of his knowledge to maps, sections, and books, was most entitled to the post, and who, from successful management of Societies, could best succeed in it. But I peremptorily declined not only this appeal, but also a gentle allusion of the President of the Board of Trade when he sounded me *in limine* [at home]. At that time my great fear was, that geology would be submerged in other affairs if a good hammer-man was not at the head of the whole.

'Who then was to be (Geology and Palaeontology apart) the *régisseur*? A split was to be deprecated – two kings would never answer, and confusion would arise. Yesterday sundry Professors, the four or five who are the oldest and most influential, met together in Jermyn Street and unanimously opined that I was the only man who could keep the whole thing together and make it work well. This opinion they conveyed to the authorities through Playfair [Secretary of the Department of Schools and Museums at the Board of Trade], and the appeal being made to me in so very flattering a way, I could not resist, particularly as I saw that I should, by accepting, prevent discord. Whether the Government will offer it to me is another question.

'Notwithstanding your mot on the triple directorate, I view it simply as the School of British Geology and Mines. The affiliated sciences are all subordinate to that fundamental point.

'If they name me, and should my health continue as good as now, you know me well enough to be certain that I will do some good at all events, though perhaps I have offered to undertake what I had better have left alone, as far as my happiness is concerned.'

Murchison was delighted to learn that a large number of important people, including his friend Sedgwick, had proposed to the Prime Minister, Lord Palmerston, that he recommend to the Queen that he be appointed as Director-General.

The entry for May 11 1855 in Murchison's journal read, 'Interview with Prince Albert at Buckingham Palace. Was complimented by H.R.H. on my appointment. Explained to him some of my views, some of our *desiderata*, and some of our doings; particularly called his attention to poor De la Beche's *Catalogue of British Pottery and Porcelain*, with which he seemed well pleased.

'The Prince then explained all his views as to the hope of realizing, at a future day, a concentration of all the chief scientific, artistic, and manufactured produce in one great building, and how the possibility of such an advance was stopped by the want of money and the unwillingness of Government to spend in these warlike times: suggested a modified scheme for the erection of a temporary building of corrugated iron with glass, slightly raised above the ground, and warmed by hot water, whereby specimens now spoiling in damp places might be kept [this project foretold the construction of "the Brompton Boilers", which were in due course replaced by the Kensington museums].

'H.R.H. then alluded to an influence now at work to have the Royal Academy transferred to the new building at Burlington House, and regretted that the men of science should not be there. I replied that we men of science should put our shoulders to the wheel, and endeavour to keep the Government to the proposed occupation by ourselves.' Later remodelling and enlargement of Burlington House provided space enough to include the chartered learned societies.

The Crimean War produced a quandary for Murchison as to whether he should wear his Russian orders, which had become part of his normal dress. He rather unwisely asked Prince Albert, who, of course, said No, which was no doubt a blow to his vanity. It was obviously now unacceptable to wear them, at least within sight of the Royal family!

In his new official capacity, Sir Roderick now entertained even more frequently at 16 Belgrave Square and elsewhere. He soon settled into what he found was enjoyable work. His health improved and he was able to lecture to a group of naturalists on the top of the Malvern Hills. He standardised the colouring and lettering of maps, regularised the titles of Records of Mines under *Memoirs of the Geological Survey* and saw to it that the fossil collection was tidied up. He arranged an expedition for Lord Clarendon to the Gulf of Nicomedia (Gulf of Izmit at the eastern end of the Sea of Marmara) in search of coal, and sent out to the American Geographical Society of New York spare copies of volumes and journals held by the British Association and Statistical Society and of those of his new organisation. He also began to distribute Survey publications to foreign bodies who would appreciate them, so that the work of his department should be more widely known.

MacLeod (2000) says, 'However, Murchison's vision was not confined to the occupation of physical frontiers. He also wished to see the RSM [Royal School of Mines] become the intellectual equivalent, to "what the *Bergakademie* of Freiburg and the *École des Mines* of Paris are to Germany and France". The fact that, over the previous decade, few students had enrolled at the RSM to study mining, did not diminish his optimism. Indeed he claimed that the mining schools later established in Vienna and Berlin were modelled on Jermyn Street; certainly, the schools in Melbourne and Sydney, were, in his words, set to copy "the very scheme and syllabus of our own establishment". In 1861, to enhance the School's new status – and perhaps to improve its intake – Murchison asked the University of London to examine and award degrees to his graduates. His request was denied – the University declined to alter its matriculation requirements, which required passes in Greek and Latin, criteria quite irrelevant to pupils of the artisan classes whom the School hoped to attract – so Murchison decided to award instead a "certificate of competency" to students who attended nine courses over three years, and who passed the School's examinations. In 1862, this qualification became (and still is) the "Associateship of the Royal School of Mines" (ARSM).'

Murchison's correspondence with Sedgwick remained on the friendliest of terms. He wrote to him on 30 May 1855, 'I am sorry to hear of your ailments. I trust that you are much too foreboding respecting your duration of life. You are no older than our Prime Minister, who has to face angry Houses of Parliament nightly, and is never in bed till one or two in the morning.

'Your *P.S.* announcing your third *fasciculus* [bundle] or introduction, shows that you are as active in mind as ever. Quite agreeing with you that half-measures in arguments in science are no measures, I would very much regret if you fire any such Minié rifle shots at your old friend as require to be answered except in a perfectly friendly manner.

'By the bye, you have no doubt heard of (if I did not already tell you of) the discoveries of fossils in our Durness limestone of Sutherland, by Peach [see p.179]. He has corresponded with me on the point, and has sent me some of the fossils. I have had them polished. The forms (rude and ill preserved as they are) look more like *Clymeniae* and *Goniatites* [two types of ammonoids] than anything else (with corals); and if so, the calcareous masses which we saw from Assynt to Durness [north-west Highlands], interstratified in the quartz rock, are high in the Devonian! I would like to hear what you say to this *éclaircissement* [clarification]. I see great difficulty in understanding it.

'If the conglomerates of the Ord of Caithness and Ben Bhragie, close to Dunrobin, are the equivalents of the West Sutherland quartz rocks, they must also be of the Scarabin hills, which are in contact with the true Old Red of the east coast. If, on the contrary, these crystalline rocks should prove altered equivalents of Silurian strata, I see nothing but what is rational.

'It is twenty-eight years since we tramped across Sutherland, and the going-over of my well-kept journal (in which I have some of your writing and much of your mind) has been a source of great pleasure to me, ruffled only by your announcement of the forthcoming continuation of our disputation on things of which neither of us had an inkling in 1827.'

These pleasant memories stirred in him a desire and later a determination to revisit the north of Scotland. He was able to combine this with attendance at the annual meeting of the British Association, this year in Glasgow, at which he would be elected to preside over Section C (Geology). On the eve of setting out, his diary entry for 7 August 1855 was: 'Last day in the office. Before I leave, I am glad to have made two good moves among, I hope many others; the one applying to my friend Lord Canning, as Governor-General of India, and begging him to look to the geological structure of India, and have surveyors in all the Presidencies; the other to Sir W. Molesworth, the new Secretary for the Colonies, urging him to do the same in many of our neglected Colonies. The answers from both are favourable, and I have hopes of something better.'

In future he continued to be deeply involved in the work of the Geological Survey, but still had time for summer excursions and to look after the interests of the Geographical and Geological Societies.

Chapter Twelve
Geology of the Scottish Highlands

At the beginning of the nineteenth century, Dr. John Macculloch had made some puzzling but important discoveries with regard to the red rocks of the far north-west of Scotland. They appeared to be the same as the Old Red Sandstones of the north-east, but had hitherto been shown on geological maps and in text books as being unfossiliferous and therefore dating prior to the appearance of life on Earth. They also passed beneath primary quartz rocks. In 1827, Murchison and Sedgwick, distracted by the Old Red Sandstone of Caithness, declared that they should be classed as the same. They dismissed Macculloch's find of what he thought were worm-burrows in the quartz as not being organic. In 1840, R.J.H. Cunningham had shown that the sandstones overlaid an old gneiss and were under quartzite and limestones, above which was more gneiss. He also was able to confirm the presence of Macculloch's worm holes in the quartzite. Cunningham observed that gneisses and schists were metamorphosed by heat and pressure, were not necessarily ancient rocks and probably post-dated the beginning of life. This was not generally accepted for another fifteen years.

Without the benefit of radiometric dating, it is not surprising that these early geologists had great difficulty in understanding the age and sequence of the rocks in this region. They were not to know that above the gneiss (probably mostly altered igneous rocks) of the Lewisian basement (the oldest rocks in the British Isles, dating from 2000 Ma (million years ago) or more) are thick sandstone deposits (the Torridonian series, named after Loch Torridon on the north-west coast of Scotland) laid down up to 1000 million years later. These have been distorted by two orogenies, one at about 1100 Ma and another at around 600 Ma – both taking place when Scotland was attached to North America. Above them are *older* rocks that have been thrust from the south-east over the top of them (the Moine Thrust), so that the Principle of Superposition does not apply. To complicate matters even further, they have been cut through in many places by igneous intrusions. Next come the magnesian limestones which range in age from Cambrian to what Murchison called the Lower Silurian (later the Ordovician). In spite of all his work and the evidence found for him by other geologists, Murchison never did, as we shall see, quite unravel the whole story.

It happened that, in 1854, Charles Peach, a Customs Officer at Wick, travelled westwards to visit the wreck of a ship off the Sutherland coast. He found in the limestones of Durness some fossil shells, which he sent to Murchison in London, who quickly realised their importance in dating the Highlands rocks. At first he compared them with Devonian fossils but concluded that this could not be their true origin. He immediately set off for the Highlands with Professor Nicol. Although it was well into August and he had promised to attend the British Association meeting in Glasgow on 12 September, he routed via the Caledonian Canal to Inverness and had a nostalgic look at Tarradale, where the tenant farmers had all gone and large well-tilled fields indicated the improved agricultural methods introduced. He also visited the burial ground of the Fairburn family in the rear of the churchyard of the Parish Church of St. Clement at Dingwall, where his uncle, the General, had repaired the family tomb (it is now in such a dangerous state that the building has been fenced off by the local authority). Murchison and Nicol eventually reached Loch Assynt in the far north-west.

To any readers who have not visited this part of Scotland, the author would say that its isolation is awe-inspiring. The sixty miles from Ullapool to Durness along the one north/south road provide an experience not to be missed. Today, the road is well surfaced, though liable to be buried deep in snow in the winter. Traffic amounts to a handful of vehicles an hour and the scenery, amongst the oldest rocks in the United Kingdom with an age exceeding 2000 million years, is truly magnificent. One can only imagine the difficulties and dangers that Murchison and Nicol were prepared to face a century and a half ago and the sheer logistics of an expedition into this wild, sparsely-inhabited countryside.

Being pressed for time, the pair did confirm what Cunningham had said about the position of the red sandstone, but could not come round to accepting that it was older than the quartz. Murchison had, some twenty-eight years earlier, sketched the relationship, showing that the quartz lay unconformably on the sandstone but still now missed the meaning of this. He insisted that the quartzite, limestones and overlying gneiss could not possibly be of Devonian age and must be much older, possibly Silurian. However, Nicol was not at all convinced of Murchison's reasoning, and suggested that the rocks could even be as young as the Carboniferous.

They returned via Wick and the east coast, looking very briefly at the geological features, then cut across to Glasgow for the meeting of the British Association, where Murchison was again elected President of the Geology and Geography Section. Sedgwick attended in spite of his ailments. He had just published the Introduction to his *Synopsis of British Palaeozoic Fossils,* in which he spoke of Murchison with a vehemence that was regretted by those who admired and respected both of them. To anyone who did not know them, it would have seemed that Sedgwick was expressing bitter animosity towards his former associate, and he was probably aware of this, for after Murchison had reported on his findings in Sutherland, he rose to speak, deliberately taking off his heavy greatcoat. Seeing that this had raised a smile in the audience, he jocularly said, 'Oh, I'm not going to fight him!' which was greeted by applause and relieved laughter.

Hugh Miller maintained that the rocks of Assynt were metamorphosed portions of Old Red Sandstone, but Murchison insisted that they must be very much older. In this he was supported by Sedgwick. However, it was clear that much work was needed to resolve the matter and Murchison was determined to undertake this.

Also at this meeting, a series of remarkable fossils from the moorlands of Lanarkshire was exhibited by Dr. Robert Slimon, a medical practitioner at Lesmahagow, twenty miles south-east of Glasgow. They were lobster-like crustaceans, identical to those found elsewhere in Upper Silurian and Lower Old Red Sandstone deposits. Here was a chance to show that the strata from which they came belonged to the Upper Silurian and to establish that such rocks were present in southern Scotland. They were in fact inliers within the Upper Palaeozoic strata of the Midland Valley. Immediately after the meeting, Murchison and Professor Ramsay went into Lanarkshire to investigate. They found that, especially on the Logan Water, a stream flowing north-eastwards towards Lesmahagow, there was an excellent example of a transition from the Lower Old Red Sandstone into Upper Silurian strata. This bore comparison with similar rocks in Hereford, Shropshire and Cumberland, and it provided a new starting-point for the determination of the geology of the country and a comparison of its rocks with those of England and Wales. It was another two years before Murchison had the opportunity to follow this up.

At the age of sixty-four, Murchison tended to look back on his achievements, rather than to look forward with youthful enthusiasm to excitement to come. Nevertheless, he was kept busy with his duties and social obligations in London. He conscientiously looked after the Jermyn Street Museum and School, saw to his official work with the Geological Survey, made occasional forays into the countryside or on to the Continent, chaired the meetings of the Geographical Society, furthered the progress of the subject, encouraging explorers and their expeditions, and polished his geological work at home and abroad. In co-operation with James Nicol, he published a large geological map of Europe, on which the Silurian, Devonian and Permian rocks were delineated.

In July 1856, he travelled down to Gloucestershire, where, joined by Professor Ramsay, he enjoyed the hospitality of Lord Ducie. They spent some time looking at the Silurian and Oolitic rocks in the Tortworth district, which he had mapped in 1835.

Murchison probably had in mind what he might describe in the new edition of *Siluria*. In the Cotswolds, they were accompanied by Robert Etheridge, who had been a businessman in Cheltenham, but given it up in favour of his interest in geology. His intelligence and knowledge of fossils so impressed Murchison that he soon afterwards appointed him Assistant Naturalist to the Geological Survey, from which position he rose to become one of the foremost palaeontologists in the country. With Lord Ducie, Ramsay and W.T. Aveline (one of the senior officers of the Survey staff), Sir Roderick revisited his old haunts in Herefordshire and Wales, returning to Cheltenham for the meeting of the British Association. While in the town he found his old nurse living there (he had not known she was still alive), and gave her £10.

Immediately after the meeting, he went over to Ireland to visit his staff there. In driving rain and low cloud, he drove via Kilkenny and Limerick to the coast of Kerry. He recorded in his journal observations of unstratified igneous rocks, grits, Wenlock fossils, Old Red Sandstone, unconformities and numerous sections. He took a welcome rest at Muckross Abbey, near Killarney, then made his way back to Dublin and over to Wales. He wrote to Andrew Ramsay: 'I had both your letters in Ireland, of which dear land I took leave this morning, believing it was no longer necessary for me to go poking into the holes and corners of Galway, where I have already seen the Silurians, so I sent Jukes and Kelly thither on a reconnaissance....

'With the exception of these oases, far far aside, I really must declare that the geology of Ireland is the dullest ("tell it not in Gath") which I am acquainted with in Europe. If St. Patrick excluded venomous animals he ought to have worked a miracle in giving to the holy isle some one good thing under ground. But no! everything has had a curse passed upon it. There are as good Cambrian rocks as need be, but they are all like the Longmynd, and won't give good slates. Then there are as good Carboniferous Limestone and Millstone-grits as any in Scotia, but it is pitiable to see the miserable small packets of broken culm [coal-dust] at intervals of scores of miles, which are dignified by the name of Coal-measures. Then as to mines it is *nil,* except what used to be called the curse of the miner (pyrites).

'Jukes is a fine energetic fellow, and I made the acquaintance of all his men (inspecting their work), who can stand a life no Englishman would tolerate. [When he returned, he said to Ramsay, "Catch me going to Ireland again!" and apparently he kept his word!].

'I am now convinced that we must have more workmen employed in the English Survey, and specially in our coal-districts, or some of these days we shall be blown up by the Parliamentaries.'

He added a postscript: 'Friday evening. – Just got back from the Stiper Stones, where I had a good tramp with [Richard] Gibbs [the Survey's fossil-collector]. It is well I went to see the things *in situ*, for by persevering I got fossils all the way down to the Stiper Stones, and under them too. It is a perfect fossiliferous descending series, with *Graptolites, Trilobites, Orthoceratites,* and *Orthidae,* as well as *Lingulae,* both great and small, and is so irrevocably dovetailed into the series that no man alive can separate them in the field whatever [John William] Salter [who had determined the species of many of Murchison's fossils and was now one of Sedgwick's palaeontological assistants] may do in his closet. I shall now adhere, with infinitely greater pertinacity than ever, to the original Silurian base, and standing on the Stiper Stones will defy all the world.'

As far as the Geological Survey was concerned, he sought to increase the manpower available, to expedite the work. It was now possible to include more detail in the geological mapping of the country. More and more attention was paid to the surface deposits, and the underlying rocks could be mapped with more precision. This became labour-intensive and Murchison, as Director-General, determined to seek money from Parliament to finance an increase in staff. This was particularly necessary in Scotland, where up until now there had been only two surveyors, sufficient while the Ordnance Survey was not yet prepared, but critical now that most of the central counties had been covered. Murchison expressed to his second-in-command, Professor Ramsay, his opinion that, if extra funds were not allocated, it would be fifty years before the survey was finished.

His request was successful and more staff were recruited. However, the rate of progress did not significantly improve, because much greater detail and perfection were sought, requiring more time. There was also the problem of loss of surveyors to more lucrative positions and the consequent requirement to train their replacements. Under Lord Derby's Government of 1866, the Geological Survey was reorganised and enlarged, the staff in Great Britain being split into two groups, one under Andrew Ramsay to deal with England and Wales, and the other under the newly-appointed Archibald Geikie (later Murchison's biographer) to work in Scotland. He had already several years' experience there under Ramsay and took up his post in April 1871. The total number of staff was increased from thirty-seven to seventy-five.

Murchison fought a proposal to transfer the control of the Geological Survey and the Museum of Practical Geology from the Board of Trade to the Education Department of the Privy Council. He feared that in time the scientific character of the institutions might be dealt with by men who had no knowledge of or sympathy with science, and whose control might fetter their free development. However, he failed to impress the powers-that-were and found himself and his establishment transferred to the custody of the Science and Art Department of the Privy Council, about which he was far from happy. In the event, the change was more apparent than real.

Sir Roderick also had frequent communication with officers in the colonies in relation to mining activities, including the search for gold in Australia, and about the defence of British territories, which he felt had been badly neglected. He wrote to Sir William Denison, Governor-General of Australia, 'Your letter stimulating me to exertion in favour of the publication, by the Government, of the natural history of the British Colonies came unluckily just as our Ministers were in agony about their untoward Reform Bill. . . .When we look at the splendid publications of the Yankees respecting the geology and natural history of their several governments, it is humiliating to be forced to confess that Britain does so little in this line. I confess that I see little prospect of inducing our Government to undertake such a scheme for all our colonies, though I have hopes that the colonies which specially called for and paid their geologists and naturalists would be assisted in any publication by the Imperial Government. . .

'You will perceive that I appeal in favour of a more efficient maritime protection for our long and exposed sea-board. It is an old hobby of mine, and I cannot yet divest myself of the apprehension that we have been too heedless of the increase of power of our Gallican allies in waters where they have neither colonies nor commerce.'

Murchison was not without his detractors, one of which was the Comptroller of the Stationery Office, J.R. MacCulloch. His office was, under Treasury orders, responsible for publishing the Survey's scientific papers, but he often described them as 'some more of Sir Roderick's trash'.

Murchison was still physically very active for a sixty-five-year old. He noted in his journal, 'At night went to the annual ball at East Grinstead. Danced a quadrille with Mrs. Mortimer West, and a tempête with the youngest Miss Sterling, Lady Caroline's lovely daughter, and a reel with Lady Arabella. Pretty well for a chicken of 1792, who had been geologising all day.'

In February 1857, Murchison wrote to his friend Joachim Barrande to tell him that he had received on his behalf the Wollaston Medal of the Geological Society. He also gave him a progress report on the amendments he was making for the second edition of *Siluria*. He had previously been loath to accept that there was a break in his Silurian series, even though Sedgwick had drawn his attention to the unconformity at the base of the Upper Silurian. He now reluctantly placed the brachiopods *Pentamerus oblongus* in the upper strata and *Pentameri* of various other species with *Atrypa hemispherica* in the intermediate character Llandovery rocks, which were themselves connected with the true Lower Silurian through certain other species. (Later, the Geological Survey traced other breaks).

Sir Roderick's duties in London provided many distractions, but a couple of years later he was able to write to Sir Philip Egerton, '*Siluria* will be out in a fortnight, with nearly 200 new figures of species in woodcuts, new tables, coloured lithograph of Assynt, and all sorts of novelties, and much additional matter.

'On Wednesday next I throw off No. 2 of my N. Highland and Orcadian contributions, and on 15th December the Old Red of Elgin comes off, followed by [Thomas Henry] Huxley's [Professor of Natural History at the Royal School of Mines] description of the wonderful reptile *Stagonolepis Robertsoni*, which must have been many feet in length, and had a swinging tail. The singular big cast which I brought away in my portmanteau and showed you at Leeds, which I told old Duff seemed to me vertebral, has, after being talked of as a Cephalopod, been proved to be the tail of *Stagonolepis*. We have lots of his footprints. Huxley makes him a Thecodont [reptilian ancestor of the dinosaurs].

'I am getting a charter for the Geographers, and going to Lord Derby for apartments to contain both the Geological and Geographical Societies at Burlington House, so as to constitute there an Institute of Science.'

In June 1857, Murchison wrote to *The Times*:

'Sir, In an elaborate letter, published in *The Times* of this day, on the subject of the survey of Scotland, Lord Elcho has done me the honour to allude to me both by name and as President of the Royal Geographical Society. His Lordship has correctly quoted my reply to a Treasury circular, in which my opinion was asked as to whether a scale 6 or 24 inches was the best for certain purposes?

'Now, the reasons I assigned for preferring the larger scale had reference exclusively to plans of estates in which each acre was to be accurately noted for tithe and parochial assessment, as well as for the enclosure of lands, and for the conveyance and transference of property.

'Adopting the views of public men of great weight on such subjects, I uniformly expressed my conviction, that such large plans or cadastres did not properly come within the scope of physical geographers or geologists.

'My opinion above stated having been cited, as if I were in favour of the publication of maps on the 25-inch scale, I beg to state that during the last 23 years I have been known to be the warm advocate of a map upon the 1-inch scale.

'Seeing in 1834 that my native highlands of Scotland were then worse mapped than any civilized country; that Cape Wrath and other headlands were out of position by many miles; I induced the British Association for the Advancement of Science to appeal to the Government upon the subject of this great national want. Heading a deputation to the Government of that day, I contended that Scotland was entitled to be furnished with the same 1-inch map which England and Wales were obtaining.

'Subsequently Ireland was surveyed, and her map published upon a 6-inch scale, that being considered the smallest measure upon which her disputed townland boundaries could be accurately laid down. The 1-inch, or generally useful map, is now in course of reduction from the larger scale.

'For a long time I remained unconvinced of the real practical value of any scale larger than that of the 1-inch, but when I became the director of the geological survey I found that in Ireland, where the 6-inch scale with contours had been used, the geological surveyors could delineate every outcrop, bend, and break of the strata, and that where this 6 inch scale had been applied in Scotland it was of high value to mining proprietors.

'I therefore stated in my evidence before a committee of the House of Commons during the last session that I had modified my original opinion, and believed that a 6-inch survey, co-ordinately with the 1-inch map, was desirable and particularly in rich mineral districts. At the same time I expressed my conviction that it would be useless and wasteful to publish any map of the 10,000,000 or 11,000,000 acres of wild lands of the Highlands on any scale larger than that of 1-inch.

I remain, Sir, your very obedient servant,

RODERICK I. MURCHISON
Royal Geographical Society, June 25.'

****

In the summer of 1857 there was a congress of scientists in Montreal and as Silurian rocks had been identified in North America, Murchison was very tempted to go, but was strongly advised by his physician, Sir Henry Holland, not to do so. In the event, the Geological Society of London was represented by Professor Ramsay. Instead, Sir Roderick determined to spend some time in Europe and looked for a good geological reason to go. He wrote on 30 July 1857 to Joachim Barrande: 'After having arranged everything for a voyage to Canada and the United States, commencing with the great meeting of savans at Montreal, I have changed my plans, seeing that my doctor rather prescribed for me rest, and the quiet amusements of Germany. The truth is, I have been working too hard this year, whether as President of the Geographers, Director of the Geological Survey, or Trustee of the British Museum, etc., and now having printed my anniversary Address to the Geographers (114 pages), I embark on Sunday night, 2d August, for Antwerp.

'Thence I shall ramble on towards the Thüringerwald, and establish myself there for ten days at the baths of Liebenstein, of which I am very fond; because one can get there pure and cold water, perfect shade, and capital Permian rocks. So write me a note to say if shall find you at Prague in case I should bend once more (and always with great profit) towards the Klein-Seite [Barrande's address in the Bohemian capital].

'The brave Peach has again discovered fossils in the crystalline limestone and quartz rocks of the north-west Highlands of Scotland – species identical with those of the Calciferous Sand-rock of North America. Is this not beautiful? I am enraptured with it. Poor Hugh Miller conceived hypothetically that these rocks represented the Old Red Sandstone, and Nicol has recently suggested that they are nothing but the coal formation changed into quartz rock and mica-schist!

Ever yours,

ROD. I. MURCHISON.'

He took with him Thomas Jones, Assistant Secretary of the Geological Society, who later became an eminent palaeontologist. Looking to examine the fossils and sections of Permian rocks, they travelled up the Rhine, then cut across to Liebenstein, where Murchison received a flattering letter from the eighty-seven-year-old von Humboldt and an invitation to visit Potsdam. Whilst there Sir Roderick paid his respects once more to the King. Going on to Prague and Vienna, the pair returned via Breslau, Berlin and the Harz mountains. A leisurely journey through Kassel and Frankfurt took them to Bonn in time for the annual meeting of the German Naturforscher. They returned to England after an absence of two months.

On 15 October, Murchison wrote to Sedgwick, 'You may have learned that I gave up a trip to North America, on which I had set my heart, because my state of health and nerves would never have stood the excitement and wear and tear of Jonathan's hospitalities.

'I went, therefore, to Germany, and to many of our old haunts and some new ones, accompanied by Jones of the Geological Society, whom I took as my aide-de-camp, and a capital staff-officer he proved. I have come here well and strong, and hope to hear you are the same. My wife is living, and will live, at St. Anne's Hill, the residence of Charles James Fox [who had been a political rival of William Pitt and had died in 1806], till the 1st March, as London does not agree with her, and I go and come thither and hither.

'My great object in Germany was to see every good natural section of Permian rocks, and to commune with the best men who had written thereon, and I have succeeded very much to my own satisfaction. . . . I have thus got all the German Permian in my pocket. Feeling that much is to be done in the English Permian, I intend to go down for a week to look again at several sections, which, in the north of England, have been laid open by railroad cuttings. . . You will much oblige me if you will send me your opinion, and a hint or two as to the spots where I am most likely to see clear data.'

About three weeks later, he wrote again to his old friend, 'I returned from my Permian skirmish on Monday night, having explored many of your old beats, and, I am happy to say, with a sincere admiration of your old and most excellent memoir. Your letter was a full proof to me that your memory was anything but an "old rotten fishing net," for I never received from you or from anyone a more clear synopsis of all that constituted truly the British Permian. . . I zigzagged across most of your old sections, and admired them all.'

A large part of Murchison's time was devoted to the affairs of the Geographical Society. He took an active interest in the Livingstone Festival of 1858, in order to ensure that the explorer's next expedition should be well manned and include a geologist. Dr. Livingstone had, a couple of years earlier, returned from a highly successful journey of exploration in southern Africa. He had struck north from the Transvaal, discovered Lake Ngami (now in Botswana) and determined to open trade routes to east and west. He accrued a vast amount of information about the country, its native tribes and products, and he found the Victoria Falls. He was now to be appointed chief of a government expedition for exploring the Zambezi.

Sir Roderick had gained a great deal of experience in presiding over meetings and conducting social affairs, and he was only too pleased to pass this on. John Phillips took over the Presidency of the Geological Society in the spring of 1858, and he wrote to him: 'One piece of advice I seriously give you. There is nothing so faithful to a public dinner (*crede experto*) as a plenitude of toasts. Ten should be the outside, including the Royal and Loyal. This was my number at the Livingstone Festival, and by my precision of firing, i.e. never losing time and yet giving them time to breathe, I got through before or just at midnight.

'I would give Cardwell [Viscount Edward, President of the Board of Trade 1852-55] a toast to propose, and not let him reply. The toast he could best give (rely upon it) is "The Geological Survey and the Government School of Mines". Having been himself the Minister under whom the whole concern acted, it is just the subject he will like to speak upon, and if you do this, and have a reporter at dinner, you will do us at Jermyn Street, i.e. your old shop, real service. As you are taxed enough, I will send a letter to the editor of *The Times* with a passport in my name for a reporter of the great Leviathan.'

In the meantime, Charles Peach had been scouring the Highlands for fossils and found enough to establish that the quartzite and limestones in the north-west were distinctly of Lower Silurian age. He had found some nineteen or twenty species and John Salter had identified at least five of them as being common to the Lower Silurian rocks of Canada. Of course geologists of this time had no inkling of continental drift, which was first suggested by a German meteorologist, Alfred Wegener, in 1915 and not generally accepted until the 1960s. So this relationship was somewhat of a mystery. We understand now that these fossils are evidence that this part of Scotland was joined to Newfoundland and today's North Atlantic Ocean only began to open about seventy million years ago.

Professor Nicol and Colonel Sir Henry James, now the Director of the Ordnance Survey, had separately traced the boundaries of these strata for long distances and shown that the red sandstones and conglomerates lay unconformably under the quartz. Nicol had also shown that the uppermost rock of the region was the gneiss. Murchison now determined to establish the relationship of all these rocks to each other and to the rest of the country's geology. Nobody had yet done this in respect of the Old Red Sandstone, which spread across Orkney and Shetland, and he readily accepted an offer from the Commissioners of Northern Lights to allow him passage on their steamer, the *Pharos*, on its annual voyage of inspection of lighthouses on the northern isles.

With Charles Peach, he started by gathering fossil fishes from the quarries of Thurso. They took the ferry from Thurso to Stromness, on the west coast of

Mainland, Orkney. As they left Thurso Bay, they noted the contrasting colour between the dark grey sandstone of Holburn Head on their left and the rich tone of the slightly younger rocks of Dunnet Head to the right. They were fascinated by the way the breakers ate away at the high cliffs and saw how storms had brought down huge chunks of rock. They noted that the whole of the western side of the island of Hoy repeated the Upper Old Red Sandstone rocks of Dunnet Head, but that, as they approached Stromness, the northern tip of Hoy was of the Middle Old Red Sandstone of Holburn Head. They took the road to Kirkwall to await the *Pharos*, which took them to the northern tip of Shetland, where Murchison, who had never been so far north before, wrote his name in the lighthouse books. This was at Muckle Flugga, sometimes called North Unst, whose lighthouse had only become operational four years before.

They only had limited opportunities to land, but could observe the geology en route with binoculars. They could see that the Orkney Islands consisted almost entirely of Middle Old Red Sandstone, frequently intruded by basalt dykes, whereas the structure of Shetland was quite different. Only the south-east coast and part of Western Zetland was similar to Orkney, though without the dykes. Most of the rest consisted of metamorphic and intrusive rocks.

The *Pharos* turned south again and dropped Murchison and Peach on Cape Wrath, from where they worked their way eastwards and southwards, revisiting sites at which sections had been drawn in 1827 and 1855 and making new traverses. It became apparent that the older strata in Sutherland were comparable to the red grits and conglomerates of Wales, classed as Cambrian. In Wales the transition from Lower Silurian to Cambrian was not clearly marked, as the two merged gradually. However, here in Scotland it was apparent that the equivalent of the Lingula Flags was not present – it had been eroded before the quartz rocks had been laid down, so the unconformity was explained. Murchison therefore classed all the rocks below the quartz as Cambrian.

Now, though, there were the gneisses of the north-west coast coming out from beneath what had hitherto been considered the oldest rocks in the United Kingdom. They were distinctively different – folded and crystallised and clearly very old indeed (today we date them as at least 2000 million years of age). Murchison called them Fundamental Gneiss and later classed them with the Laurentian Gneiss of Canada, recognised as far back as 1846 by Sir William Logan, Director of the Geological Survey of that country, then with the status of a colony. Starting with these as a base, he traced a section through the Lower Silurian limestones and the vast overlying schists and gneisses to the Old Red Sandstone on the east coast of the Highlands. Since there were Lower Silurian fossils beneath them and Devonian rocks above them, Murchison reasoned that the metamorphic rocks must be Silurian, thus negating the previously-held belief that gneisses and schists must pre-date any fossiliferous rocks, an unprecedented change to geological thinking. However, Professor Nicol dissented from this view, believing that the schists were really part of the fundamental gneiss brought up by faulting. In time he was shown to be right and Murchison's error seriously impeded the progress of petrology in the Scottish Highlands.

Murchison worked his way across to the east coast north of Helmsdale, to explore the 2000-foot peak of Scaraben high in the desolate moorland. He managed to choose a day of violent winds and storms, but pressed on regardless. It was not surprising that, at the age of sixty-six, he rather overdid things and made himself ill. Fully recovered after a few days, he made a leisurely journey down the coast via Dingwall to Inverness and across to Elgin. On the way he enjoyed the hospitality of old friends but conscientiously also sought out all the outcrops he could find of the Old Red Sandstone, about which he reported later to the Geological Society in an elaborate memoir. Continuing by way of Aberdeen, he reached Rossie Priory, on the north bank of the Firth of Tay, the home of Lord Kinnaird. From here he led a party across the Tay to visit the Upper Old Red Sandstone of Dura Den, which had already become famous for its abundance of fossil fishes. They were so complete that it was clear that their death was sudden and they had been covered with sand before their bones became loosened and separated.

Murchison described the day's work: 'After finding a few remains and fragments, Lord Kinnaird's eye caught the end of a fish. On quarrying into the rock, after much perseverance the head and a considerable portion of a grand *Holoptychius* came forth, to the exuberant joy of all concerned. The dark and red tints of the scales and bones of this fine large fish shone out in striking contrast to the white and yellow stone. Grand as was this discovery, it was clear that we were only on the threshold, and that by patience the whole fish might be extracted. So thereon we went to lunch under the trees – a most picturesque party, our noble host, having worked harder than the quarrymen, in his shirt sleeves, and Lady Kinnaird presiding with her attractive manners. We carried off our trophies, hoping still for more, recrossed the Tay, and dined at eight at the Priory – a very joyous party. But our excellent and eloquent explorer of Dura Den [Rev. Dr. Anderson of Newburgh] resolved to complete our gratification. Next morning he went back by rail, and in the evening returned with an immense booty, and all the remainder of the huge fish in a large box completely covered up in wool. This day has passed in uniting the head with the remainder of the animal, cleaning, fixing, cementing, and securing the whole. The animal thus put together measures thirty-three or thirty-four inches by thirteen in width, and is thus considerably larger than the *Holoptychius nobilissimus* which I acquired for the British Museum some years ago.'

****

The 1858 meeting of the British Association was held in Leeds and Murchison was again elected President of the Geography and Ethnology Section. He gave a short report on the progress of the faculty and did not ignore the geology section, to which he outlined what he had been doing in the Highlands and the great change he proposed to their accepted structure. However, Professor Nicol expressed strong opposition to his conclusions. He contended that everywhere the upper layer of gneiss overlaid the other strata, it was separated from them by intrusive igneous rocks and must therefore be the lower gneiss brought up by faulting. Although Murchison was confident that he had made no mistake, he determined to revisit the Assynt and Durness region with Professor Ramsay to settle the matter.

The revised edition of *Siluria* was at last published at the beginning of 1859. Murchison sent a copy to Sedgwick, but received no acknowledgement of it. His old friend had expressed in his *Synopsis of Palaeozoic Fossils* his very strong feelings over the controversy regarding their findings and he felt that Murchison had taken all the kudos for their work together. His bitterness had grown beyond a scientific argument into deep personal ill-feeling. A week later Murchison sent a note to Sedgwick: 'I have sent a copy of my new edition of *Siluria* for your acceptance, earnestly hoping that the passages relating to yourself in the Preface, p. viii, and the alteration of a phrase or two in the body of the work, may remove from your mind the impression produced by the perusal of the first edition.

'Time rolls on, and as we passed many a happy day together, I trust that you will have some gratification in turning to these pages, particularly those relating to the Highlands of Scotland. Little did we think, when we first united the yellow and white sandstones of Elgin with the Old Red, that those beds would be found to contain such reptiles as the *Telerpeton and Stagonolepis*!

'Clinging to the hope that the only bit of sorrow I have experienced in my scientific life may pass away, and that your friendly feelings towards me may return, I am always, my dear Sedgwick, - Yours most faithfully, ROD. I. MURCHISON.'

Sedgwick wrote a very cool reply from Dent in Cumbria, beginning 'Dear Sir Roderick', instead of his former 'Dear Murchison'. It was no more than a formal acknowledgement of the gift, with no hint of healing the rift between them. Two years later, in 1861, Murchison was honoured by Cambridge University with the degree of Doctor of Laws (LL.D.). Using the occasion, Murchison tried once more for reconciliation, writing:

'Dear Sedgwick,

I cannot be once more in Trinity College without having brought vividly to my mind our former friendship and your kindliness to me on many an occasion. Permit me to assure you that I have at this moment as strong a regard for you as ever, and that although I yesterday received an honour which you had secured for me at the installation of Prince Albert, if the University law would have permitted, I consider this, and all worldly distinctions that might be bestowed on me, as nothing, in my estimation, compared with one kind letter from yourself, in your old manner. I should, of course, have infinitely preferred to make the appeal to yourself in person, and was much disappointed when I found you were not to be present at the Convocation of yesterday.

'After the ceremony I went to visit your museum, and was perfectly astonished at the immense improvements and additions which have been made in and to it since I was in Cambridge. I recollect full well how slightingly you always spoke of the Upper Greensand of Cambridge, and how, when we were together in Westphalia, you looked to me as a sort of authority on the "Malm Rock." But who could ever have imagined that your little Cambridge zone would have given forth such riches as it has afforded? I was really quite astounded at the quantity, variety, and value of the fossils. . . .

'Among the few old friends left here I was vexed to see Hopkins so much broken, though he officiated in the ceremony, and will, I trust, now recover his wonted vigour. If you will, at your leisure, gratify me with a line, and let me know that you are in better health than when I saw you last at the Athenaeum, you will sincerely gratify me. The days of "auld lang syne" are perpetually recurring to me, and when I transmit to you, as I shall when I go to town, a copy of my last memoirs on the Highlands, including one to refute Sharpe's errors about the cleavage of the Highland rocks, you will see how I recur to your dicta on that point, as well as to our original observations in Scotland. Yours always most truly,   ROD. I. MURCHISON.'

In fact Sedgwick was so bitter over what he saw as unfair treatment that he withdrew from all further contact with Murchison and the Geological Society. He only wrote to him twice more, once on the occasion of Lady Charlotte's death.

In the summer of 1859 Murchison and Ramsay set off on their planned north-west Highlands trip, completing the last part of the journey by steamship. They traced out in detail the rock boundaries and concluded that the great mass of the crystalline rocks of the Highlands were altered strata of Lower Silurian age. This gave Murchison considerable gratification.

The pair cut across to the east coast and worked their way down to the Moray Firth, looking carefully at the Old Red Sandstone, eventually reaching Aberdeen in time for the 1859 meeting of the British Association, this year under the presidency of Prince Albert. During the meeting, Murchison gave an address on his geological discoveries in the Highlands. Quite unexpectedly a deputation from the Royal Society of Edinburgh came on to the platform and presented Sir Roderick with the first gold medal, founded by Sir Thomas Makdougall Brisbane [the Scottish General and astronomer, after whom the capital of Queensland is named], for the encouragement of science in Scotland.

At the close of the meeting, Her Majesty Queen Victoria invited the members of the Association to Balmoral to witness some Highland games. The Queen had braved heavy showers to remain in the open, when Sir Roderick requested an audience with her. He was able to tell her that he had just received a telegram reporting the discovery by Captain M'Clintock of the Franklin records and log book.

Sir Roderick had made a very substantial contribution to the affairs of the Geographical Society since its inception in 1830. He now, feeling his sixty-six years, decided that he must ease his burden somewhat, and in 1859 he resigned his chair in favour of Lord Ashburton, though remaining on the Council. Unfortunately, the peer's health failed, and Murchison found himself still carrying much of the day-to-day responsibility of running the Society, which involved world-wide correspondence and connections. In 1861, with Lord Ashburton called away by family illness, he was left to prepare the annual Address. Two years later, he was entreated by his colleagues to take the chair again, and he held it until just before he died in the spring of 1871. During his stewardship geographical knowledge had been greatly extended, often with the encouragement and financial backing of the Society of a number of intrepid explorers, and the subsequent dissemination of their discoveries to the public. He had increased its membership from 600 to 2400, enabling substantial funds to be raised, and he had been instrumental in persuading the Government to provide large sums for the exploration of East Africa. There were three areas of particular importance that had been opened up – Australia, the interior of Africa and the Arctic.

In Australia, John McDouall Stuart had made seven expeditions into the interior and reached Lake Eyre. He made three attempts to cross the continent, the last one in 1861/2 successful. Murchison's interest in the development of the colony is reflected in a number of places and geographical features named after him (see Appendix 3).

The African explorers Baker, Burton, Grant, Livingstone, Speke and many others featured frequently in the Society's *Journal*. In particular, Murchison had strongly proposed the sending of Livingstone to confirm the source of the Nile by establishing the position of the central African watershed. Even though reports of his murder on the west side of Lake Nyasa by a member of the Mazite tribe reached home, Murchison was aware that the Johanna men (from the Comoros Islands) who had deserted Livingstone and brought the news, were notoriously mendacious and he was adamant that the great explorer was safe and well.

From central Africa at that time letters were entrusted to caravans which could take months to reach the coast. News was then forwarded to England, often by the political agent in Zanzibar via the Seychelles or the Cape, and it usually took six more weeks to arrive. (The Suez Canal was not opened until 1869). So there was much anxiety as to the welfare of explorers commissioned by the Royal Geographical Society and others.

DR. LIVINGSTONE'S RETURN.

TO THE EDITOR OF THE TIMES.

Sir,—The public will be glad to learn that this great African traveller will shortly be at home. By a letter which I have just received from him, and which was finished at Malta on the 17th inst., I learn that he reached Bombay on the 13th of June, after a voyage of 42 days from Zanzibar in his own little steamer, the Lady Nyassa.

Far from being downcast at the failure of the efforts hitherto made to check the slave trade on the east coast of Africa, my dauntless and energetic friend writes that he " cannot find it in his heart to abandon his object." He is therefore bent upon returning to Africa, after a stay of about four months at home, during which time he will consult friends on the subject of those future labours in which he purposes to employ his steamer, now left at Bombay. Of this vessel, built at his own expense for river and lake navigation chiefly, Dr. Livingstone writes :—" The Lady Nyassa is a first-rate little sea-boat, and she rose like a duck on the huge waves of the ocean."

The projected new expedition of Dr. Livingstone is not, he says, " so much exploration, as to set in train operations by merchants and others by which the slave trade shall be eventually worked out."

I trust that at the meeting, of the British Association, to be held at Bath on the 14th of September, this truly disinterested and good man will give us an account of his last bold adventures.

Your obedient servant,
RODERICK I. MURCHISON.

Belgrave-square, July 22.

Letter from Murchison to *The Times*, published on 23 July, 1864

Murchison had bid God-speed to Franklin's expedition to find the Northwest Passage and, deeply saddened by the lack of any news of it, he still held out hope that some members at least had survived and were eking out an existence with friendly Eskimoes. He put forward a petition to the Government to mount a search but failed to persuade them to do so, even though reports had given a good indication as to where they might meet with success. It was Lady Franklin herself, who, with some small help from her friends, had equipped the *Fox* under Captain M'Clintock and sent it off to seek news of the fate of her husband. In his Address of 1857 to the Geographical Society, Sir Roderick said, 'May God crown their efforts with success, and may M'Clintock and his companions gather the laurels they so well merit, in their noble endeavour to dissipate the mystery which shrouds the fate of the *'Erebus'* and *'Terror'* and their crews! If however this last effort, which, in the absence of other aid save that of her friends, Lady Franklin is now making, should fail in rescuing from a dreary existence any one of our countrymen, and should not even a plank of the *'Erebus'* and *'Terror'* be discovered – still, for her devotion in carrying out the exploration of the unvisited tracts wherein we have every reason to believe the ships were finally encompassed, every British seaman will bless the relict of the great explorer, who has thus striven to honour the memory of her husband and his brave companions.

'My earnest hope is that this expedition of Lady Franklin may afford clear proofs that her husband's party came down with a boat to the mouth of the Back River in the spring of 1850, as reported on Esquimaux evidence by Dr. Rae, and thus demonstrate that which I have contended for, in common with Sir Francis Beaufort, Captain Washington, and some Arctic authorities, that Franklin, who in his previous explorations had trended the American coast from the Back River westward to Barrow Point, was really the discoverer of the Northwest Passage.'

M'Clintock brought back the records of the lost expedition, which showed that Franklin had, indeed, crossed from the Atlantic to the Pacific. It was tragic that the Northwest Passage was found to be useless, after it had been sought for centuries. Nevertheless, it was still considered that reaching the North Pole was a worthwhile goal and possible. Murchison also pointed out the desirability of Antarctic exploration, with a view to finding sites for the observation of the transition of Venus in 1874 [to study its atmosphere against the background of the Sun]. When Murchison finally gave up the chair of the Geographical Society, his successor, Sir Henry Bartle Frere, said of him, 'It is no exaggeration to say that during the past thirty years no geographical expedition of any consequence has been undertaken in our own or, I believe I might say, in any other country, without some previous reference to him for advice and suggestion, often entailing laborious research and correspondence.'

Archibald Geikie said of him, 'In passing from the Geographical Society we may take notice of one feature of the anniversary Addresses on which Murchison always laid great stress – the obituaries of deceased members. These afforded an opportunity, of which he never failed to avail himself, to sketch the services and good qualities of old scientific friends and companions. Most of his compeers in the Geological Society were likewise enrolled among the geographers. Hence year by year he had occasion to pronounce an *éloge* over the grave of one after another of the early magnates in geology. At one time it is the genial Buckland to whose memory he has to pay a kindly tribute, remembering not only the lasting services of that able man to science, but the many kindnesses which he had himself received, and not least among these, the friendly guidance which led him to the banks of the Wye in 1831, and indirectly to the Silurian System and his after fame. Again he has to chronicle the quenching of another of the lights under which geology in its early days spread and prospered in England – William Conybeare. Of the leaders who upheld the science when he first began to study it, the author of the *Silurian System* was indebted to no one more deeply than to this able observer and admirable writer. Conybeare and Phillips' *Geology of England and Wales* had been, as he said, his scientific Bible. From his earliest geological paper onwards, the influence of that book may be traced in all his geological writings. These obligations he gratefully acknowledged. At another anniversary, when death had been busy among the leaders of science, and especially among the President's own circle of friends, he had to record the loss of Robert Brown, to whom he was sincerely attached; Alexander von Humboldt, from whom he had received so many proofs of respect and esteem, and to whose assistance and stimulation he now gratefully recounted his obligations; Hallam, one of the most welcome guests at his gatherings of scientific, literary, and artistic friends; the Archduke John [Johann] of Austria, the frank, open Styrian prince with whom he had been so delighted among the valleys of the eastern Alps.'

****

Darwin's *Origin of Species* appeared in 1859. Murchison was strongly opposed to the principles behind it, but had, as he had had throughout his career, the common sense not to broadcast opinions too loudly on subjects he had not studied in detail. However, in conversation and private letters he held nothing back. He wrote to Professor Harkness: 'If you read the work of Darwin on the *Origin of Species*, which has given us an earthquake shock, you will easily see that in reality my geological postulates, if not upset, destroy his whole theory. He will have no creation – no signs of a beginning – millions of living things before the lowest Silurian – no succession of creatures from lower to higher, but a mere transmutation from a monad [simple organism] to a man. His assumption of the position of the Lyellian theory, that causation never was more intense than it is now, and that former great disruptions (faults) were all removed by the denudation of ages, is so gratuitous, and so entirely antagonistic to my creed, that I deny all his inductions, and am still as firm a believer as ever that a monkey and a man are distinct species, and not connected by any links, i.e. are distinct creations. The believers in a lower, and a lower still, have never answered, and cannot answer, the fact that the rich marine Lower Silurian fauna is invertebrate, and that the Cambrian rocks of Ireland, Wales, Shropshire, and the north-west of Scotland, though less altered than the Lower Silurian, have afforded nothing distinct which is higher than an Oldhamia or a worm.'

Again, he wrote to Sir William Denison: 'I am a geologist of the school of Buckland, Sedgwick, De la Beche, Greenough, and I may add, of myself. I flatter myself that I have seen as much of nature in her old moods as any living man, and I fearlessly say that our geological record does not afford one scintilla of evidence to support Darwin's theory.

'Recently we have had the grandest trumpeting about the discovery of the *Eozoon canadense* in the Laurentian rocks below all Cambrian. And what does it amount to? Why, simply that the lowest imaginable order of zoophyte is found in the lowest discoverable rock. It changes nothing. We are just where we were. Simply the lowest created things are found in a stage lower. This only confirms the doctrine of a commencement with the lowest grades of creation, and a succession in after ages to higher and higher types of life successively. As for the transmutation of types, I look upon it as simply an ingenious piece of sceptical puzzling without the least basis.'

In a letter to Sir Charles Lyell, Darwin commented on Murchison: 'How singular so great a geologist should have so unphilosophical a mind.'

There would seem to be here some confusion about the significance of older fauna with regard to evolution. Sir Charles Lyell, author of *Principles of Geology,* had changed his position after Darwin's publication and embodied his amended ideas in *Antiquity of Man*. Murchison did not seem to have grasped this and wrote to a friend, 'I presume you will get Lyell's new volume on the Antiquity of Man, and will marvel at and perhaps admire the bold efforts now made to throw back the origin of our noble species Homo to the accumulations immediately succeeding the glacial period, when half of modern Europe was either under snow and ice or icy seas. Huxley's "Place of Man in Nature" completes the view by showing us that man is only the front-rank leader of a succession of apes. This little book is beautifully written. My gifted colleague runs far ahead of my knowledge. I must apply to myself "Ne sutor ultra crepidam [let the cobbler stick to his last];" as yet however I am not a Darwinian, and see numberless objections to his theory.'

****

In preparing his memoirs on the geology of the north of Scotland for the Society, Murchison felt that he should compare the north-west to the more southern parts of the Highlands and that this should clarify the whole structure. So in the summer of 1860 he wrote to Archibald Geikie, then one of the field-geologists of the Geological Survey in Scotland: 'Requiring some speedy change of air or absence from over-excitement, I would have liked to have had a real holiday in the Pyrenees or elsewhere. But seeing that Ramsay and Jukes, my generals of division, are both abroad, I have resolved not to quit the British Isles. I propose, therefore, to get away in the middle of next week, and go to Scotland. Being there, I consider it my duty to work out with your assistance the problem of how far the order and classification which are clear and established in Sutherland and Ross are applicable to the more southern parts of the Highlands.

'I think, therefore, of taking you with me in the first instance to Jura and the adjacent mainland, where zones of quartz-rock and limestone abound, and which may prove to be equivalents of my Durness and Assynt Silurians. Having ascertained whether that zone subsides under micaceous flags (as I surmise), I will test the same again between Balahulish [sic] and Fort-William. Having settled these points, and having re-explored the heads of Loch Duich, Loch Alsh, etc., I will test the thing again at the head of Loch Maree (one of Nicol's obstructive cases), and, having looked around that tract, will revisit Loch Broom, where the Ross-shire succession is as clear as that of Sutherland. Finally, we will cross to the Lewis, where I wish to satisfy myself still more conclusively as to the fundamental gneiss.'

The two carried out this plan, though it was considerably extended. They completed a series of traverses across the Highlands, attempting to show for the first time the general geological structure of the region, from the old gneiss in the north-west to the Old Red Sandstone in the south-east. They reported their findings in detail to the Society in a memoir entitled *On the altered rocks of the Western Islands of Scotland and the north-western and central Highlands*. The expedition laid the foundation of a close friendship between the two. Writing Murchison's biography some fifteen years later, Geikie says, 'From this time forward he treated me with almost paternal kindness, frankly taking me into his intimate confidence, and showing on many occasions a thoughtful and tender solicitude for my welfare, which has endeared the memory of his friendship as one of the brightest recollections of my life.

'His own journal of the tour, like the rest of his journals in this latter part of his life, contains scarcely an entry save what is geological. Its pages, after the interval of years, recall to me the eagerness with which he pursued his quest, the shrewdness with which he could guess at the probable structure of a hill several miles away, where most eyes would have detected nothing, but where, after a good hard climb, one found his conjecture to be true; the pertinacity with which, in spite of the attractions of Highland sport and Highland hospitality, to both of which he yielded so far, he yet held on his way until he had accomplished his task.

'A few of the incidents of the tour which impressed themselves on my memory, though of little note, may perhaps fitly find a place here. No one who has often heard Sir Roderick Murchison address public meetings can have failed to notice how characteristically his Highland blood would show itself. He was proud of being a Highlander, and seldom lost a chance of proclaiming his nationality. Back in that picturesque region of Kintail and Lochalsh, where his forefathers had lived, his patriotism glowed again with renewed ardour. He revisited, with undiminished interest and pride, the scenes where Donald Murchison had baffled the King's troops. When we were together in Loch Duich, though no geological necessity called him, he must needs once more make a pilgrimage to the Bealloch of Kintail. Standing on a rising knoll, his left hand stuck into the arm-hole of his waistcoat, and his right holding a stout staff, with which he pointed out the leading features of interest, historical or geological, his face would kindle with the old martial fire as he went over again the events of "the '15." In the same spirit, he solicited and obtained from the proprietor of the ground leave to choose a site for a monument to commemorate the deeds of his illustrious kinsman. A bright autumnal afternoon was given to that pious quest. We went by boat, creeping in and out among the islands and promontories at the mouth of that wonderfully fine inlet, Loch Duich, and fixing at last upon a knoll of rock amid the heather and bracken, from which we could look over to Eilan Donan Castle, and away up to the mountains of Kintail and Glenelg on the one side, and over to the peaks and glens of Skye on the other – a site which the annual crowds of steamer-carried tourists would be sure to see when the obelisk should be placed upon it (see p.129).

'Again – the Murchison sept had not been all as prosperous in the world as the Laird of Tarradale. Some of them still remained in the original district in humble circumstances, but, with the genealogical skill of true Highlanders, they could yet count their kinship to the geologist. I remember, on one of our excursions, we halted at some fern-thatched cabins, and were met by one or two plaided cottars, with whom I left Murchison in talk. I was told afterwards that they were some of his distant relatives, or clansmen, whom he always visited and assisted when he returned to that part of the country.

'While still in this Ross-shire district, we attended the English service in the parish church, which, in spite of a very rainy day, was crowded by a Gaelic congregation of some 500 people in wet clothes, who gave a good illustration of that loud and deep groaning during the sermon, which is sometimes so marked in the churches of the north-west Highlands. Murchison's face was a curious study during the service. Naturally reverent, and evidently with a strong desire to compose himself to the frame of mind and posture of body proper to the occasion, he yet wore a droll expression of wonder as he watched the gravity of the bearers amid sounds which, anywhere else, he would have supposed indicative of the deepest anguish or pain. When the service was ended, and we were again in the pure air outside, he drew a long breath, and remarked to me that it was the last time he should ever enter a Presbyterian church!'

The following weekend, they went round the coast in a small boat and sailed up Loch Torridon. At the hamlet of Torridon they were able to hire neither horse nor carriage, and so had to walk the twelve miles up the glen to Kinlochewe, which Murchison managed easily, possibly because there was so much of geological interest on the way. The next morning, a Sunday, dawned bright and clear, and after breakfast they separated. Murchison went up to Loch Maree and explored the east side of it, stopping from time to time to sketch the strange mountain outlines, while Geikie climbed the mountains to the west, thoroughly enjoying the landscape and wild life. He wandered so far across trackless moorland that darkness fell when he still had several miles to go to get back to the inn at Kinlochewe, which he did not reach until midnight, fortunately with the help of a bright moon. Murchison was naturally extremely worried by his absence and tried to get people from the inn to set out with lanterns. Because it was the Sabbath, they were indifferent to the situation and, had Geikie been lost, they would have said it was his own fault for venturing abroad on the Lord's Day!

The pair then went southwards to make a series of traverses across the central Highlands. They found the metamorphic rocks crumpled and folded, so that they cropped out at successive points. They were able to trace them across wide areas of the countryside and taught them about the history of metamorphism. Although the rocks were substantially changed, they could identify them and map them just as easily as the ordinary unaltered strata. They were able to establish the general structure of the Highlands, though the finer detail would have to await the availability of accurate maps. Geikie tried to persuade Murchison that everything did not fit harmoniously into his views as he wished or imagined, and that the upper rocks of the south-east did not appear in the north-west, but Murchison was adamant in his opinions. In the Blair Atholl district (on the Perth to Inverness road) Geikie was driven to distraction, trying to reconcile the chaotic assemblages with the structures in the Assynt region.

The partners produced a joint memoir to the Geological Society and plans were made to prepare a small geological map of Scotland, embodying the latest findings. Writing in 1875, Geikie stated that 'this little sketch-map was the first, and as yet the only one, in which the rocks of the country from bottom to top were treated in rigid stratigraphical order, and delineated so as to show the structure of the country.' This turned out to be Murchison's last great geological task, and he derived great satisfaction from it.

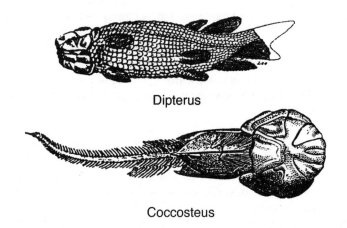

Dipterus

Coccosteus

Fishes of the Old Red Sandstone of Scotland

Chapter Thirteen
Lady Murchison's Ill Health

Back in London, Sir Roderick began preparations for the 1862 International Exhibition. In his official capacity at Jermyn Street, in connection with the Department of Science and Art, he had plenty to do. He wrote to his friend, Sir Henry Barkly: 'The Commissioners of the International Exhibition of 1862 have applied to me to know if it will not be possible to test in this establishment the economic value of the various coals of the British Colonies, of which, in the event, the Governors would send specimens. This is indeed an important affair, and I will endeavour to have it carried out, provided the Home Government will pay for the cost of the inquiry. We have no staff in this building, nor any space for such an inquiry (on the great scale). We must, in fact, have ground, set up large boilers, and employ several chemists, etc. Nor can it be done in a hurry, if a really valuable result is wanted. . . I find that our metallurgical Professors think we can sufficiently analyse the various Colonial coals for general purposes of comparison without going into the tedious and expensive details formerly employed by Sir H. de la Beche for our own navy. . . .

'Geological surveys are all the fashion in New Zealand. I have already sent out Dr. Hector to Otago on a three years' survey, with a good assistant, and I have no doubt he will do capital work. His portion of the labour in defining the character of the upper region of the Saskatchewan and the Rocky Mountains, also of British Columbia, was admirably done.

'I have now an application from Wellington province for another surveyor. In replying thereto, and hunting out a fit man, I could not avoid the expression of my satisfaction in reading two reports in the New Zealand Gazette, by the Honorable L.C. Crawford, on the geological structure of the province of Wellington.

'23d June 1862. – Here I am again President of the Geographers, my eighth year of office. I presided over 200 people at dinner in Willis's Ball-room, and as I had some of the foreign chairmen of classes in the International Exhibition, I contrived to make the evening pass with liveliness and point. Gladstone spoke admirably, but they scarcely noticed his speech, and omitted all my sayings and doings in The Times.

I have had, besides, very hard work as chairman of Class I of the Exhibition. With 2000 exhibitors in my class, it has been no small difficulty to adjudicate with fairness some 300 to 400 medals. The weather has been positively horrible, - wet and cold rains for ever, but today there seems to be a genial change. It is marvellous that the Exhibition should succeed as well as it does, despite the Palace shut up, the Court absent [Prince Albert had died the previous year], and half of our cotton mills closed.'

In August, Murchison took himself off to the spa at Marienbad (now Mariánské Lázně) in Bohemia. He was welcomed there by Professor Antonin Fric, Curator of the zoological collections in the Museum of the Czech Kingdom, whom he had recently met in London. Feeling better for his rest, Sir Roderick, with the help of Mining Councillor Lipold, acquired the newest geological maps of Northern Bohemia from the Geological Institute of Vienna and revisited, for the third time, the Silurian basin around Prague, where there were new exposures in railway cuttings. He also wanted to see if there were gneissose rocks of the same great age as those in Scotland, to assess their relationship to the Silurian there and to visit a location where the older gneiss was in contact with the younger.

An article in the Czech journal *Ziva* by Professor Fric, was translated for *The Edinburgh Geologist* by a Corresponding Fellow, Raduan Horny. In it he says, 'Stopping at the village of Ejpovice, we saw the Cilina Hill on the southern side, built of impressive beds of the Drabov quartzites. The valley below us led off to the north through a depression between the Komarov and Rokycany beds, where iron mines run into the ground in all directions. A short time before, railway cuttings had exposed the beds and made it easier to interpret the structure.

'After being cared for that evening by the Czech family of Mr. Antonin Jelinek, an owner of a spinning mill in the town of Lochoviche, the next day Murchison studied the landscape around the town of Zdice, where shales and quartzites of the lower Silurian system border with basaltoids, supporting the Lower Silurian limestone basin. Murchison had already visited the region between Veroun and Prague in 1848 and therefore went by railway directly to Prague. He said candidly that he did not want to visit the enigmatic sites of the so-called Colonies, because he had not enough time to spend there, and neither did he want to take a part in a dispute that concerned his old friend Barrande. Staying for two days in Prague, he visited Barrande again and examined the beautiful fossil collection of the Abbot Zeidler, being enormously surprised by the splendour and beauty of the specimens. He examined the collections in the Czech Museum very thoroughly, and discussed for a long time with Professor Krejci [a stratigrapher, mineralogist and structural geologist] the relationship between the gneiss and the so-called Archaic shales in Bohemia which he, in analogy with northern Scotland, considers not to be Archaic but metamorphosed lowermost beds of the Silurian age....

'On September 4th I again attended our distinguished guest on his way via Josefov to Ratiborice, from where we intended to make an excursion to a fossilised forest near the village of Radvanice. Murchison had letters of recommendation to Duke Lippe who, unfortunately, was away. We were received so unkindly by a deputy officer (an alien), that I blushed for shame and, being unable to get any hay for our weary horses, we had to return disappointed all the way to Josefov on the same day.

'The next day we went to Horky by railway where we made an excursion to the Permian, observing here beautifully developed red sandstones and melaphyres [darker than usual porphyritic rocks]......

'He was troubled at the present time by the over-learned Germans who wanted to re-christen the old and honourable name of the Permian to the Dyas, and feared that his exhausting work in the Permian region would be forgotten.

'On the same day we arrived at Semily and followed the beds in a railway cutting, as recorded in the excellent maps of the Imperial Survey.

'On September 6th we went from Semily to Libstat, where Mr. Maryska, a parish priest and a keen collector of natural objects, was our guide for the whole day. Here we saw an excellent fish locality in black shales near Kostalov and coarse-grained conglomerates with malachite sandstone in a railway cutting.

'Quickly flying by railway through the Cretaceous system near Turnov and the Archaic slates at Zelezny Brod, we made the last excursion on the next day near Rychnov, where again Archaic slates, limestones and porphyries occur.

'Murchison left this place for Dresden to see the famous geologist Geinitz, and I went back to Prague. So I was rather surprised when after about three days, Murchison again appeared in Prague, going by the Plzen railway to Bavaria, where he wanted to continue his observations along the banks of the Danube. Seeing him to the Smichov railway station, as a farewell gesture I drew in his notebook a profile of beds from the glorious Vysehrad over Dvorce and Branik, as it was possible to see from the stairs of the railway building.

'A week after Murchison's departure, that well-known secret circular was sent out, in which the political officers were instructed to watch both of us travellers, to ensure that we were not engaged in political canvassing. As far as I myself was concerned, this matter did not surprise me, as our family had for many years had the pleasure of special attentiveness in this regard. The fact that even our celebrated guest, according to the style of the circular, was suspected, has been deplored by public opinion in domestic and foreign journals. A study of Murchison's biography best confirms how unsubstantiated were the apprehensions of the authorities.'

****

At Munich he visited some of the art galleries and listened to mass with Mozart and Haydn's *Offertorium* in the cathedral. He went by rail to Paris, where he found his old friend, de Verneuil, and visited the Louvre. He went on to Cherbourg, to see if he could discover any of his 'fundamental gneiss' there. On his way home he succumbed to some infection which practically undid all the benefits of his stay in Marienbad. He had found in the past that the best therapy for this sort of problem was to go out shooting pheasant and he had several standing invitations from landed gentry. Among others, he went to visit Lord Palmerston at Broadlands, where he enjoyed some good sport with the Prime Minister and Admiral Bowles.

Some of the places in Bohemia visited by Murchison in 1862

Lady Murchison, now seventy-three years of age, was also not in good health and had stayed at Brighton while her husband visited his friends. She suddenly fell seriously ill and Sir Roderick was called to join her from East Anglia. Among his papers was found the following note:

'Clermont, Norfolk, Nov. 5th, 1 p.m., 1862. -   Alas! The telegram received calls me to my dear wife's sick-bed at Brighton, and here I am fast bound for three or four hours for the want of any railway train, and doubting whether I shall catch the Brighton train at night! What a painful state of suspense, and what a journey I have before me! What a happy retrospect, and what a sad prospect!

'I look to her as having been my safeguard and guardian angel for forty-six years. She first imbued me with a love of science, and weaned me from some follies of the world. She accompanied me in the three or four first years of my geological career by land and by water; she sketched for me, collected fossils for me, and encouraged me onwards. Even when I was working at my Silurian System, twenty years and upwards after our marriage, she was often by my side, and from those days to these, when unable, from feeble health, to accompany me, she has been my best adviser, and my infinite solace when I returned to my own fireside. Her goodness, her deep sense of religion, and her practical benevolence, devoid of all cant and profession, have often made me reflect with sincere sorrow on my unworthiness of her goodness, - on my vanity and love of the world and its pleasures, as contrasted with her humility and true Christian piety.

'I ought to be a much better man than I am after so many years of so good and excellent example before me. May the Great Disposer of all events have so pre-arranged all human destinies in a future state that I may be able to witness her heavenly abode (for that surely it must be) should such a miserable sinner be far removed from her!

'*Brighton, Nov. 6.* – A tedious and anxious journey by the Eastern Counties railroad from five till ten (Brandon to Shoreditch). Delayed by accident. Reached this at midnight, and thank God to find her rather easier, and most grateful to me for coming.

'*Nov. 9.* – Three intensely anxious days. My dear wife cannot shake off the bronchitis. Coughing all night, and incapable of eating. Nourished by beef-tea and arrowroot. Has had intense suffering. Mind wandering occasionally. Mr. Turner, the experienced surgeon and practitioner, was doing all in his power. Myself in a state of deep affliction, and oppressed with the calls on my duty tomorrow as President of the Geographical Society.'

He was obliged to leave her to a slow and only partial recovery.

****

There was an alarming suggestion that Britain's coal-mines would soon be exhausted. Murchison was nominated as a member of a commission of enquiry. In their report they expressed the opinion that a productive coalfield probably existed under the Chalk and other sediments of south-east England. Murchison strongly protested against this conclusion. He felt that the geological structure was not conducive to the formation of coal, even though rocks of Carboniferous age might well be found at no great depth. Exploratory boring took place some years later, and a small coalfield was found in Kent.

In the summer of 1863, Murchison tore himself away from his duties in London and went with Professor Harkness to spend a few weeks in Cumberland, Westmorland and Lancashire, ending up in Newcastle for this year's meeting of the British Association. He afterwards wrote to Sir Henry Barkly, 'Our meeting at Newcastle was a very good one. I was, of course, well satisfied, inasmuch as my section of Geology and Ethnology was the most popular by far of the divisions of our Parliament of Science.

'I have effected a considerable change in our geological maps of England in this recess. There is always something to be done, even at home! If you look at any one of the geological maps of England, including my own little one, you will see that in Westmoreland and Cumberland, all the valley of the Eden, up to Carlisle and round into Lancashire, by the coast of Whitehaven and Furness, is laid down as New Red or Trias. Now I have demonstrated, in conjunction with Mr. Binney and Professor Harkness, that all this region is Permian. I have further shown, what these two gentlemen were at first indisposed to admit, that on the western side of the Pennine chain the Permian group exhibits a large mass of sandstone, superior to the Magnesian Limestone (near Bees Head), which is also an integral part of the group, as in tracts in Germany (see *Siluria*).

'Harkness and myself also determined a fact of some importance to the amplification of my Permian group, viz., that the hematite iron ore of Cumberland, which lies in cavities of the Carboniferous Limestone, is a part of the Rothliegende or Lower Permian. This fact is quite new.

'When I look round the world I cannot help saying how grateful we ought to be who live at home and ease in these islands. With such horrors as are going on in America, where the mob rules supreme, or where their President is as odious a tyrant as Imperial Rome could have produced, it is wonderful that such men as Everett and Agassiz should write to me from Boston as if nothing were occurring that would not soon pass away, and as if the great republic would soon be one and indivisible!'

Writing to his wife after the meeting, he said:

'Dearest C.,

We had a right capital day yesterday. [James] Grant [who had just returned from exploring the sources of the Nile with John Speke] filled the section to repletion. There were 1200 persons in the Assembly Rooms, and he performed twice as well as he did in London. I am anxious that you should read the accounts given in the Newcastle Express, which goes today, because every word I said is well reported, and I always wished my anecdote about Grant's gallantry in India to be well put forth. . . .

'To-day we had a no less successful day – beginning with a paper by Lord Lovaine on newly discovered pile lake-habitations in Wigtownshire, which I got Lyell to attend, and at which he spoke well.

'Half of this day was devoted to the Geological, where I held forth at some length on my Permian rocks of the west of England with Harkness, and on the reptiliferous sandstones of Morayshire. Yesterday I proposed we should meet at Bath, and Lyell for President, and it was carried by a large majority.

'Yesterday, also, they gave us a dinner, at which I had to propose their healths, with all due estimates and comparisons of past and present Newcastle.

'I go to Alnwick Castle on Thursday, and write to me thither. The Duke kindly wrote to me to bring Speke and Grant. . . . I have been asked to Corby Castle, and numerous places, including Clumber (Duke of Newcastle), so that if my forces hold out, and I make my tour to the Highlands, God knows when poor Pincher [Lady Murchison's favourite terrier], to say nothing of my loving wife, will see me.

Ever yours,

Rod.

'P.S. I told you that that the Durham boys had asked the "old Boy" to get them a holiday, and I wrote to the head-master for it. . . . . . .Dr. Holden came up to me after the meeting, and congratulated me, and told me he had given the boys a holiday for the day, at my request. The section thanked me warmly when I took leave. We beat all the others in popularity.'

****

In 1863, Sir Roderick was made a Knight Commander of the Most Honourable Order of the Bath (K.C.B.), an order of chivalry second only in England to the numerically-restricted Most Noble Order of the Garter. Murchison's keen interest in world affairs is brought out in a letter written in August 1863 to his friend Sir William Denison: 'On a Sunday afternoon, when far away from the smoke and noise of the metropolis, in which I have been presiding, chattering, eating, and drinking for the last eight months (barring a little pheasant shooting up to February last), here I am in the middle of my Permian rocks in Lancashire. . . .

'I tried hard before I left town to get some honours of the Crown from my good friend Lord Palmerston for the men of the Nile, Speke and Grant, and though I failed for the moment I am sure the right thing must be done. (See the postscript to my Address.)

'I never expected to see my country drifting again into a war for an idea. We did so in the Crimean War, and as Mr. Bull required to be let blood after so many years of stagnation, I suppose that, folly as it was, the thing was inevitable. But as the only result of that war was to raise France egregiously, and above all in her maritime condition, and almost to elevate her beyond us, I could not have conceived that we should have been on the point of still further raising her and advancing her to the Rhine on account of the Poles – a people who have never known, and will never know, how to govern themselves. Mr. Bull has strangely changed from his old character if he thus Quixotizes.

'We are all dead sick of the brutal American struggle. I have always wished for the South, because they fought like noble fellows for their independence.'

The meeting of the Association in 1864, at which Murchison was again elected President of Section E (Geography and Ethnology), was duly held at Bath with Sir Charles Lyell in the chair. It was attended by the great African explorers, David Livingstone, Sir Richard Burton and John Speke. The occasion was deeply saddened by the death of Speke, who accidentally shot himself, when, one afternoon when a speech of his had been deferred, he went out into the country after some pheasant.

In Archibald Geikie's *Life of Murchison*, he says, 'The last edition of Siluria was published in the autumn of 1867. If we compare it with the first edition of the work we see how much progress had been made in Palaeozoic geology during the interval of thirteen years. Among other changes, the Laurentian system had been established. The Cambrian, which had been purposely omitted from special description in the first edition, now receives recognition in the limited sense in which the term was used by the Geological Survey; the physical break between Lower and Upper Silurian contended for by Sedgwick is now admitted, and a zone of passage between the two series is described under the name of "Llandovery rocks." The important discovery that the rocks of the Scottish Highlands, formerly thought to be of an origin anterior to the existence of life upon the globe, consisted really of altered Lower Silurian rocks, is pointedly dwelt upon. Great improvements and additions are introduced into those portions of the book treating of organic remains. Especial attention is likewise given to the foreign equivalents of the British formations, and thus the book is made truly an indispensable handbook to all geologists who are intent upon deciphering the history of the oldest fossiliferous rocks. No better evidence of the practical utility of the work could have been given than the fact that, in spite of its technical character, its total want of literary attractiveness, and its high price, four editions were called for in thirteen years.'

Geikie goes on to say, 'Quitting his own special domain of Palaeozoic geology, Murchison in his later years took considerable pains to reiterate his faith in a former greater intensity of Nature's operations, and to oppose the doctrines of the opposite or uniformitarian school. His opinions on this subject are strongly expressed in the closing pages of the last edition of Siluria. He used often to announce them from the chair of the Geographical Society, but the greatest vigour of language was reserved for his private correspondence. Some illustrations of his opposition may be given here.

'For some years there had been growing among the younger and more active geologists of Britain a conviction that the old doctrine of Hutton as to the origin of valleys by the erosive action of running water – a doctrine which, in spite of the admirable confirmation of it adduced by Mr. Scrope from Central France, had never been generally adopted – was substantially true. Foremost among those who maintained this view, and enforced it by cogent argument and illustration, were the Directors of the Geological Surveys of Great Britain and Ireland – Ramsay and Jukes. The former, moreover, started and worked out the remarkable idea that besides the excavation of valleys by river action and the slow washing of the land by rain, there has been an extensive erosion of hollows and basins by glacier ice, and that to this process we must attribute the great predominance of rock-basin lakes scattered over those tracts of the northern hemisphere which can be shown to have been buried under land-ice. As may be supposed, the President of the Geographical Society regarded these doctrines as rank heresy, not to say sheer nonsense. He opposed them chiefly in his addresses to that Society; but his opposition, though vigorous in its language, dealt more in strong denial and protest, with the citation of the crowd of geological authorities who sided with him, than in serious argument. (In one of these addresses he gave great prominence to the question of glacier-erosion, especially in reference to Professor Ramsay's then recently broached doctrine. Not content with the publicity given by the Journal of the Geographical Society, he extracted that portion of his Address, and circulated it far and wide among the geologists of Europe and America. Professor Ramsay's reply in the *Philosophical Magazine* (October 1864) was valuable as a protest against the attempt or tendency to crush opposition by weight of authority). The force of evidence had constrained him to yield somewhat of the old exclusiveness with which he had fought for his icebergs, but having given up some points, and consented to admit the power of glaciers to polish and score the face of a country, and to pile up huge moraine-mounds, he felt himself free to set his foot down firmly and refuse to go a step further in the way of excavation, as his friends, the "ice-men," would have had him.'

Writing about the fourth edition of *Siluria* in the *Quarterly Review* in 1868, Geikie said 'The third edition of the late Sir Henry de la Beche's 'Geological Manual', published in 1833, enumerates 126 genera and 547 species as having up to that time been found in the 'Grauwacke group'. But no attempt had yet been made to use these organic remains as tests for the chronological subdivision of the rocks containing them, as had been so happily done for the secondary rocks of England. It was believed that the strata had been so broken and altered by subterranean movements during the long succession of geological periods, that little order could be drawn from them. They were known to contain the earliest traces of life upon the globe, but the record had been so sadly defaced and mutilated that no one had yet been able, or perhaps had ever deemed it possible, to piece the fragments together and gather a connected story from them. This, then, was the task to which Sir Roderick Murchison set himself so far back as the year 1831. Guided by the advice of his friend, the late Dr. Buckland, he broke ground upon the banks of the Wye, and gradually during several years working his way among the strata which rise out from under the old red sandstone in Hereford, Radnor, and Shropshire, discovered the clue to the history of the oldest fossiliferous deposits. He found that instead of being hopelessly broken and obscure, these strata could be separated into distinct formations, each characterised by its own peculiar assemblage of organic remains, and that a gradual progression from lower to higher forms of life could be traced between the oldest and the newest rocks of the series. Thus he established a hitherto unknown group of formations, which he classed together under the name of "the Silurian System". The work which he published with that title contained a chapter in the world's history which up to that time had remained unwritten. Originally the name had reference merely to a comparatively small tract of England and Wales; but it was soon found to be of world-wide application. The succession of organic existence discovered in the most ancient fossiliferous rocks of this country was ascertained to be repeated in other and widely separated regions. Thus Sir Roderick in elucidating the geological structure of a limited part of Britain, in reality found the key to the order of succession among the rocks of a large portion of the surface of the globe, and the "Silurian System", instead of retaining merely a local significance, became at once a familiar term to the geologists of every country.

'Thirty years have since passed away. Hundreds and thousands of observers have been at work all over the world, and though many new facts have been brought to light, and much detail added to the earlier researches of Murchison, the grand outlines first traced by him have been only the more firmly established. Some notion of the progress which has been made, from the fact that while in 1833 only 547 species of fossils had been obtained from all the rocks older than the carboniferous system, in the recent edition of "Siluria" nearly 1300 species are enumerated from the British Silurian rocks alone. And if to these are added the species found in other parts of Europe and America, where Silurian strata are largely developed, the number will be enormously increased. But besides these additions to the fauna of the system, the succession and arrangement of rocks of Silurian age have been laboriously traced over many thousands of square miles. In Scandinavia and Russia, and through central Europe to the shores of the Atlantic and the Mediterranean, these rocks have been correlated with the original British types; throughout America a like identification has been made. And now, gathering up the fruits of all this research, Sir Roderick has issued a new and much enlarged edition of his treatise on these ancient formations.'

****

In 1859 Jules Marcou had proposed that Murchison's Permian period should be renamed Dyas, causing him some irritation. Dr. H.B. Geinitz in Germany resurrected the idea in 1861, causing Murchison to write to his friend, Professor Harkness: 'My good friend Dr. Geinitz has, I regret to say, revived the ridiculous term of Dyas as a substitute for Permian. Taking it from Marcou, who had most absurdly applied it to a union of the Permian with the Trias as "the hard red series," Geinitz, wholly disapproving that absurdest of projects (for he knows the one is palaeozoic, the other mesozoic), still proposes the name as a substitute for Permian, because, forsooth, in the limited tracts of Germany which he knows, the Rothliegende and the Zechstein constitute the group. I have already written a paper, which I am sending to the printer, to quash this nonsense (for it is truly such) at once. Trias is the worst word we ever had in use, for in England it is, as you know, a Dyas, in other tracts abroad a Monyas, and in others a Tetraias. So it is with the Permian. That name involves no necessary number of physical or lithological divisions; and, proposed by me twenty years ago, it has been in current use everywhere for fifteen years.

'In Russia it is one great series of alternating limestones, marls, sandstones, gypsums, copper ores, and conglomerates, the Zechstein fossils occurring at various horizons. But I need not dilate. You will read my paper soon, for I will print it myself, and send it all over Europe and America. . . .

'The logic, or want of all logic, on the part of good Geinitz is lamentable. But the Germans are reviving old Grauwacke.'

On Murchison's seventy-second birthday (19 February 1864) he was presented with the Geological Society's highest award, the Wollaston Medal. There was no doubt that he had earned it a quarter of a century earlier, but having been a member of the Council of the Society continuously for thirty-two years, he had been disqualified from receiving it under the rules. He recalled Dr. Wollaston himself welcoming him with wise and friendly advice into the scientific circles of London. It was also very gratifying to him to receive the medal from the hands of the then President, Professor Ramsay, who was able to say, 'Perhaps on this occasion I may be pardoned for recalling the memory of a time I well remember, when of all the geologists of weight, you sir, were the first who held out the hand of fellowship to me as a young man, when four-and-twenty years ago I was struggling to enter into the ranks of geologists.'

Only three years after he received his knighthood, Sir Roderick was, in 1866, created a Baronet and he received honours from other European sovereigns. He was sent by Czar Alexander II, the son of his old patron, a friendly and flattering message and a gold snuff-box set with diamonds. On the death of Michael Faraday, he was chosen to fill the vacancy in the list of the eight foreign members of the Académie des Sciences in the Institut de France.

Portrait of Sir Roderick Murchison in the 1860s
(*The Illustrated London News,* 10 March, 1866)
(*The Illustrated London News* Picture Library)

Chapter Fourteen
The History of Harting

In 1877, the Rev. H.D. Gordon published *The History of Harting*, a small village in the Weald near the Sussex/Hampshire border. To form part of the book, he had invited Murchison, ten years earlier, to write a chapter on the *Geological Structure of the Parish*. Sir Roderick had started his married life in the house of his wife's parents in the next parish, Buriton, and was a frequent guest of Sir Harry Featherstonhaugh at nearby Up Park, where he enjoyed shooting pheasant. The chapter is quoted in full, to show his deep knowledge of this part of Sussex. Note that he stuck to his belief that valleys resulted from upheavals of the Earth's crust and torrential flows, not accepting Hutton's theory that they were worn down by the rivers that flowed in them. He makes no mention of the dry valley of the Devil's Dyke near Brighton, nor of that of the Devil's Punchbowl near Hindhead. The 'chalk with flints' mentioned is, of course, the Upper Chalk, the life-forms which turned into flints not existing at the time of formation of the Middle or Lower Chalk.

'Upwards of half a century having elapsed since I became acquainted with the country around Harting, and forty-two years having passed since I described the geological relations of the western extremity of the great Wealden valley between the South and North Downs, I gladly comply with the request of the Vicar of Harting, the Reverend Henry D. Gordon, and will endeavour briefly to delineate the main geological features of a parish, in which, through the kindness of my valued friends, the late Sir Harry Featherstonhaugh and his excellent Widow, I have enjoyed so many pleasant days. [The lady to whom he refers here was Mary Ann, Sir Harry's dairymaid, whom he had married when he was seventy and she twenty years old].

'I must first beg the reader to cast his eye over a geological map of England, in order to understand that the several formations which I am about to describe, as exhibited in and near the parish of Harting, are simply segments of the several zones of rock which constitute the sides and centre of the great Wealden valley of Sussex, Surrey, and Kent, as subtended on the north and south by the chalk of the North and South Downs, and on the west by the range of the Hampshire hills of Selbourne, &c. He will then understand that the following is simply the description of one slice across the successive ledges of strata which rise to the surface as you advance from the South Downs to the centre of the great valley.

'In taking a bird's-eye view from the lofty ground near the ruined tower in Up Park, the spectator commands within his vision a large portion of the parish of Harting, and sees, in looking northwards, in the distance of little more than five miles only, all the formations, from the Upper Chalk on which he stands, to the Wealden deposit which forms the base of the whole Cretaceous series. These different formations and their subdivisions are exhibited in the accompanying general diagram, and the observer who proceeds from the high road by Up Park, through Harting and Rogate, and thence over the sandstone hills to the valley of Harting Combe, will pass over successively the following strata: - Chalk with Flints; white Chalk passing down into grey Chalk and Chalk marl; Upper Greensand or Malm Rock; Gault clay; Lower Greensand, the upper part iron shot and yellow; the inferior greenish grey; and, lastly, the Weald Clay in Harting Combe. This succession, from the highest to the lowest strata in the district is given in the accompanying geological section.

'As every one of these formations, and even their subdivisions, has a separate stony structure, so the decomposition of each gives to the stony soil above it a distinctive agricultural character. In consequence, the parish of Harting, for the most part the property of Lady Featherstonhaugh, embraces a variety of soils very rarely to be found within the same compass.

'In the following description the reader is conducted from the highest to the lowest formation in the parish and adjacent grounds. He must further understand, that if he extended his research, and proceeded from the valley of Harting Combe, either to the north-west or to the north, he would pass across the same formations, in ascending order, as those over which he has descended; and whether he reached the hills of Hampshire above Selbourne, or the North Downs of Surrey above Godalming, he would again meet with the same Chalk with Flints from which he began his journey at Up Park.

'In geological language the intervening depression between these two chalk ranges is called a "Valley of Elevation," because the lowest strata of the region, as at Harting Combe, have been raised to the surface, and have thrown off the formations which once covered them. In other words, the time was, when the Chalk, the Upper and Lower Greensand, and the Gault, were all continuous over this now bare country. The great natural convulsions by which this state of things was brought about were necessarily accompanied by vast deluges of water; and as all the overlying deposits were formed under the sea, so it is supposed (by me at least), that powerful waves of translation necessarily resulting passed over the surface, and removed all the immense heaps of broken materials, which must have been produced by such great earthquakes and upheavings from a common centre of elevation. That such a denudation took place is indeed proved by the fact, that, with the exception of a few very limited patches of broken flints for the most part that lie near the bottom of the escarpments of the South Downs, the great valley of the Wealden has been clean swept, and its flanks nearly so, of all such *debris*. The exceptions are in this western extremity of the Wealden denudation only, as in the Lower Greensand of Trotton Common, and near the west end of Harting Combe, where patches of broken chalk flints strew the surface. It is from this great denudation that the parent rock is so constantly near the surface, and that its decomposition has had, and has, so great an influence on the soil.

'The youngest rock in the parish is the Upper Chalk, or Chalk with Flints, which, inclining gently to the south of Up Park and Lady Holt Park, is eventually covered by the Tertiary clays and sands, which occupy all the low maritime tract extending from Bognor to Portsmouth.

'The Upper Chalk is named by many geologists the "Chalk with Flints," as distinguished from the mass of chalk beneath it in which a flint is very rarely discernible. The great and central mass, consisting of white chalk becomes less purely calcareous and more argillaceous, assuming a greyish colour in its lower part, as is well seen in the sides of the steep road descending from Up Park to South Harting. At the base of the hill this grey chalk is underlaid by a thin band of chalk marl, much used as a manure for certain soils and crops. The Chalk formation, so constituted from top to bottom, exhibits the same structure in its range, whether we proceed to Butsor Hill on the west or to the Brighton Downs on the east.

'(Note.- Butsor Hill is 990 feet above the sea, and is the highest point of the adjacent South Downs. The tower at Up Park is about 690 feet. Boundary of the Park at Two Beech Gate, 646·6 feet. Spithead Bench, 672·5. Near north end of Kill-devil Lane, 626·8. Beacon Hill, the eastern boundary of Harting parish, over 790. The Leith nearly 1000.)

'As a whole, the chalk formation is a great absorbent of the rain-fall on the hills, the water of which penetrates downwards through chinks and fissures, until it is held up by the tenacious chalk marl; and hence at Harting, as at Buriton on the west and at numerous places to the east, a series of ponds of crystal clear water is formed.

'At the mansion of Up Park, long the residence of Sir Harry Featherstonhaugh, Bart., and now the property of his relict, standing upon the Chalk with Flints, and at an elevation of 650 feet above the sea, water was only reached by sinking a well to the depth of 250 feet. To have rendered this supply useful would have been most costly and irksome, and hence the water which gushes out from the base of the hill near Harting was turned to account for working an ingenious but simple mechanical contrivance, by which water is thrown up, by the action of an overshot wheel, from the valley to the summit of the hill.

'In its range to the east, as to the west, the Chalk formation of the South Downs is charged with numerous marine remains of various groups of animals, whether zoophytes, mollusca, or fishes, though few have been found in the escarpment south of Harting and the hills of Up Park. On the whole, the following species of fossils characterize the Upper Chalk: *Inoceramus brongniarti, Lima spinosa, Ammonites lewisiensis, Nautilus radiatus, Belemnitella mucronata*, and the fishes *Beryx lewisiensis*, and palates of *Ptychodi.*

'As might be expected from the scanty covering of soil, the hills consisting of chalk with flints are most favourable to pasture, and it is on the short, sweet bite of the grass that the far-famed and fine-shaped South Down sheep are reared; whilst the lower parts of the undulations of the same rock, as at the Castle Farm and Huck's Holt, where the soil is mixed with flints, yield fair crops of barley, turnips, &c.

'The Lower Chalk and Chalk Marl are distinguished from the Upper Chalk by containing the following well-marked species:- *Inoceramus cuvieri, I. mytiloides, Pecten beaveri, Pholadomya decussata, Pleurotomaria perspectiva, Ammonites mantellii, A. variolaris, A. Rhotomagensis, Nautilus pseudo-elegans, Turrilites tuberculatus.*

'It is, however, when we reach the next formation beneath the Chalk marl, as spread out in a broad plateau of about a mile and a half in width, that we find ourselves upon lands which constitute the real wealth of the parish, i.e., upon some of the finest wheat soils of the kingdom. This soil is literally made up of the decomposition of the rock on which it lies, *i.e.*, the Malm Rock or Upper Greensand of geologists. The name of "Upper Greensand," though well applied in Wiltshire, is wholly inapplicable to it in the parish of Harting, or, indeed, in any part of its range from Weston and Nursted on the west to the sea near Eastbourne, *i.e.*, all along the escarpment of the South Downs. Far from being a sandstone, this rock is highly argillaceous, and yields a very stiff soil. Examples of it are seen in the sides of numerous deep lanes and natural ravines, and of the latter the low cliffs on either side of the narrow dell called the Mill Hanger, so renowned for its preserves of pheasants. A clear section of the strata, showing how the Malm Rock is surmounted by chalk marl and the lower chalk, is exhibited at the north end of Tarberry Hill. This is a singular narrow promontory of chalk, which protrudes and stands out from the escarpment of Harting Warren and the Side Hills. Lying upon the plateau of Malm Rock, it is what geologists call an "outlier," since between it and the main range of the hills, the chalk has been worn away or denuded to its base.

'The upper beds of Malm Rock are the most chalky in appearance, but in some central parts of the deposit the grey colour gives way to a bluish tint, and in these cases the stone is more compact, and hence preferred as a building stone; the ordinary grey Malm Rock being of a very decomposing nature. Composed of clay, sand, and lime (the first predominating), the best soils are those where there is a due admixture of each, and particularly where the calcareous matter reaches 25 to 30 per cent. of the mass; this soil, though very tenacious, is highly fertile in the production of wheat, clover, beans, &c. On the whole, there is a striking unity of composition in this soil, whether we examine it in the farms of South, East, and West Harting, or in the adjacent lands of Nursted.

'The formation beneath the soil has a thickness varying from 80 to 120 feet, as known by the wells sunk in it, for, just as the water which percolates through the chalk is held up by the Chalk Marl, so is that which sinks by fissures through the Malm Rock, sustained by the argillaceous shale or clay beneath it, which, in geological language, is termed the "Gault."

'The fossils of the Malm Rock which are most common were formerly enumerated by me as *Ammonites rostratus, A. varians, Pecten orbicularis, Gryphæa vesiculosa, Avicula,* with forms of the Sea Urchins, *Echino spatangus,* and portions of fishes. In other tracts, and where the formation is sandy, it affords a vast quantity of organic remains. Among which the following may be cited as most characteristic:- *Pecten asper, Exogyra conica, Cardium gentianum, Panopœa plicata, Solarium ornatum, Nautilus elegans, N. fittoni,* with numerous Sponges, Ventriculites, &c.

'In some parts of England, particularly in Cambridgeshire, remains of fishes, including their excrement, called Coprolites, so abound in this Upper Greensand or Malm Rock, that these, mixed with other animal matter, constitute a phosphatic manure of high value to the proprietor; but the paucity of such fossil remains in the district under review forbids the anticipation of any discovery of this source of wealth in or near the parish of Harting.

'In proceeding northwards down Bohemy or Bohemia Hill, the student will observe that the Malm rock becomes gradually darker-coloured and more argillaceous, and that at the bottom of the hill it passes into a pure, stiff, blue, shale clay, which is the Gault. Occupying a zone of about a mile or more in width, this clay, usually free of all superficial foreign cover, or flints and gravel, is as continuous all around the great Wealden denudation as the Malm Rock or the Chalk above it. Everywhere, in short, whether in the parish of Harting, or in that of Buriton on the west, and of Elstead on the east, it yields grass and trees only, and is scarcely ever turned into arable land. In short, the outline of the Gault is everywhere marked as enclosed between the grey Malm Rock above it and the yellow and white sands on which it lies. Fine specimens of the meadows on this formation are those of Down Park; and it is by this same clay that the adjacent large ponds, the property of Lady Featherstonhaugh, are held up. The woodlands called the Severalls are also on it. Houses are rarely built on the Gault; and if people value good health, and eschew rheumatism, they would never live on this retentive clay, which is only suitable for fattening bullocks and raising oaks.

'Though rare in this parish, fossils occur in great abundance elsewhere in the Gault, and notably at Folkestone, where the *Ammonites dentatus,* which I have found in West Sussex, is associated with *Plicatula pectonoides, Inoceramus concentricus, I. sulcatus, Cucullæa fibrosa, Nucula pectinata, Dentalium decussatum, Rostellaria carinata, Natica gaultina, Ammonites splendens, A. tuberculatus, A. interruptus,* and *Hamites intermedius.*

'The junction of the Gault with the upper beds of the Lower Greensand is admirably exposed at the Kilns to the right of the road that runs between Down Park and the Ryefield Farm, where the contact of clay and sand has led to the manufacture of bricks. There the sands, both ferruginous and pure white, rise up from beneath the Gault to form the beautiful low hills called West Heath, the most northern portion of the Up Park estate, and distant from the mansion upwards of three miles. A very instructive section of these sands is exhibited on the side of the road as you advance to the valley of the Rother; and they are in parts so fine and incoherent, and of so purely white a colour, as to be used by ladies in washing. In a recent cutting of the railroad from Petersfield to Midhurst, which passes by the north side of West Heath, a rich argillaceous ironstone, found by Mr. Buxton, exhibited on its surface small circular cavities in pairs, evidently the work of a marine worm or annelid, together with casts of, probably, the remains of seaweeds. In many other places the ferruginous structure of this band is very conspicuous. This is well seen on the side of the road from Petersfield to Midhurst, particularly to the east of the latter town, where the ironsand assumes singular concretionary forms. Where the black oxyde of iron prevails, the stone found in this layer rings under the hammer, and is the clinkstone used in road making.

'It is on the western termination of this ferruginous portion of the Lower Greensand that the town of Petersfield stands. There the geologist has only to explore southwards to Butser Hill, or northwards to the Froxfield Hangers, and he passes successively upwards over all the formations I have enumerated to the Chalk with Flints inclusive; the pointed mass of sandstone at Petersfield being wrapped round to the north-west and north by the confluence of the younger formations of the Gault, Upper Greensand, and Chalk.

'The fossils of this upper band of the Lower Greensand are not numerous hereabouts. In other tracts, as at Parham park, the following are characteristic – two or three of them, however, were found by me many years ago on the commons north of Petersfield:- *Gervillia acuta, Trigonia alæformis, Cytherea (Venus) parva, Panopæa plicata, Cucullæa decussata, Thetis sowerbii, Modiola æqualis, Tellina æqualis, Cyprina angulata, Rostellaria parkinsonii, Ammonites dentatus.*

'Though not exhibited in this neighbourhood, the calcareous conglomerate called Bargate Stone, occasionally burnt for lime, and abundant near Godalming, in Surrey, lies at the base of the upper zone of the Lower Greensand.

'To render the geological description complete, we must quit the parish of Harting, and, entering that of Rogate, continue our little trip to the north. By so doing we pass over other and inferior members of the Lower Greensand until we reach the Weald Clay of Harting Combe.

'The River Rother, on which is placed Fair Oak, the seat of the Honorable J. Carnegie, runs from west to east, between the higher or Petersfield and Shanklin sand; and the next lower portion of the formation, or the Sandgate beds of Kent, is the Rogate Sandstone of this tract. To the north other and inferior strata rise into hills of some altitude, on the southern slopes of which are situated the country houses of Rogate Lodge.and Dangstein. It is in this portion of the formation that the greater number of fossils occur, particularly near Hythe in the so-called Kentish Rag at Maidstone and Sevenoaks. The following are typical forms:- *Perna alæformis, Pinna crassa, Trigonia spectabilis, Trigonia alæformis, Corbis corrugata, Astarte obovarta, Cyprina angulata, Pholas giganteus, Ammonites nutfieldiensis.*

'There are thin layers of clay in both the sandstones above described, which serve to hold up lines of ponds, as at Petersfield, Spring, Woolmer Forest, &c.

'The hills which constitute the escarpments of the valley of Harting Combe are composed of a sandstone, a variety of the Kentish Rag, which is no longer so ferruginous as the upper portion of the deposit, green grains being abundant in the body of the rock, which constitutes an imperfect building stone, and becomes more and more argillaceous as you descend into the valley.

'Farther to the east, *i.e.,* at Petworth and beyond it, this sandstone is a more compact building stone, though affording few fossils here.

'The bottom bed of the Lower Greensand is a zone of dark clay, which was formally, from its mineral character, not distinguished from the subjacent Weald Clay, but is now clearly recognised to be very distinct, and to represent the Atherfield rocks of the Isle of Wight, and the lower Neocomian of foreign geologists, *i.e.,* the lowest of all the marine deposits of the Cretaceous age.

'Though I do not believe that as yet any fossils of this zone have been detected in Harting Combe, I have observed them in great quantities near Haslemere, where the railroad has been cut through this same zone of clay.

'The fossils are all marine, viz.:- *Gervillia anceps, Ostræa frons, Perna mulleti, Trigonia dædalea, T. caudate, Venus parva, Panopœa neocomiensis, Rostellaria robinalbina, Pteroceras fittoni, Ammonites deshayesii, A. martini, A. hambrovii, Crioceras bowerbankii,* and *Ancyloceras gigas.*

'The agricultural characters of the Lower Greensand necessarily vary considerably in its several parts. Thus in the uppermost portion we find West Heath yielding little more than heather and ferns, while the adjacent farm of Ryfield produces excellent barley, root crops, and fine grass. Indeed the character of a good loamy soil characterises this zone all along the course of the Rother to Habing Bridge and Trotton.

'On the other hand, the lower portion of the formation, which rises into the commons of Rogate and Vining, and constitutes Holder Hill, is usually sterile and heathy.

'In descending from the hills of Rogate and Vining Commons to Harting Combe, we reach the Weald Clay, the lowest formation to be seen in our downward exploration from the summit of the South Downs. Let me here remind the reader that he will pass over the very same strata downwards if he proceeds from the Chalk of the North Downs across the Lower Greensandstone of Hind Head, or from the Hampshire plateau above Selbourne, across Woolmer Forest, to this same valley of Harting Combe.

'Unlike all the formations which cover it, the Wealden is a fresh-water deposit, or one which was formed at the mouth of some great marshy river, inasmuch as it only contains shells of fresh-water origin, and fragments of bones which belonged to great aquatic and terrestrial lizards. It is the upper portion only, however, of the vast deposit, which, having this character, and occupying the larger portion of the Wealden of Sussex, Surrey, and Kent, has its nether termination in Harting Combe.

All the lower part, consisting of alternations of sands and clays, constitutes what was formerly called the Hastings Sands; and in their range to Crowborough Beacon and Pevensey Bay they are marked at intervals by strong bands of sandstone, as at Horsham, Tunbridge Wells, Hastings, &c.

'This whole series, from the base to the summit, is eminently ferruginous; and even in the little nook of Harting Combe, as at Lynch and Redford, when I first examined the tract in 1824, the old slag of the iron furnaces was used as a road material – having been found where the ore was smelted with the charcoal resulting from the burning of the wild forests of this "Anderida" of the Romans.

'The uppermost or purely argillaceous member of the Wealden, particularly where the valley widens between the promontories of Green Sandstone of Black Down on the north and Holder and Bexley Hills on the south (points all visible from the hills of Up Park), is characterized by containing at intervals the shelly limestone called Petworth Marble, and in which the shells of the *Paludina fluviorum* are often covered with layers of compact clay or shale, replete with the minute white bivalve crustacean *Cypres faba*.

'It would lead me too far from the interest attached to the parish of Harting and its neighbourhood to discourse at greater length on the structure of the Wealden deposits, or those which surround or overlap them, whether on the north, west, or south. It suffices if I have by this brief sketch so placed the subject before the general reader that he may see at all events how intimately the agriculture, drainage, and well being of the district are based upon its geological structure.

'Those persons who wish to pursue their geological enquiries as respects this region must consult the important Memoir of my lamented friend, the late Dr. Fitton, in which they will find a full account of all the rocks mentioned, not only as respects this tract, but all the region in and around the Weald, and extending over the south-east of England, with accurate lists of their fossils, and descriptive maps and sections.

'Lastly, I specially recommend the reader to provide himself, at small cost, with a copy of the geological map of the tract in which he may reside – for, as I have been the Director-General of the Geological Survey during the last eleven years, so I have had the truest satisfaction in seeing that the maps finished by my associates have so well illustrated that very part of England in which my geological researches began.

RODERICK I. MURCHISON.

Jan. 3, 1867.'

Chapter Fifteen
The Close

In the final chapter of his *Life of Sir Roderick*, Archibald Geikie says, 'For many years Lady Murchison's health continued to be delicate. Now and then she seemed almost at the point of death, while, even when comparatively well, her condition rendered great care necessary. It was under such trying circumstances that she had striven for many years to do her part in the social gatherings which made her house in Belgrave Square one of the chief scientific centres of London. At last she died on the 9th February 1869.'

Murchison buried his wife in Brompton Cemetery, West London, erecting a large pink-granite sarcophagus inscribed:

THIS TOMB WAS ERECTED BY SIR RODERICK IMPEY MURCHISON
BART KCB FRS &c &c
IN MEMORY OF HIS DEVOTED WIFE
CHARLOTTE
ONLY DAUGHTER OF GENERAL HUGONIN
BORN 18th APRIL 1788
DIED 9th FEBRUARY 1869

Geikie continues: 'Bound to her by a tender attachment, and by the respect which her many excellencies of character never failed to inspire, Murchison acknowledged to the last his gratitude to her as the real source of all his scientific work and fame. A long union of mutual help and sympathy was now severed, and he stood alone in the world, wifeless and childless. At first the blow seemed to have fallen so heavily as to paralyse him, but he quickly rallied. One of his first efforts was to pen the following sketch of his wife, which shows at least the writer's deep affection and gratitude to his life-long companion:-

'"March 3, 1869. – My dear Geikie, I will give you a few words upon my beloved wife's influence over me for whatever good I may have done in the walks of science. In the year 1815, the Battle of Waterloo having submerged all my ambition, as well as that of the great Napoleon, and seeing no 'avenir,' I fell in love with Charlotte Hugonin, and married her when I was but twenty-three, she being three and a half years older than myself. Her father, the old General of the 4th

Dragoons, was a remarkably intelligent man, and a fair astronomer; her mother a most skilful florist and botanist, so that their only daughter was brought up under the most auspicious circumstances. She was a good sketcher of scenery, having been taught by the famous Paul Sandby [dubbed the father of the watercolour school]. Passing our first winter in Hants, I naturally profited much by the instructions of herself and parents in all natural history subjects, and we then prepared ourselves for a foreign tour in France, the Alps, and Italy, which we undertook in the spring of 1816. I was then a prodigious walker, and more than once did on foot distances in one day which occupied Swiss horses and carriages two days, my wife (when practicable) accompanying me on horseback, and always making me recognise the numerous wild-flowers peculiar to certain rocks, altitudes and mountains. Passing the winter at Genoa (1816-1817), we became together good Italian scholars, and acquainted with all the fine art of that noble city. In the spring we travelled to Rome, and were so enchanted that we stayed on till the 29th June, a most imprudent act, by which my wife, who had been riding late in the Borghese Gardens, caught a malarian fever, by which I very nearly lost her, and the malady hung about her through her long life. We passed summer at Naples, where she made numerous coloured sketches, and where we enjoyed the charming society of that capital in those days, and all the enchanting scenery of the environs.

"In our journey homewards we visited every remarkable object, and of all the sights, pictures, and statues I have notebooks full, for all that time I was a virtuoso and dilettante.

"Reaching England in 1818, I took to a country residence in the house of my wife's grandfather, recently deceased – the old General who led the 4th Dragoons in one day from Canterbury to the Borough of London, and dispersed the mob in the evening, - a service which George the Third always spoke of with admiration and gratitude. I then gave myself up recklessly but jovially to a fox-hunting life. It was during the years 1818-22 (three in the north country, and two seasons at Melton Mowbray) that my wife was always striving to interest me in something more intellectual than the chase, and began to teach herself mineralogy and conchology. Just at that time (1823), I happened to meet Sir Humphry Davy at Mr. Morritt's of Rokeby, the eminent scholar, and friend of Walter Scott; and Sir Humphry, seeing how my wife was striving to lead me into other paths, gave me words of encouragement, which, coming from so good a man, flattered me, and led me to try and acquire some knowledge of science. He saw that as a sportsman I had a quick and clear eye for a country, and that with most mountain forms and features I was already acquainted, and so he stimulated me to sell my horses, settle for the winter in London, and attend the chemical and mining lectures of the Royal Institution.

"Thus my fate was decided. My first burst of enthusiasm when I got my lessons from Buckland, Greenough, Fitton, Warburton, Webster, and others, was unbounded, and I was then, to the great delight of my wife, another man.

"Immediately I had acquired this taste my wife and self resolved to explore for ourselves (1825) the whole southern coast of England, from the Isle of Wight inclusive, where all our home phenomena were repeated, to Land's End. For this purpose I had a nice little pair of horses, a light carriage, and with saddles strapped behind to use the nags for riding when at any centre of attraction. At some places we examined the cliffs in boats, she never failing to make good sketches. When we reached Lyme Regis, she being rather fatigued, I left her to recruit there and amuse herself, and become a good practical fossilist, by working with the celebrated Mary Anning of that place, and trudging with her (pattens on their feet) along the shore; and thus my first collection was much enriched.

"The year 1826 was very dear to me, for then it was that my good wife accompanied me to the Yorkshire coast, and made many a sketch of cliff and fossil for me, and thence travelled with me to Brora, and various parts of the Hebrides. There also we had our little horses; and many were the rides she took in Skye and many other places, where wheels could not go. Then it was, too, that she found the Ammonites murchisoniae, and many other fossils, first described by Sowerby.

"When we were boating it along the shores of Arran in 1826, old Ronald Macalister, the guide of Jameson, who, with a little boy to help, was our only boatman, got quite 'fou' with his too frequent drams, and as I was thus obliged to row back most of the way from Loch Ranza to Brodick, he amused my poor wife much when, sitting coiled up in the bow, he kept saying, 'Noo, I'm the Laird.'

"In 1828 she saved my life by her energy in treating me for a violent fever caught in Frejus, in the south of France, when walking with Lyell.

"To go on narrating, even in this superficial way, all her adventures with me – all the happy hours we have spent together at the tables of Cuvier, Brongniart, and many eminent men of France, Italy, and Germany, is impracticable in a hurried letter, in scribbling off which all the deepest wells of my heart are opened out.

"In 1830 she explored a large portion of Germany, and the Austrian and Tyrolese Alps, with me, and was with me at Vienna when George the Fourth died, and when we dined with Lord Cowley, at whose table Prince Metternich was quite pleased with her conversation. The Archduke John of Austria (a highly intellectual man) was also her great admirer.

"Need I say that in originating and completing the Silurian classification, from 1830 to 1838, she was very frequently at my side.

"Then as years rolled on, she became more infirm, she necessarily could not encounter long journeys, and to bivouac with me in Russia and Siberia was out of the question; but the intense interest she took in my exploration of these regions is best told in her affectionate and dear letters to me, which I cherish, and which buoyed me up through all my difficulties and illnesses in the hope of rejoining her.

"Still feeling that though she was unequal to a Russian campaign she was equal to one in the Alps and Italy, she again set out with me in 1847, when, making the round of Germany, we were together at the last meeting of the Scienziati Italiani at Venice, where all the leading men of science paid her the most marked attention, including Leopold von Buch, Robert Brown, Carl Ritter, etc.

"After this my younger friends came upon the scenes of life. You as well as any one know how much my good, generous, and kind wife did, when other physical powers failed, to cheer and encourage all those who were striving to advance natural knowledge. – Yours ever sincerely, Rod. I. Murchison.

"P.S. – I may tell you that when the Prince Consort, many years ago, called in Belgrave Square to see my great Russian vase, which my wife was showing to him before I could get to the spot (for I was in my dressing gown), H.R. Highness said to me, 'I know who made you a geologist.' It would appear that our gracious Queen has always recollected this fact, for not only on all occasions has Her Majesty been most attentive and kind, but on this last melancholy occasion she has specially condoled with me in most touching terms. Among great people the Queen of Holland and Comte de Paris have also sympathised with me, and I have at least 150 letters of condolence, some of them beautifully expressed. Those of yourself and your good Surveyors shall all be bound up with those of other friends in the album of souvenirs of Lady M.'"

Sedgwick wrote a letter of deep sympathy in the fondest terms, recalling Lady Murchison's hospitality to him and his happy memories when she and her husband had visited him at Cambridge. He called her 'one of the dearest of those friends whose society formed the best charms of my life.'

Geikie says of her, 'She could have been no ordinary woman whose memory drew such an encomium from such a man. Her influence upon the career of her husband was not her only title to the grateful recollection of lovers of science. To the courteous bearing of a cultivated woman she added a brightness of conversation, an intelligence, and a range of knowledge which gave her a peculiar charm, and enabled her to please people of the most varied tastes and acquirements. To her presence the success of her husband's social gatherings was largely due, and there can be little doubt that these gatherings, by commingling students of science with statesmen and politicians, men of letters and men of rank, helped to give science and its cultivators a better hold on the sympathy and goodwill of the rest of society.

'Though Murchison came to Jermyn Street as of old, and wrote letters or transacted other business there, and though he soon renewed his energy at the Geographical Society, he did not seem ever to recover from the shock of his wife's death. In these public matters, as well as in the socialities of private life, he appeared, indeed, to mingle as much as ever. But though Lady Murchison had been more or less an invalid for some years, she could share up to the last in her husband's cares and interests. Her death broke up therefore the daily intercourse and habits of more than half a century. From such a blow it was hardly to be expected that he should wholly rally.

'Of the incidents in Sir Roderick's life after this event no special mention need be made. They continued to be much what they had been for some years before. Among them however there is one which remains to be noticed, as the last effort made in his lifetime for the advancement of the science to which he had given his unremitting energies and from which in return he had reaped so large a measure of renown – the founding of a Professorship of Geology in the University of Edinburgh. When, on the death of Edward Forbes, the Chair of Natural History became vacant in that University, the Crown, in whose hands the patronage lay, having regard to the enormous strides made by the various sciences which had been taught under that title, anticipated the probable necessity of dividing the Chair into at least two. Various movements were subsequently made to induce the Government to carry out this idea and make the subject of Geology and Mineralogy the business of a new and distinct Professorship. Murchison had taken a part in the negotiations which, however, proved unsuccessful.

'In the summer of 1869 he went north for the last time to Scotland to get a little rest, and once more to breathe the air of his native Highlands. The time of his arrival in Edinburgh happened to coincide with the graduation day at the close of the summer session of the University. With some difficulty he was persuaded to remain for the ceremony, and to receive himself on that occasion the degree of LL.D. It so chanced that the announcement of a memorial Fellowship for the encouragement of Geology and Palaeontology, recently instituted in the University by the friends of the late Dr. Hugh Falconer, was made at the same time. In a short speech on the occasion he by a slip of the tongue alluded to the Chair of Geology which had just been made, but instantly correcting himself, he added that he hoped that there would before long be a Chair too. The way in which this was said seemed to indicate that he already meditated founding the Chair himself.

'In the summer of the following year, Professor Allman, who had succeeded Forbes, resigned his appointment, making the Natural History Chair once more vacant. Murchison then determined to carry into effect in his lifetime a proposal which he had already provided for in his will. He applied to the Government to divide that Chair into one of Natural History or Zoology, and one of Geology and Mineralogy, and offered to provide more than half (£6000) of the endowment of the new Professorship. Eventually this proposal was accepted, and on 10th March 1871 a Royal warrant was issued founding the Chair and appointing the Professor [Archibald Geikie].

'It was the first Professorship which had been founded in any Scottish University for the special teaching of Geology, and there was a peculiar fitness in the fact that it should have been founded by one who had himself done so much for Scottish geology. In his remembrance, he wished it to be known in all time coming as the

"Murchison Professorship."

'Before the negotiations connected with this matter were brought to a close, the veteran geologist, still vigorous alike in mind and in body, was struck down by paralysis. On the morning of 21st November 1870, while dressing, he had a shock which deprived him of the use of his left side. For a time his life was in some danger, but in a few weeks he so far rallied as to be able to be wheeled into his library. As his speech had only been slightly affected, and as he seemed for a while to be regaining the use of his disabled left hand, he spoke in a cheerful way of his probable recovery. Hence he continued to take a lively interest in current affairs, dictated his correspondence, saw his old friends when they came to inquire for him, and was taken out almost daily in his carriage. In the spring of 1871 he prepared his last Anniversary Address to the Geographical Society, dictating it to his nephew. He knew it would be his last, for even should he recover from the attack, he felt that he could never again take the same active part in life. He had been altogether fifteen years President of the Society, had given sixteen anniversary discourses and had seen its membership increased from 600, when he was first called to preside, to the large number of 2400. He now resigned the Chair, and with an expression of pride in the success which had attended his efforts to promote the Society's interests, handed the seals of office to his successor. As a recognition of his services, both to the Society itself and to the cause of Geography all over the world, his associates gave him the Founder's medal.

'This and other tokens of esteem and grateful recollection cheered the invalid. Unable to walk or stand, he could no longer resume his place at the School of Mines, or at any of the many meetings where he used to be so constant an attendant. But driving about in London, receiving visits from his more intimate friends, and reading, as he did, a good deal, he by no means felt himself cut off from all interest and participation in what was going on in the world. Throughout the summer he continued in this condition, making no visible progress towards convalescence, but yet retaining so much vivacity, and looking so well, that it seemed as if he might yet live for some time to come. He carried on his correspondence, usually by the help of an amanuensis, but sometimes with his own hand, down to the month of August. Some of his letters to myself, written even as late as the early part of that month, though not suitable for quotation here, show little change in the keenness of his interest in the progress of geology, of the British Association, of the School of Mines, the Geological Survey, and other matters with which he had long been so closely connected.

'The malady, however, made great progress in the autumn. He had repeatedly expressed a wish to see me, and at the end of September I rejoined him. The lapse of a few weeks had produced a marked and sad change. His speech had become so affected that even his nephew, who assiduously watched him daily, could not make out what he said. His face brightened with the old friendly smile as I sat down beside him for the last time. There was something which he wished to say, but he tried in vain to express it in words. He then had recourse to the pencil, which for a week or two had served to make his wants known to those about him. But the fingers could no longer form any intelligible writing. His eyes filled with tears, and he sank back into his chair.

'The end, now plainly near, though sad, could not but be welcome. He had never all his life been given to speaking on religious subjects, but he seemed to enjoy the Psalms and other passages of scripture as read to him. His nephew asked him if he felt perfectly happy, and received in return a smile and an affirmative pressure of the hand. In the middle of October, in the course of his usual drive, he caught cold. An attack of bronchitis followed, under which, on the 22d of the month, after a lapse of only three days, he quietly and almost imperceptibly passed away.

'On the 27th of October the remains of the old soldier and geologist were laid beside those of his wife in the Brompton Cemetery. A goodly company of mourners followed them to the grave, including representatives from the varied circles of life and activity where he had moved for so many years, and from which his presence would long be missed. The Queen and the Prince of Wales testified their respect by sending their carriages to join the funeral procession. Among those who walked bareheaded behind the bier the most conspicuous form was that of the Prime Minister, Mr. Gladstone. And thus, amid the deep regrets of his personal friends, and with the respect and esteem of every rank and condition of men, the earth closed upon all that was mortal of Roderick Impey Murchison.'

The sarcophagus stands in Compartment 5 West, right by the central pathway through Brompton Cemetery, immediately to the north of the arcades. This historical burial ground is presently in the care of the Royal Parks Agency. It is situated south-east of Earls Court Exhibition Centre (nearest Underground station West Brompton on the District Line). It is one of the finest Victorian cemeteries in London and some 200,000 people, some world-famous, lie buried here. The inscription on the north side of the vault reads:

TO THE MEMORY OF
SIR RODERICK IMPEY MURCHISON
BART KCB FRS DCL LLD &c
DIRECTOR GENERAL OF THE GEOLOGICAL SURVEY
FOREIGN MEMBER OF THE INSTITUTE OF FRANCE
MEMBER OF THE IMPERIAL ACADEMY OF SCIENCES OF ST. PETERSBURG
AND OF MANY OTHER SCIENTIFIC SOCIETIES
KNIGHT GRAND CROSS OF THE IMPERIAL ORDER OF
ST. ANNE AND ST. STANISLAUS OF RUSSIA &c &c
AUTHOR OF THE SILURIAN SYSTEM OF ROCKS
AND OF RUSSIA AND THE URAL MOUNTAINS
BORN AT TARADALE ROSS-SHIRE 19th FEBRUARY 1792
DIED IN LONDON 22nd OCTOBER 1871

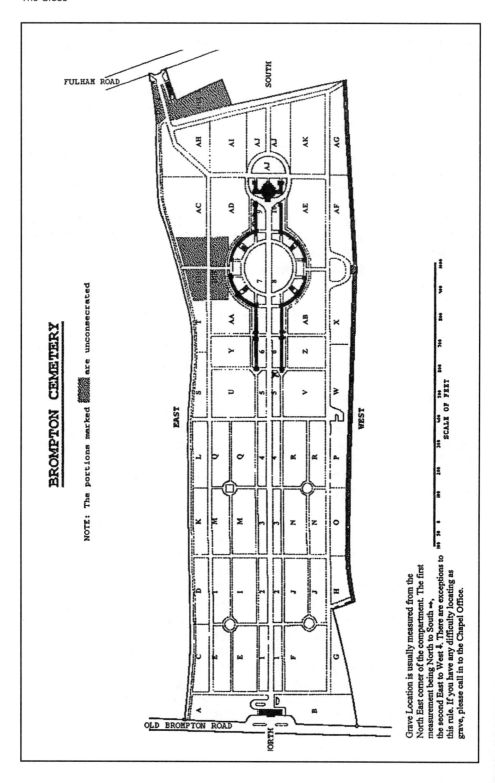

BROMPTON CEMETERY

NOTE: The portions marked ▨ are unconsecrated

Grave Location is usually measured from the North East corner of the compartment. The first measurement being North to South ↦, the second being East to West ↦. There are exceptions to this rule. If you have any difficulty locating as grave, please call in to the Chapel Office.

SCALE OF FEET

Register of Burials in the West of London and Westminster Cemetery, Earl's Court, Old Brompton.

ESTABLISHED BY ACT OF PARLIAMENT, 1st VICTORIA, CAP. 130.

NAME AND DESCRIPTION	Place where Death occurred	When Buried	Age	By whom this Ceremony was performed	Place of Burial and No. of Grant.	From what Parish, &c. removed.	Church.	Dissent.	REMARKS.
65526			65						
65527			72						
65528			70						
65529			62						
65530			4						

Register of Burials in the West of London and Westminster Cemetery, Earl's Court, Old Brompton.

ESTABLISHED BY ACT OF PARLIAMENT,

17 VICTORIA, CAP. 130.

NAME AND DESCRIPTION.	Place where Death occurred.	When Buried.	Age.	By whom the Ceremony was performed.	Place of Burial and No. of Grave.	Present Parish Address.	Church.	Dissent.	REMARKS.
53154		1860	60						
53155									
53156									
53157									
53158									

Chapter Sixteen
Epilogue

'Archibald Geikie concludes his *Life of Sir Roderick I. Murchison* as follows:

'Here the task of the biographer might fitly end. Yet not without reluctance can he lay down the pen. For many months it has seemed to him as if he had been living again with the friend whose life and work he has been tracing, and from whom the completion of these pages brings as it were a final and irrevocable parting. Here then at the close he would ask what that friend was, and what he did, that his death should have called forth so general an expression of regret. Looking back upon the foregoing narrative, we can perceive that the services by which Murchison earned the esteem and grateful recollection of his fellow-men were twofold. There was first the value of his scientific work, and secondly, the influence of his personal character.

'1. It is probably still too soon [1875] to attempt an estimate of the actual and lasting contributions made by Murchison to science. But as to the general nature and tendency of his work there can be little diversity of opinion. He was not gifted with the philosophic spirit which evolves broad laws and principles in science. He had hardly any imaginative power. He wanted therefore the genius for dealing with questions of theory, even when they had reference to branches of science the detailed facts of which were familiar to him. The kind of opposition he offered to the views of the evolutionists, and to the doctrines of those who gainsaid his own favourite faith in former convulsions of nature, showing as it did a warmth of antagonism rather than an aptitude for coherent and logical argument, may be cited as evidence of this natural incapacity as well as the want of early training in habits of accurate scientific reasoning.

'But though his name may never be inscribed among those of the recognised magnates in science who are both consummate observers and philosophic reasoners, and who mould the character of science for their own and future times, he will ever hold a high place among the pioneers by whose patient and sagacious power of gathering and marshalling facts new kingdoms of knowledge are added to the intellectual domain of man. He was not a profound thinker, but his contemporaries could hardly find a clearer, more keen-eyed, and careful observer. He had the shrewdness, too, to know wherein his strength lay. Hence he seldom ventured beyond the domain of fact where his first successes were won, and in which throughout his long life he worked so hard and so well.

'In that domain he had few equals. The patient industry and untiring perseverance with which year after year he returned to the attack of the old grauwacke rocks of his Silurian region form a lesson of hope and encouragement to all students who seek to advance our knowledge of the earth. His Silurian System, in its original elaboration, and in its subsequent extension to the rocks of other countries, may be taken as the type of his scientific work, as it certainly constitutes the ground on which his name will most securely rest. Theories and speculations which now seem firmly established may eventually be swept away before the onward march of research, but such solid contributions of fact as the details of the Silurian System will remain as part of the common stock of knowledge out of which new theories and speculations will be evolved. That system embodied the results of such patient toil as enables a traveller to bring a new and unexplored country to the knowledge of the rest of the world. Murchison's labours among the older rocks stood indeed to geology in a relation not unlike that which his friend Livingstone's work in Africa bore to geography. Round these rocks there had gathered some share of the mystery and fable which hung over the heart of Africa. And he dispelled it not by intuitive genius, but by plodding and conscientious toil, directed by no common sagacity, and sustained by an indomitable courage. For this service his name will be held in lasting and honoured remembrance.

'It was in the province of Palaeozoic geology that Murchison exerted his chief influence upon the progress of science. But, as we have seen, there were other spheres of work wherein he did good service, though its value may be even less easily appraised. No man could be so long and so actively concerned in the direction of some of the leading scientific Societies of his day without materially affecting the advancement of the studies to which these Societies were devoted. To none of its founders and promoters, for example, did the British Association owe more than to him. His work, too, at the Geographical Society, was directly related to some of the best achievements of modern geography. But in this and similar cases his scientific endowments were probably less concerned than his personal character, to which we may now, and lastly, turn.

'2. A man's face and figure afford usually a good indication of the general calibre of the spirit which lodges beneath them. The picture which rises to the mind when one thinks of Murchison is that of a tall, wiry, muscular frame, which still kept its erectness even under the burden of almost fourscore years. It seemed the type of body for an active geologist who had to win his reputation by dint of hard climbing and walking almost as much as by mental power. It was moreover united in his case with a certain pomp or dignity of manner which at one time recalled the military training of the Peninsular days, at another the formal courtesy of the well-bred gentleman of a bygone generation. No learned body or business meeting or anniversary dinner could well be presided over by one who possessed in a greater degree the preliminary and often very useful advantage of a commanding presence. The dignity, however, was blended with a courtesy and kindliness of manner which usually conciliated even those who might have been most disposed to object to any assumption or appearance of assumption, of authority on his side.

So he moved among his fellows as a leader under whom, in the conduct of affairs, his comrades, even when confessedly his own superiors in mental power and scientific achievement, gladly, and indeed instinctively, ranged themselves.

'Fortunately his social position and wealth were such as to give him the full use of these personal advantages. Like Sir Joseph Banks, he made his house in Belgrave Square, one of the centres where the most truly representative gatherings of men could be met with. Ministers of State, men of rank, of science, of literature, of art and of travel mingled there together, and came to see and know each other. And yet in the midst of this general intercourse Murchison never lost sight of his scientific position. His guests, too, though they saw him to be a man of the world, were in various indirect ways reminded that he took a pride in his science. It may be hardly possible to estimate the value of this influence. But assuredly among the causes which have helped, during the last thirty years, to give science and its votaries a firmer hold upon society, and especially the higher classes of society, we must count as by no means unimportant the liberal way in which Murchison displayed his excellent social qualities.

'But above and beyond this mere external aptitude for a place of eminence, Murchison had many higher claims to such a position. Foremost we should place his vigorous energy, his unwearied and almost restless activity. He seemed never to be without a definite and well-planned task. When his hands were fullest of his own work, he appeared to have almost unlimited time for assisting the labours of others, and co-operating with them for the general advancement of knowledge. That he could do this in so great a degree arose not only from his capacity for work, but from a certain method and orderliness of mind which characterized him in every period and phase of his life. The spirit which led him in early days to tabulate the deeds and fate of his respective hunters was the very same which guided him through the labyrinths of grauwacke, and prompted his exertions for the welfare of the Geographical Society. Men could not but respect one who, while doing so much honest independent work himself, was ever ready to take his place with others in efforts for the general good.

'Another leading feature of his character, and an element which largely aided his success, was shrewd common sense and knowledge of the world. We see this feature conspicuously manifested in all his scientific undertakings, where he derived more help from it than some of his contemporaries did from undoubted genius. He never allowed himself to be led astray from the track which he was patiently and ploddingly following by any will-o'-the-wisp in the shape of speculation or theory; nor in the management of affairs did he bind himself to lofty and impracticable principles. He took men and things as he found them, and tried to work upon them by firmness or concession, as seemed most likely to aid his object. Now and then, when provoked by opposition, he manifested a certain impatience, and even imperiousness of manner, which provoked rather than conciliated. Nevertheless, in the tact which enables a man to manage his fellows successfully for many years, he had few rivals. He showed it in the conduct of the various learned Societies of whose governing bodies he was a member. But nowhere did he display it more conspicuously than in the way in which he gained from different Ministries a recognition of the claims of scientific discovery. Probably no man had so much influence with the Governments of his day, and no man more honourably, persistently, and courageously used it.

'There was still another characteristic which secured to Murchison the esteem as well as the respect of his fellow-men – his thorough kindliness and goodness of heart. Separate instances of this have been given in the foregoing narrative, but it was a feature which showed itself all through his life. Many a humble fellow-worker in science did he encourage and materially assist. When he had given the right hand of friendship to a man he stuck to him, even in the face of baseness and ingratitude. The devotion, indeed, with which he espoused the cause of a friend, had, at times, something altogether chivalrous about it. Of this, the instance which will naturally rise to most men's minds is his hearty and energetic devotion to Livingstone, whose interests he so entirely identified with his own.

'With the recollection of these features which go to make up the picture of what Murchison was, there must needs mingle some slight remembrance of his foibles of character. But if this narrative of his life has been as faithful as its writer has wished that it should be, these superficial weaknesses have already appeared and need not be touched on here. Rather let us carry with us through the rest of life the lessons which the other and dominant features of his character and work may teach – his persevering industry, his readiness to be helpful, his loyalty to a friend, and, above all, his life-long and entire devotion to the advancement of knowledge. It will, perhaps, be many a day before another man arises to fill among us the honourable and useful place from which we shall long miss the presence of Roderick Impey Murchison.'

Appendix 1

The Primary Publications of Sir Roderick Murchison

Selected from his own definitive Bibliography
by Anthony Brook (see p. 7)

1. On the Coal-field of Brora, in Sutherlandshire, and some other Stratified Deposits of the North of Scotland, [1827]
    Transactions of The Geological Society Series 2,**2**, pt. 2 (1827) 293-326, plus Plates 31 and 32.

2. Supplementary Remarks on the Strata of the Oolitic Series, and the rocks associated with them in the Counties of Sutherland and Ross, and in the Hebrides, [1827]
    Transactions of The Geological Society Series 2, **2**, pt. 3 (1827) 353-68.

3. With Adam Sedgwick
    On the Geological Relations of the Secondary Strata in the Isle of Arran, [1828]
    Transactions of The Geological Society Series 2, **3**, pt. 1 (1829) 21-36.

4   With Charles Lyell
    On the Excavations of Valleys, as illustrated by the Volcanic Rocks of Central France,   [1828]
    Edinburgh New Philosophical Journal , **7** (April-October 1829) 15-48, plus 3 Plates.

5. On the Tertiary and Secondary Rocks forming the Southern Flank of the Tyrolese Alps, near Bassano, [1829]
    Philosophical Magazine NS, **5** (1829) 401-10, plus fold-out Plate of Sections

6. With Charles Lyell
    On the Tertiary Deposits of the Cantal, and their relation to the Primary and Volcanic Rocks, [1829]
    Annales des Sciences Naturelles, **18** (1829) 173-214

7.   With Charles Lyell
        On the Tertiary Freshwater Formations of Aix, in Provence, including the coalfield
        of Fuveau, [1829]
        Edinburgh New Philosophical Journal, **7** (April-October 1829) 287-98, plus 2
        Plates.

8.   With Adam Sedgwick
        A Sketch of the Structure of the Eastern Alps; with Sections through the Newer
        Formations on the Northern Flanks of the Chain, and through the Tertiary Deposits
        of Styria, etc, [1830]; with Supplementary Observations, Sections and a Map by
        Roderic Murchison, [1831]
        a) *Philosophical Magazine* NS, **8** (1830) 81-134, with large fold-out Plate of 7
        Figures (Sections).
        b) *Transactions of The Geological Society* Series 2, **3**, pt. 2 (1832) 301-420, plus
        Plates 35-40 and Explanation thereof.

9.   Supplementary Observations on the Structure of the Austrian and Bavarian Alps,
        [1831]
        Philosophical Magazine NS, **9** (1831) 213-19

10.   The Structure of the Cotteswold Hills and country round Cheltenham; and on the
        occurrence of Stems of Fossil Plants in vertical positions in the Sandstone of the
        Inferior Oolite of the Cleveland Hills, [1832]
        Proceedings of The Geological Society, **1** (1826-33) 388-92

11.   On the Sedimentary Deposits which occupy the western parts of Shropshire and
        Hertfordshire, and are prolonged from Northeast to Southwest, through Radnor,
        Brecknock and Carmarthenshires, with descriptions of the accompanying rocks of
        intrusive or igneous characters, [1833]
        Proceedings of The Geological Society, **1** (1826-33) 470-77

12   On the Old Red Sandstone in the Counties of Hereford, Brecknock and
        Carmarthen, with collateral Observations on the Dislocations which affect the
        northwest margins of the South Welsh Coal-basin, [1834]
        Proceedings of The Geological Society, **2** (1833-38) 11-13

13.   On the Structure and Classification of the Transition Rocks of Shropshire,
        Herefordshire and part of Wales, and on the Lines of Disturbance which have
        affected that Series of Deposits, including the Valley of Elevation of Woolhope,
        [1834]
        Proceedings of The Geological Society, **2** (1833-38) 13-18 plus extensive fold-out
        Table.

14.   On the Gravel and Alluvial Deposits of those Parts of the Counties of Hereford,
        Salop & Worcester, which consist of Old Red Sandstone; with an Account of the
        Puffstone, or Travertin of Spouthouse, and of the Southstone Roch near Tenbury,
        [1834]
        Proceedings of The Geological Society, **2** (1833-38) 77-78

15. On certain Trap Rocks in the Counties of Salop, Montgomery, Radnor, Brecon, Carmarthen, Hereford and Worcester; and the Effects produced by them upon the Stratified Deposits, [1834]
     Proceedings of The Geological Society, **2** (1833-38) 85-93

16. A General View of the New Red Sandstone Series, in the Counties of Salop, Stafford, Worcester and Gloucester, [1835]
     Proceedings of The Geological Society, **2** (1833-38) 115-18

17. On the Silurian System of Rocks,
     Philosophical Magazine Series 3, **7** (1835) 46-52

18. On certain Lines of Elevation and Dislocation of the New Red Sandstone of North Salop and Staffordshire, with an Account of Trap Dykes in that Formation, at Acton Reynolds, near Shrewsbury, [1835]
     Proceedings of The Geological Society, **2** (1833-38) 193-95

19. With Adam Sedgwick
     On the Silurian and Cambrian Systems, exhibiting the order in which the older Sedimentary Strata succeed each other in England and Wales,
     Philosophical Magazine Series 3, **7** (1835) 483-85

20. On the Geological Structure of Pembrokeshire, more particularly on the Extension of the Silurian System of Rocks into the coast cliffs of that County, [1836]
     Proceedings of The Geological Society, **2** (1833-38) 226-30

21. The Gravel and Alluvia of South Wales and Siluria, as distinguished from a northern drift covering Lancashire, Cheshire, North Salop, and parts of Worcester and Gloucester, [1836]
     Proceedings of The Geological Society, **2** (1833-38) 230-336 [7pp. only: 230-32, 333-36]

22. On the Silurian and other Rocks of the Dudley and Wolverhampton Coalfield, followed by a Sketch proving the Lickey Quartz Rock to be the same age as the Caradoc Sandstone, [1836]
     Proceedings of The Geological Society, **2** (1833-38) 407-14

23   With Adam Sedgwick
     Description of a Raised Beach in Barnstaple Bay, on the north-west coast of Devon, [1836]
     Transactions of The Geological Society Series 2, **5**, pt. 2 (1840) 279-86

24. With Hugh E. Strickland
     On the Upper Formations of the New Red Sandstone System in Gloucestershire, Worcestershire and Warwickshire; showing that the Red (Saliferous) marls with a peculiar Zone of Sandstone represent the Keuper; and that the underlying Sandstone of Ombersley, Bromsgrove and Warwick is part of the "Bunter Sandstein" of foreign geologists, [1837]
     Transactions of The Geological Society Series 2, **5**, pt. 2 (1840) 331-48

25.   With Adam Sedgwick
        On the Physical Structure of Devonshire, & on the Subdivisions & Geological
        Relations of its Old Stratified Deposits, [1837]
        Transactions of The Geological Society Series 2, **5,** pt. 3 (1840) 633-704, plus
        Plates 50-58

26   *THE SILURIAN SYSTEM, Founded on Geological Researches in the*
        Counties of Salop, Hereford, Radnor, Montgomery, Carmarthen, Brecon,
        Pembroke, Monmouth, Gloucester, Worcester and Stafford, with
        Descriptions of the Coalfields and Overlying Formations, 2 Vols., Quarto,
        John Murray, London, 1839 768pp. 39 plates

27.   With Adam Sedgwick
        On the Classification of the Older Rocks of Devonshire and Cornwall,
        Philosophical Magazine Series 3, **14** (1839) 241-60 and 317 and Vol. 15 (1839)
        401-07

28.   With Adam Sedgwick
        On the Classification and Distribution of the Older or Palaeozoic Rocks of the
        North of Germany and of Belgium, as compared with Formations of the same age
        in the British Isles, [1840]
        Transactions of The Geological Society Series 2, **6**, pt. 2 (1842) 221-302, plus
        Plates 23-28

29.   First Sketch of some of the Principal Results of a Second Geological Survey of
        Russia, in a letter [from Roderick Murchison] to Mr Fischer de Waldheim,
        Philosophical Magazine Series 3, **19** (1841) 417-22

30.   With E. de Verneuil
        On the Geological Structure of the Northern and Central Regions of Russia, [1841]
        Proceedings of The Geological Society, **3** (1838-42) 398-408

31.   On the Glacial Theory,
        Edinburgh New Philosophical Journal, **33** (April-October 1842) 124-40

32   With E. de Verneuil and Count von Keyserling
        On the Geological Structure of the Central and Southern Regions of Russia in
        Europe, and of the Ural Mountains (being a General Summary of a Second
        Geological Survey during 1841) London; Richard and John Taylor, 1842 40pp

33.   With E. de Verneuil
        On the Permian System as developed in Russia and other parts of Europe, [1844]
        a) *Proceedings of The Geological Society*, **4** (1843-45) 327-33
        b) *Neues Jahrbuch* (Leonhard und Bronn) (1844) 81-87

34.   On the Palaeozoic Deposits of Scandinavia and the Baltic Provinces of Russia,
        and their relations to Azoic or more ancient crystalline Rocks; with an account of
        some great features of Dislocation and Metamorphism along their northern
        frontiers, [1844]
        a) *Proceedings of The Geological Society*, **4** (1843-45) 601-28
        b) *Quarterly Journal of The Geological Society*, **1** (1845) 467-94

35   **With E. de Verneuil and Count von Keyserling**
         THE GEOLOGY OF RUSSIA IN EUROPE AND THE URAL MOUNTAINS
         Vol. 1 (English) – Geology – 662pp., 15 plates   John Murray, London [For
         Title- Page, see Back Cover]
         Vol. 2 (French) – Palaeontologie – 511pp., 50 plates   P. Bertrand, Paris   1845

36.   Habitation and Destruction of the Mammoths,
         Edinburgh New Philosophical Journal, **40** (Oct 1845- April 1846) 344-61

37.   On the Superficial Detritus of Sweden, and on the probable causes which have
         affected the surface of the rocks in the central and southern parts of that Kingdom,
         Quarterly Journal of The Geological Society, **2** (1846) 349-81

38.   A brief Review of the Classification of the Sedimentary Rocks of Cornwall (with
         opinions on the Gold of Australia),
         Transactions of The Royal Geological Society of Cornwall, **6** (1846) 317-26

39   On the Silurian and associated Rocks in Dalecarlia, and on the Succession from
         Lower to Upper Silurian in Smaland, Oland and Gothland, and in Scania, [1846]
         Quarterly Journal of The Geological Society, **3** (1847) 1-48, plus fold-out of
         Sections

40   On the Meaning originally attached to the term 'CAMBRIAN SYSTEM' and on the
         evidences since obtained of its being geologically synonymous with the previously
         established term 'LOWER SILURIAN',
         Quarterly Journal of The Geological Society, **3** (1847) 165-79

41.   On the Silurian Rocks of Bohemia, with a few remarks on the Devonian Rocks of
         Moravia,
         Edinburgh New Philosophical Journal, **44** (October 1847- April 1848) 66-79

42.   On the Geological Structure of the ALPS, APENNINES and CARPATHIANS, more
         especially to prove a transition from Secondary to Tertiary Rocks, and the
         development of Eocene Deposits in SOUTHERN EUROPE, [1848]
         Quarterly Journal of The Geological Society, **5** (1849) 157-312, plus fold-out of
         Sections

43.   On the Earlier Volcanic Rocks of the Papal States, and the adjacent parts of Italy,
         Quarterly Journal of The Geological Society, **6** (1850) 281-310

44.   On the Vents of Hot Vapour in Tuscany, and their relations to Ancient Lines of
         Fracture and Eruption,
         Quarterly Journal of The Geological Society, **6** (1850) 367-84

45.   The Slaty Rocks of the Sichon, or Northern End of the Chain of Forez in Central
         France, shown to be of Carboniferous Age, [1850]
         Quarterly Journal of The Geological Society, **7** (1851) 13-18

46   On the Origin of the Mineral Springs of Vichy, [1850]
         Quarterly Journal of The Geological Society, **7** (1851) 76-84

47.   On the Silurian Rocks of the South of Scotland,
        Quarterly Journal of The Geological Society, **7** (1851) 139-69,
        plus Geological Sketch Map of the Coast of Carrick, Ayrshire.

48.   The Silurian System,
        The Literary Gazette, a) No. 1835, (March 20 1851) 278-79   b) No. 1840, (April 24
        1851) 369-70

49.   On the Distribution of the Flint Drift of the South-East of England, on the Flanks of
        Weald, and over the Surface of the South and North Downs,
        Quarterly Journal of The Geological Society, **7** (1851) 349-98

50   On the Meaning of the Term "SILURIAN SYSTEM" as adopted by Geologists in
        various Countries in the last 10 years,
        Quarterly Journal of The Geological Society, **8** (1852) 173-84

51.   On the Basin-like Form of Africa,
        Edinburgh New Philosophical Journal, **54** (October 1852-April 1853) 52-56

52.   ***SILURIA   The History of the Oldest Known Rocks containing Organic
        Remains, with   a brief Sketch of the Distribution of Gold over the Earth***
        John Murray, London 1854   xvi + 523pp.
        4th Edition B 1867 xix + 566pp. (including "The Silurian System")
        Maps, Plates, Tables, Figures (including Sections)

53   With John Morris
        On the Palaeozoic and their Associated Rocks of the Thüringerwald and the Harz,
        Quarterly Journal of The Geological Society, **11** (1855) 409-50, plus large fold-out
        Table of Strata

54.   The Silurian Rocks and Fossils of Norway, as described by M. Theodor Kjerulf,
        those of the Baltic Provinces of Russia, by Professor Schmidt, and both compared
        with their British equivalents,
        Quarterly Journal of The Geological Society, **14** (1858) 36-53

55.   On the Succession of the Older Rocks in the Northernmost Counties of Scotland;
        with some Observations on the Orkney and Shetland Islands,
        Quarterly Journal of The Geological Society, **15** (1859) 353-418, plus Plates XII
        and XIII

56.   On the Sandstones of Morayshire (Elgin, etc) containing Reptilian Remains; and
        on their Relations to the Old Red Sandstone of that Country, [1858]
        Quarterly Journal of The Geological Society, **15** (1859) 419-39

57   Supplemental Observations on the Order of the Ancient Stratified Rocks of the
        North of Scotland, and their associated Eruptive Rocks,
        Quarterly Journal of The Geological Society, **16** (1860) 215-40

58.   With Archibald Geikie
        On the Altered Rocks of the Western Isles of Scotland, and the North-western and
        Central Highlands,

Quarterly Journal of The Geological Society, **17** (1861) 171-228

59   Thirty Years' Retrospect of the Progress in our Knowledge of the Geology of the Older Rocks,
American Journal of Science, Series 2, **33** (1862) 1-21

60.   On the Permian Rocks of Northeastern Bohemia,
Quarterly Journal of The Geological Society, **19** (1863) 297-306

61   On the Gneiss and other Azoic Rocks, and on the superjacent Palaeozoic Formations, of Bavaria and Bohemia,
Quarterly Journal of The Geological Society, **19** (1863) 354-68

62   With Robert Harkness
On the Permian Rocks of the North-west of England, and their extension into Scotland,
Quarterly Journal of The Geological Society, **20** (1864) 144-65

63.   On the Antiquity of the Physical Geography of Inner Africa,
Journal of The Royal Geographical Society, **34** (1864) 201-05

64.   Observations on the Classification of the Silurian Rocks, being an Introduction to the Description of the Brachiopoda of that system, in *A MONOGRAPH of the BRITISH FOSSIL BRACHIOPODA,* Thomas Davidson, 3   DEVONIAN and SILURIAN SPECIES Part 7 The Silurian Brachiopoda.
London; Palaeontographical Society, 1866, 19-31

Appendix 2

Geographical Features named after Sir Roderick Murchison

Murchison, Victoria, Australia	Small town 100 miles north of Melbourne.
Murchison, Mount, Western Australia.	370 miles north-east of Perth (520m, 1706').
Murchison Range, N.T., Australia.	200 miles north of Alice Springs.
Murchison River, Western Australia	Enters Indian Ocean 300 miles north-north-west of Perth (north of Kalbarri).
Roderick River, Western Australia.	Tributary of River Murchison.
Murchison, New Zealand.	Small town 50 miles east of Westport, South Island.
Murchison, Mount, New Zealand	Southern Alps, 80 miles north-west of Christchurch (732m, 2402').
Murchison Mountains, New Zealand.	Fiordland National Park, Southland.
Murchison Falls, Uganda.	On Victoria Nile east of Lake Albert (renamed Kabalega).
Murchison Range, Transvaal, S. Africa.	24 miles north-east of Johannesburg.
Murchison Rapids, River Shire, Malawi	Tributary of the Zambezi, south of Lake Nyasa.
Murchison Sound, Greenland.	West coast, north of Thule Air Base.
Murchison Island, Canada	In Lake Nipigon (north of Lake Superior), Ontario.
Murchison, Texas, U.S.A.	Town 75 miles south-east of Dallas.
Murchison, Mount, Antarctica	Near the coast, 300 miles from Scott Base (3502m, 11490').

Appendix 3
The Geological Periods

Cambrian: 590 to 505 Ma (million years ago). Sediments deposited during the period include the first organisms with skeletons. Common fossils include brachiopods, trilobites, ostracods, and late in the period, graptolites.

Ordovician: 505 to 438 Ma.   Named after an ancient Celtic tribe, the Ordovices. Noted for the presence of various rapidly evolving graptolite genera and of the earliest jawless fish.

Silurian: 438 to 408 Ma.   The end of the period is marked by the climax of the Caledonian orogeny and the filling of several Palaeozoic basins of deposition.

Devonian: 408 to 360 Ma   The period of the Old Red Sandstone. Abundant invertebrate fauna.

Carboniferous: 360 to 286 Ma.   Marine limestones with a rich coral-brachiopod fauna. Vast forests gave rise to extensive coal measures.

Permian   286 to 248 Ma   Corals, trilobites and blastoid echinoderms vanished at the end of this period in a mass extinction.

Triassic: 248 to 213 Ma   Many new faunal and floral elements, including ammonites, modern corals, various molluscs, the dinosaurs and certain gymnosperms.

Jurassic: 213 to 144 Ma   Clays, calcareous sandstones and lime-stones. Brachiopods, bivalves, and ammonites and many other Invertebrate stocks. Reptiles flourished on land and in the sea, but mammals were relatively insignificant and presumed to have been predominantly nocturnal. The first birds, including *Archaeopteryx*, appeared late in the period.

Cretaceous: 144 to 65 Ma.   Noted for the deposition of chalk and the mass extinction of many invertebrate and vertebrate stocks, including the dinosaurs, mososaurs, ichthyosaurs and plesiosaurs.

Tertiary: 65 to 2 Ma.

Quaternary: The last 2 million years. Numerous major ice-sheet advances in the northern hemisphere.

Appendix 4
The Will of Sir Roderick Impey Murchison

On the 14th day of November 1871, the Will with two Codicils thereto of

Sir Roderick Impey Murchison

formerly of the Estate of Taradale in the County of Ross in North Britain

but late of No. 16 Belgrave Square in the County of Middlesex, Baronet KCB

deceased, who died on the 22nd day of October 1871

at No. 16 Belgrave Square aforesaid

was proved in the Principal Registry of Her Majesty's Court of Probate, by the Oaths of

Kenneth Robert Murchison of No 16 Belgrave Square aforesaid Esquire and Robert Maingy Murchison of Limpley Stoke in the County of Wilts Esquire the Nephews, Trenham Reeks of the Geological Museum Jermyn Street in the said County of Middlesex Esquire and John Murray of No 50 Albemarle Street in the same County Publisher Executors named in the said Will they having been first sworn duly to administer.

Resworn at the Stamp Office - under £300,000 April 1873.

Effects under £250,000. Leaseholds.

This is the last Will and Testament of me Sir Roderick Impey Murchison, formerly Proprietor of the Estate of Taradale, Ross-shire in North Britain and now of No 16 Belgrave Square in the County of Middlesex, Baronet K.C.B. I direct my body to be interred in the same vault as that in which the body of my dear wife is interred in the Brompton Cemetery and that the sum of five hundred pounds be expended by my executors in having such desirable and suitable memorials raised as they may approve, unless I shall previously have done so in my life time, such sum of five hundred pounds to be divided and applied as follows – four hundred pounds for a tombstone of memorial in the Brompton Cemetery and one hundred pounds for a memorial to be placed in the Church at Bathhampton near Bath, where my father, mother, uncle and other relatives are interred, to explain that I and my wife "are buried in the Brompton Cemetery London".

I bequeath to my eldest nephew, Kenneth Robert Murchison, late a Lieutenant in the 58th Regiment, for his life, my leasehold house No 16 Belgrave Square aforesaid, with the coach house and stables thereto belonging, including the benefit of the ground rent reserved by the lease, under which I hold the same premises and which ground rent I some time since purchased, he my said nephew keeping the said house and premises duly insured against fire and in proper repair and condition, according to the lessee's covenants contained in the lease under which I hold the same; and in case my said nephew shall fail to observe this condition, then I authorise the executors of this my Will to observe and perform the same on his behalf out of the income arising from my residuary estate, hereinafter bequeathed in trust   But I expressly declare that my said executors shall incur no responsibility to my residuary legatees for any omission to exercise that authority, and I empower my said executors at any time during the life time of my said nephew, with his consent, to let at said rent or sell my said leasehold house, coachhouse, stables and ground rent, and, in case of sale, the net proceeds of such sale shall be invested in the names of my executors in such manner and upon such securities as they shall think fit, and the interest or income to arise therefrom and the rent of the premises whilst let and until sold, shall be paid to my said nephew during his life for his own use, and subject thereto I direct my said leasehold house and premises to form part of my residuary estate. I bequeath to the said Kenneth Robert Murchison the cash balance which may be to the credit of my drawing account in the hands of my Bankers, Messrs Coutts and Company, at the time of my decease, and also the sum of one thousand pounds for his own use. I also bequeath to my said nephew all my furniture, plate, linen, china, books, prints, pictures, wines, liquors and other effects whatsoever at 16 Belgrave Square aforesaid, except securities for money, and except that several articles and things specifically bequeathed by this my Will, and also by way of bequest and not of exception, my horses and carriage with their appurtenances for his absolute benefit.

And I bequeath my large picture of Donald Murchison called "The Great Day" in the Exhibition of one thousand eight hundred and sixty eight by Sir Edwin Landseer to the Trustees of the National Gallery of Scotland in Edinburgh, to be well

This is the last Will and Testament

of me Sir Roderick Impey Murchison formerly Proprietor of the
Estate of Tarradale Rossshire in North Britain and now of Nº 16 Belgrave
Square in the County of Middlesex Baronet K. C. B. I first my body to be
interred in the same vault as that in which the body of my dear wife is interred
at the Brompton Cemetery and that the sum of five hundred pounds be
expended by my executors in having such desirable and suitable memorials
raised as they may approve unless I shall previously have done so in my life
time such sum of five hundred pounds to be divided and applied as follows
four hundred pounds for a tombstone or memorial in the Brompton Cemetery
and one hundred pounds for a memorial to be placed in the church at
Bathhampton near Bath where my father, mother, uncle and other
relatives are interred to explain that I and my wife "are buried in the
Brompton Cemetery London" I bequeath to my eldest nephew Kenneth
Robert Murchison late a Lieutenant in the 58th Regiment for his life
my leasehold house Nº 16 Belgrave Square aforesaid with the coach house
and stables thereto belonging including the benefit of the ground rent
reserved by the lease under which I hold the same premises and which
ground rent I some time since purchased at my said nephew keeping the
said house and premises duly insured against fire and in proper repair
and condition according to the lessees covenants contained in the lease under
which I hold the same and in case my said nephew shall fail to
observe this condition then I authorize the executors of this my Will to
observe and perform the same on his behalf out of the income arising from
my residuary estate herein after bequeathed in trust But I expressly declare
that my said executors shall incur no responsibility to my residuary legatees for
any omission to exercise that authority and I empower my said executors at
any time during the life time of my said nephew with his consent to let at a
rack rent or sell my said leasehold house coach house stables and ground rent
and in case of sale the net proceeds of such sale shall be invested in the names
of my executors in such manner and upon such securities as they shall
think fit and the interest or income to arise therefrom and the rent of the
premises whilst let and until sold shall be paid to my said nephew during
his life for his own use and subject thereto I direct my said leasehold
house and premises to form part of my residuary estate I bequeath to the
said Kenneth Robert Murchison the cash balance which may be to the
credit of my drawing account in the hands of my Bankers Messrs Coutts
and Company at the time of my decease and also the sum of one thousand
pounds for his own use I also bequeath to my said nephew all my furniture
plate linen china books prints pictures wines liquors and other effects what
soever at 16 Belgrave Square aforesaid except securities for money and except
the several articles and things specifically bequeathed by this my Will and
also by way of bequest and not of exception my horses and carriage with their
appurtenances for his absolute benefit and I bequeath my large picture of
Donald Murchison called "the Rent day" in the Exhibition of one
thousand eight hundred and sixty eight by Sir Edwin Landseer to the

placed in the best light in that gallery and to have a tablet or inscription affixed thereto, stating that it was presented by me.

And I bequeath my great vase of Siberian Aventurine with Porphyry pedestal and inscription, and my gold snuff box with diamonds with enamel portrait of Alexander Second Emperor of all the Russians, and also my Russian Damascene Stool Sideboard Plaque to the Museum of Practical Geology in Jermyn Street, London, to be deposited in such Museum, but in the event of the said Museum being at any time broken up or removed from Jermyn Street, then I bequeath the said vase with pedestal and inscription and the said snuff box to the Trustees of the British Museum, to be deposited in the Mineralogical Department of that Museum and I direct that the gilt inscription relative to the said vase, and which is now loose, shall be fastened into the Porphyry pedestal as soon as conveniently may be after my decease, and I direct that the said vase and snuff box shall always be kept together and be inseparable, whether they shall be in said Museum in Jermyn Street or in the British Museum or elsewhere, and as to the said Plaque in the event of the said Museum of Practical Geology being at any time broken up or removed from Jermyn Street, I direct that the same to be deposited in the Fine Arts Collection of the South Kensington Museum under the Lords of the Committee of Enquiry on Education And I direct that the said picture and vase and snuff box and plaque shall remain at No 16 Belgrave Square aforesaid for the space of one year from my decease.

And I bequeath the two large pictures of the Hugonin Family that hang in the Dining room, as well as the picture of two young girls in pink dresses in my late wife's Bedroom, and also the picture in crayon of my wife in the Boudoir by Brocchi, and the water colour drawing of Falaise by my late wife also in the Boudoir, to my late wife's niece Mrs. Catherine Pannel the wife of Charles Pannel of Torquay. And I request my executors to hand over the old Family Bible in which my late wife's birth is recorded, as well as any books having the Hugonin names or roots in them, to the said Catherine Pannel, to whom I bequeath the same accordingly.

And I bequeath to my nephew Robert Maingy Murchison, late a Captain in the 50th Regiment, the sum of one thousand pounds for his own use.

And I bequeath to my niece, Charlotte Barbara Cox, wife of Lieutenant Colonel Cox, R.A., the sum of one thousand pounds for her sole and separate use.

And I bequeath the sum of twelve thousand pounds to my trustees hereinafter named upon trust to invest the same in their names in such manner as they shall think proper, with liberty to vary the same investments at discretion, and upon trust to pay the annual income of the investment thereof unto the said Robert Maingy Murchison during his life, and from and after his decease unto his surviving wife, if any, for her use, and subject as aforesaid to hold the capital and income thereof in trust for all and every the children and child of the said Robert Maingy Murchison, who being sons or a son shall attain the age of twenty one years, or die under that age having issue, or being daughters or a daughter shall attain that age or marry, in equal shares if more than one such child, and if there shall be but one then in trust for such one child, and in case there shall be no such child, then the capital thereof to form part of my residuary estate. And I empower the trustees or trustee for the time being of this my Will, after the decease of the said Robert Maingy Murchison and his surviving wife, if any, or in the life time of the said Robert Maingy Murchison and any wife of his, or of the survivor of them with their, his or her consent in writing, to apply any part not exceeding one half of the vested or presumptive share of any such child aforesaid for his or her advancement, or otherwise for his or her benefit.

And I bequeath the sum of twelve thousand pounds to my trustees hereinafter named upon trust to invest the same in their names in such manner as they shall think proper, with liberty to vary the same investments at discretion, and upon trust to pay the annual income of such investment unto the said Charlotte Barbara Cox, during her life and during her present or any future coverture, for her sole and separate but inalienable use and benefit, and from and after her decease, then if her present husband Colonel Cox shall survive her, unto him for his life, and from and after the death of the survivor of them, then as to the capital and income thereof in trust for their son Kenneth Murchison Cox absolutely, if he shall attain twenty one or die under that age leaving issue, and if not, then the capital thereof to form part of my residuary estate. Provided always and I empower my said trustees or trustee for the time being after the decease of the said Charlotte Barbara Cox and Colonel Cox, or in the life time of them or the survivor of them, with their, his or her consent in writing, to apply any part of the said capital fund not exceeding two thousand pounds sterling for the advancement, or otherwise for the benefit, of the said Kenneth Murchison Cox.

And I bequeath unto Miss Georgiana Scott, my mother's half-sister, the sum of two thousand pounds.

And I bequeath unto my half sister, Henrietta Cathrine [sic] Hull, wife of William Varley Hull Esquire, the sum of one hundred pounds, considering that, by the Will of my late aunt Mary Massit, she is well provided for; and also the sum of one hundred pounds to her husband William Varley Hull.

And I likewise bequeath as remembrances unto each of my late wife's nephews and niece, Francis James Hugonin of Nursted House, and Roderick Hugonin recently residing in Nova Scotia and now of Torquay, and the said Catherine Pannel, and unto each of my own nieces, Mrs. Louisa W. Cumming, Mrs. Annie Urile, the wife of Colonel Henry Urille, C.B., Mrs. Harriette R. Rownham, the wife of the Reverend Mr. Rownham of Combe Down Vicarage, and Mrs. Charlotte Greaves, the wife of the Reverend Mr. Greaves, the sum of one hundred pounds.

And I bequeath to John Charles William Paul Graham of Dricnie in North Britain, the sum of one thousand pounds and to his mother, Anne Pauline Camille Graham, the sum of five hundred pounds. And I bequeath to Mademoiselle Marie Elise Carolina Losenegger of Berne, Companion of my late wife, and to Miss Mary otherwise Marie Macrae, formerly of Demerara but now residing at 82 Hill Street Glasgow, the sum of one hundred pounds each.

And I bequeath to Lieutenant Colonel John Bartleman of Her Majesty's Indian Army and now in New Zealand the sum of three hundred pounds, and in the event of his death in my life time, then I bequeath the same sum to his present wife, if she shall be then living; but if the said John Bartleman and his said wife should both have died in my life time, then I bequeath the same sum to their son, who is named after me, or in case of his death in my life time unto such of the children of the said John Bartleman by his present wife as shall be living at the time of my decease, to be equally divided between them. I also bequeath to Miss Margaret Bartleman, the daughter of the said John Bartleman by his former wife, the sum of one hundred pounds.

I bequeath to my friends Archibald Geikie, Director of the Geological Survey of Scotland, Thomas Rupert Jones, Professor in the Royal Military College Sandhurst, Harry William Bates, Assistant Secretary of the Royal Geographical Society, and Trenham Reeks, Curator of the Museum of Practical Geology, the sum of three hundred and fifty pounds each, to assist my executors and act as editors of any Publications to be selected from my journals and memoranda, or in preparing a sketch of my life.

And I bequeath as remembrances to the following friends the sum of one hundred pounds each, videlicet Professor Andrew Ramsey of the Geological Survey; Charles Murchison M.D. of 79 Wimpole Street, London; James William Salter, late Palaeontologist of the Geological Survey; William Talbot Aveline of the Geological Survey; Professor John Morris, University College, London; Kenneth Murchison of New Kelso, Lochcarron, Ross-shire; Dr. James Watson of Bath; Henry William Bristow of the Geological Survey; Monsieur Edouard de Verneuil, Member of the Institute of France; Count Alexander von Keyserling, Rector of the University of Dörpat, Russia; George Anderson of Inverness, W.S.; Major R. Murchison, late of the 29th Regiment; John Murchison of Melbourne, Victoria; Daniel Boys of 5 Lincolns Inn Fields and Charles Stark, late of the Custom House, Wick, North Britain; and in case of the death of the said Charles Stark in my life time, I bequeath the same sum of one hundred pounds to his widow, and in case of her death in my life time to his oldest son.

And I bequeath to the Geological Society of London the sum of one thousand pounds.

And I bequeath the like sum of one thousand pounds to the Royal Geographical Society of London, such two sums to be respectively paid to the President and Treasurer for the time being of each of those Societies, whose receipts respectively shall be good discharges for the same; and my will is that the sum so bequeathed to the first mentioned Society shall be styled "The Murchison Geological Fund", and that the sum so bequeathed to the secondly mentioned Society shall be styled "The Murchison Geographical Fund", and that such sums shall respectively be funded in the respective names of those Societies, or of the trustees for the time being thereof, or be otherwise invested by them in such securities as they respectively shall think proper; and the annual interest thereof respectively shall be applied in every consecutive year, in such manner as the Councils of the same Societies respectively may deem most useful in advancing Geological and Geographical Science respectively, whether by granting sums of money to Travellers in pursuit of knowledge, to Authors of memoirs or to persons actually employed in any enquiries bearing upon the Sciences of Geology and Geography respectively, or in rewarding any such Travellers, Authors or other persons whom such respective Councils may consider deserving of recompense. And I direct that the Council of the Geological Society shall, in every consecutive year, give a bronze cast of the Murchison Medal executed by Mr. Leonard Wicon, which I have hereafter directed to be annually furnished to the Geological Society, to some person to whom such Council shall grant any sum of money or recompense in respect of Geological Science.

I bequeath to the Director and Professors for the time being Officers of the Royal School of Mines, Jermyn Street aforesaid, the sum of five hundred pounds, to be invested in the Public funds of Great Britain, the income arising from such investment to be applied annually to purchase books for a prize to be styled "The Murchison Prize", to be accompanied by a cast of the said Murchison Medal. And I bequeath the Die of the said Murchison Medal to the Director for the time being of the Royal School of Mines in Jermyn Street aforesaid, and in order further to carry out my intention, I request that a cast of the said Murchison Medal be annually furnished by the Director of that establishment to and at the expense of the Geological Society. And in respect of the Royal School of Mines I direct such prize to be awarded annually to the Student who stands highest in the Geological Examination and high in any out of the other subjects taught in the Royal School of Mines. And I direct that the receipt of the Rector for the time being of the Royal School of Mines shall be sufficient discharge for the said sum of five hundred pounds.

And I bequeath the sum of six thousand pounds for the purpose of founding a Chair of Geology in the University of Edinburgh, to be called "The Murchison Chair", such sum of six thousand pounds to be paid to the Senatus of the said University, or the Trustees, Treasurer or other person or persons authorised to receive sums bequeathed to the said University, whose receipt shall be a sufficient discharge for the same. Provided always that in case I should found a Chair of Geology in the said University in my life time, then the said bequest of six thousand pounds to be void.

I bequeath the sum of two thousand pounds to the Honorable [sic] and Reverend Robert Siddell of St. Paul's Church, Knightsbridge, and also the sum of two hundred pounds to the Reverend Richard Burgess of Trinity Church, Sloane Street, or to the respective Incumbents for the time being of the same Churches respectively, to be distributed or applied by them respectively amongst the Poor around their respective Churches in the Parishes or Districts of Knightsbridge and Chelsea, as they shall think proper, and their respective receipts to be sufficient discharges.

I bequeath to the Minister for the time being of the Parish of Urray, Ross-shire, in which I was born at Taradale, the sum of two hundred pounds, to be distributed or applied by him among the Poor of that said Parish, as he shall think proper, and his receipt to be a sufficient discharge for the same.

I bequeath to Jane Haley, the widow of my old servant John Haley, the sum of ten pounds for mourning and also an annuity of twenty pounds during her life.

I bequeath the same sum for mourning to Elizabeth Rosse (my late wife's maid) and an annuity of twenty-five pounds during her life.

I bequeath to my old Coachman, William Vincent, an annuity of twenty pounds during his life.

I bequeath to my head Housemaid, Lesbiana Wharton, an annuity of fifteen pounds during her life; and I direct that the said annuities shall be considered as arriving from day to day but to be paid half yearly.

I bequeath to my Butler, William Chator, the sum of one hundred and fifty pounds and all my wearing apparel.

And I direct all the servants in my establishment at the time of my death to be put into devout mourning, and, in addition to any other benefit they take under this my Will, to each of them who has been in my service five years or upwards I bequeath one year's wages, and to each of them who has been in my service two years and upwards, half a year's wages.

And I bequeath to Samuel Pond, Messenger to the Geological Museum, the sum of one hundred pounds.

And I bequeath to James Holmes, House Keeper of the Geological Museum, and to Zachariah Chapman, Lecture Attendant at the Geological Museum, the sum of twenty-five pounds. And I hereby declare that all the legacies and annuities bequeathed by this my Will shall be paid free of duty, and that such of the legacies as are bequeathed to Charities or for Charitable purposes shall be paid exclusively out of such part of my personal estate as the law permits to be appropriate to Charitable purposes.

And as to the Residue of my Property, subject to the payment of my debts (including my liability to pay twenty five pounds a year to the said Georgiana Scott for her life, being the half of fifty pounds per annum to which she is entitled under the Will of my late uncle, General Sir Alexander Mackenzie) and my funeral and testamentary expenses and legacies and annuities, I bequeath the same to my nephews, the said Kenneth Robert Murchison, Robert Maingy Murchison, and the said Trenham Reeks, and John Murray of No. 50 Albemarle Street, upon trust that they or the survivors or survivor of them or other the trustees or trustee for the time being of this my Will do and shall continue my residuary property, or such part thereof as may consist of investments or securities for money in their then state of investment, or do and shall sell and convert the same into money, when and as they or he in their or his discretion shall think fit, or do and shall collect sell and convert into money all other parts of my residuary property, whether arising from the conversion of investments or securities existing at my decease or otherwise, and do and shall invest the same in their or his names or name in such manner as they or he shall think proper, with liberty to vary the same investments at discretion, and do and shall stand possessed thereof in trust for my said nephew, Kenneth Robert Murchison.

Provided always, and I hereby declare my Will to be that, if my said nephew, Kenneth Robert Murchison, shall die without leaving lawful issue living at his decease, who being a male shall have attained or shall attain the age of twenty one years, or being a female shall have attained that age, or have married, or shall attain that age or marry, then in such case my said trustees shall stand possessed of my said residuary estate from and after the decease of the said Kenneth Robert Murchison, upon trust out of the annual income of my said residuary estate to pay an annuity of six hundred pounds, free of legacy duty, to Harriet Isabella Murchison, the wife of the said Kenneth Robert Murchison, during her life, and, if she shall survive him, by equal half yearly payments and subject thereto in trust for my said nephew, Robert Maingy Murchison.

And if the said Robert Maingy Murchison shall die without leaving issue living at his decease, who being a male shall have attained or shall attain the age of twenty one years, or being a female shall have attained that age, or have married, or shall attain that age or marry, then and in such case my said trustees shall stand possessed of my residuary estate from and after the decease of the said Robert Maingy Murchison, in trust for my niece, the said Charlotte Barbara Cox, for her life, and during her present or any future coverture, for her sole and separate but inalienable use and benefit. And from and after her decease upon trust to pay thereout the sum of five thousand pounds, free of legacy duty, to Colonel William Cox, the husband of the said Charlotte Barbara Cox, if he shall survive her, and subject thereto in trust for Kenneth Murchison Cox, the son of the said Charlotte Barbara Cox, and if the said Kenneth Murchison Cox shall die without leaving issue living at his death, who being a male shall have attained or shall attain the age of twenty one years, or being a female shall have attained that age, or have married, or shall attain that age or marry, then from and after the decease of the said Kenneth Murchison Cox upon the trusts following, that is to say Upon trust out of such part of my said residuary estate as by Law I am enabled to devote to Charitable purposes, to pay the following legacies, free of legacy duty, that is to say to the Hospital at Brompton for Consumption and Diseases of the Chest the sum of one thousand pounds; To the Scottish Hospital of London, Crane Court, the sum of one thousand pounds; To the Caledonian Asylum at Holloway the sum of one thousand pounds, and to the Infirmary of Inverness the sum of one thousand pounds, and I direct the last mentioned legacies to be paid to the Treasurer for the time being of the respective Hospitals, Asylum, and Infirmary, whose receipt for the same legacies respectively shall be a sufficient discharge to my said trustees for the same.

And subject thereto in trust to pay or transfer my said residuary estate unto the said Francis James Hugonin, Roderick Hugonin, and Charles Murchison, provided they respectively shall be living at the time of the failure of the preceding trusts, in equal third shares as tenants in common. Provided always that if any of them my said last residuary legatees shall be then dead leaving issue then living, such issue shall take the share which such residuary legatee or legatees who shall be then dead would have taken if then living, such issue to take per stirpes [through family lineage] and interest as tenants in common, and the same principle of distribution shall be applicable, if the issue of any of them my said last named residuary legatees shall be of different degrees.

And I further declare that on failure of the trusts of any of the said third shares, the share or shares, the trusts whereof shall so fail with all additions thereto under this clause, shall accrue to the others, or equally among the others of the said third shares, and be subject to the trusts herein before declared concerning the share or respective shares to or among which such accrual shall take place.

Provided always I declare my Will to be that, if the said Kenneth Robert Murchison shall die leaving issue, none of whom shall at his death being a son or sons have attained the age of twenty one years, or being a daughter or daughters have attained that age or married, then and in such case whilst it shall be in suspense whether he the said Kenneth Robert Murchison shall have become entitled indefeasibly to my residuary estate, the income thereof from and after his decease shall be accumulated in augmentation of the capital thereof, and such accumulation and the resulting income thereof shall follow the ultimate destination of the capital of my residuary estate, and this provision shall be applicable in the like case and in the like manner after the successive deaths of the said Robert Maingy Murchison and Kenneth Murchison Cox, in case the indefeasible ownership of my residuary estate shall not have previously been determined but nevertheless without prejudice to the life interest of the said Charlotte Barbara Cox, in case she shall become entitled to a life interest in possession.

Provided always, and I hereby declare that, if under the aforesaid trusts of my residuary estate any person shall eventually become entitled thereto, whether for life or absolutely, and whether defeasably or indefeasibly, and who shall not already bear and use the surname and arms of Murchison, he or she, and in case of a female if married her husband, shall, in addition and in recognition with and after his or her own surname, take and use during his or her life the surname of "Murchison", and bear with his or her arms the arms of "Murchison", and obtain the Royal Licence or other necessary official authority for that purpose, and in default of which for the space of twelve Calendar months after becoming entitled to such entirety as aforesaid, or attaining the age of twenty one years or marrying as the case may be, such entirety shall go over and be enjoyed under the next ulterior trust, if any, of this my Will relating thereto.

And I appoint my said nephews, Kenneth Robert Murchison and Robert Maingy Murchison, and the said Trenham Reeks and John Murray, Executors and Trustees of this my Will. And I bequeath to the said Trenham Reeks (in addition to the sum I have already bequeathed to him) and to John Murray the sum of one thousand pounds each for their trouble in acting in the execution hereof, and for the purpose of arranging as soon as may be all my manuscripts and journals, with a view to the publication of such parts of them as may either illustrate my Biography, or advance Science, but without any liability to account for the said legacies or the application thereof.

And I bequeath the copyright of my said manuscripts and journals, and the profits of the publication thereof, to the said Archibald Geikie, Thomas Rupert Jones, Henry William Bates, and Trenham Reeks equally, but so nevertheless, and on the express condition that none shall be published without the consent of my executors.

And I devise all estates vested in me as a trustee or mortgagee unto my said executors, subject to the trusts and equities affecting the same. In witness whereof I, the said Sir Robert Impey Murchison, the testator, have to each sheet of this my last Will and Testament contained in twelve sheets of paper set my hand, this tenth day of March in the year of our Lord one thousand eight hundred and sixty nine --- Rod: I. Murchison --- signed acknowledged and declared by the said Sir Roderick Impey Murchison, the testator, as and for his last Will and Testament in the presence of us, who, at his request, in his presence and in the presence of each other, all being present together at the same time, have hereunto subscribed our names as witnesses --- Alex Forbes Tweedie, 5 Lincolns Inn Fields, London, Solicitor --- Fred: Du Camo Robinson, 5 Lincolns Inn Fields, Gentn.

This is a Codicil to the Will of me Sir Roderick Impey Murchison of No. 16 Belgrave Square in the County of Middlesex, Baronet, K.C.B., and which Will bears the date the tenth day of March one thousand eight hundred and sixty nine. I revoke the bequest contained in my said Will to my friends Archibald Geikie, Thomas Rupert Jones, Henry William Bates, and Trenham Reeks of the sum of three hundred and fifty pounds each. And I also revoke the bequest, contained in my said Will, of the copyright of my manuscripts and journals and the profits of the publication thereof, to the said Archibald Geikie, Thomas Rupert Jones, Henry William Bates, and

Trenham Reeks.

And I hereby direct that the same shall fall into and form part of my residuary estate. And I direct my executors to hand over all letters, books, and other documents in my possession necessary for the preparation of the Memoir of my life, to my friend the said Archibald Geikie, to be entirely under his control. He will select from them such portions as may seem to him proper for publication, either in my own words or otherwise as he may see fit, and the responsibility of the preparation of the Memoir of my Life is to rest with him. Provided always that he or his representatives shall be bound to return to my executors, books and other documents which they may have delivered to him, upon the completion of the publication of the memoir of my life, or upon the death or illness, or the happening of any other event whereby the completion thereof may be prevented or delayed beyond a reasonable time; and in any such event it shall be incumbent upon my executors to recover possession of the said letters, books, and other documents, and to hand them over to such other person or persons as they may consider competent to write or complete the said Memoir.

I bequeath to the said Thomas Rupert Jones, Henry William Bates, Trenham Reeks, and to my friend Professor John Morris, F.G.S., the sum of three hundred and fifty pounds each, in the expectation that they will contribute such assistance as they can give to the said Archibald Geikie, or to other the person or persons engaged on my Memoir. And I declare that, as regards the said Trenham Reeks, the said legacy of three hundred and fifty pounds shall be in addition to the legacy of one thousand pounds bequeathed to him by my said Will.

And I bequeath to the said Archibald Geikie the sum of one thousand pounds in recognition of his labor [sic] on my Memoir, and to be paid to him within the period of twelve months after my decease, notwithstanding my Memoir may not be then completed.

And I direct that the legacies of one thousand pounds each by my Will, bequeathed to the said Trenham Reeks and John Murray, shall be respectively given to them as executors and trustees without regard to the duty imposed upon them, as indicated by my said Will in connection with such bequest, and without any liability to account for the same legacies or the application thereof.

I bequeath to my nephew, Kenneth Robert Murchison, the diamonds formerly belonging to my late wife and now in the custody of my Bankers, Messrs. Coutts and Company, for his absolute use and benefit.

With regard to the bequest to the National Gallery of Scotland in Edinburgh of my large picture of Donald Murchison by Sir Edwin Landseer, I direct that the tablet or inscription to be affixed thereto shall contain an explanation of the Scene and of the History of Donald Murchison, as derived from the volumes of Robert Chambers' Domestic History of Scotland.

I bequeath to the trustees of the National Portrait Gallery the two large portraits of my God-father and God-mother, Sir Elijah and Lady Impey, and Lady Impey, by Zoffani, together with the portrait of their dear friend, my father, by Raeburn.

I bequeath to the said Trenham Reeks my Monorloid desk in my Dressing, but not the contents of such desk.

I bequeath to the widow of the late Lieutenant Colonel John Bartleman the sum of three hundred pounds, in addition to the like sum bequeathed by my said Will, and in the event of her death in my life time, then I bequeath the same three hundred pounds to their son, or other children, as in my said Will expressed with regard to the sum of three hundred pounds thereby bequeathed to them.

I bequeath to Margaret Bartleman, the daughter of Lieutenant Colonel Bartleman by a former marriage, the sum of one hundred pounds, in addition to the life sum bequeathed to her by my said Will.

I bequeath to Barbara Hort, the grand daughter of my half sister, Barbara Murray MacGregor, the sum of five hundred pounds on her attaining the age of eighteen years, the interest thereof to be paid from my decease to her mother, Mrs. Neame, to be applied by her for the education of her said daughter.

I bequeath to Mary E. Macrae the sum of one hundred pounds, in addition to the like sum bequeathed to her by my said Will.

I bequeath to John Charles William Paul Graham the sum of five hundred pounds, in addition to the sum of one thousand pounds bequeathed to him by my said Will.

I bequeath to my good friend and Physician, Dr. Henry Bruce Jones, who has attended me in my recent illness, the sum of one thousand pounds.

I bequeath the sum of one hundred pounds as a remembrance to each of the following friends videlicet Professor Thomas H. Huxley, F.R.S., Henry William Bristow, F.R.S., Professor Wareington Smyth, F.R.S., John Percy, M.D. F.R.S., Robert Hunt, F.R.S., and F. Macdonald of Druidag, Lochalsh, Rossshire.

I bequeath to Thomas William Newton, Assistant Librarian of the Royal School of Mines, the sum of one hundred and thirty pounds.

I bequeath to Elizabeth Rose, my late wife's maid, a legacy of two hundred pounds and an annuity of twenty five pounds during her life, in addition to the annuity of twenty five pounds already bequeathed to her by my said Will.

I bequeath to my Butler, William Chater, the sum of one hundred and twenty pounds, in addition to the legacy of one hundred and fifty pounds already bequeathed to him by my said Will. And I also bequeath to him, the said William

Chater, all my wearing apparel, other than my shooting clothes.
I bequeath to my footman, Richard Beaumont, the sum of seventy pounds and my shooting clothes, and also my shooting apparatus, including four double-barrelled guns.

I revoke the annuity of twenty pounds given by my said Will to my old Coachman, William Vincent, and I substitute in lieu thereof a legacy of one hundred pounds.

I bequeath to my Cook Maid, Emma Cronk, the sum of fifteen pounds.

And I bequeath to Diana Minors and Eleanor Jones Owen, the two Nurses who have attended me in my recent illness, the sum of twenty-five pounds each.

I direct that all legacies given by this Codicil shall be free of legacy duty, and lastly I revoke all former Codicils to my said Will.   In witness whereof I, the said Sir Roderick Impey Murchison, the testator, have to this Codicil to my last Will and Testament set my hand this twenty first day of April in the year of our Lord one thousand eight hundred and seventy one.

Rod: I. Murchison

Signed acknowledged and declared by the said Sir Roderick Impey Murchison, the testator, as and for a Codicil to his last Will and Testament, in the presence of us, who, at his request, in his presence, and in the presence of each other, all being present together at the same time, have hereunto subscribed our names as witnesses.

Richard Walter Tweedie, 5 Lin: Inn Fields, London. Solr.
Wm. Pound, Clerk to Messrs. Boys and Tweedies, 5 Lincolns Inn Fields. Solrs.

This is a further Codicil to the Will of Sir Roderick Impey Murchison of No 16 Belgrave Square in the County of Middlesex, Baronet, K.C.B., and which Will bears date the tenth day of March one thousand eight hundred and sixty nine.

I give and bequeath unto Mary Forster and Mrs. Grinbon, the two nurses now attending me, the sum of twenty five pounds each, to be paid to them respectively, free of legacy duty.

And in all other respects I confirm my said Will. In witness thereof I, the said Sir Roderick Impey Murchison, the testator, have to this Codicil to my last Will and Testament set my hand this twentieth day of July in the year of our Lord one thousand eight hundred and seventy one.

Rod: I. Murchison

Signed, acknowledged, and declared by the said Sir Robert Impey Murchison, the testator, as and for a Codicil to his last Will and Testament, in the presence of us, who at his request, in his presence and in the presence of each other, all being present together at the same time, have hereunto subscribed our names as witnesses.

Richard Walter Tweedie, 5 Lin: Inn Fields. Solr.

Alex A. Forbes, Clerk to Messrs. Boys & Tweedies.

Proved at London with two Codicils 14th Novr. 1871 by the oaths of Kenneth Robert Murchison Esqre. And Robert Maingy Murchison Esqre. the Nephews, Trenham Rooks Esqre. and John Murray the executors to whom Admon was granted.

References

Black, R.M., (1988) *The elements of Palaeontology*. C.U.P.

Brook, A., (2001) *Aspects of Murchison*. West Sussex Geological Society.

Brook, A., (2002) *Gideon Mantell – Memento Mori – 2*. West Sussex Geological Society.

Dana, J.D. & E.S., (1890) Sedgwick and Murchison. *Amer. J. Sci.*, ser. 3, **39**, 167-180.

Fric, A. (1863) Murchison in Bohemia. Ziva, Bohemia. Translated by Raduan Horny, *The Edinburgh Geologist*, **38** (Spring 2002).

Geikie, A, (1871) Sir Roderick Murchison (Obituary). *Nature,* Nov. 2, 1871.

Geikie, A., (1875) *Life of Sir Roderick I. Murchison*. Murray, London.

Geikie, A. (1903) Textbook of Geology. Macmillan, London.

Hawley, D. (1997) 'The first true Silurian': an evaluation of the site of Murchison's discovery of the Silurian. *Proc. geol. Soc. Lond.*, **108**, 131- 140.

Knell, S.J. (2000) *The Culture of English Geology* 1815-1851. Ashgate, Aldershot.

Lyons, Sir H., (1944) *The Royal Society 1660-1940: A history of its administration.* C.U.P

Morton, J.L. (2001) *Strata*. Tempus, Stroud.

Murchison, R.I., Verneuil, E. de and Keyserling, A. von (1845) *The Geology of Russia in Europe and the Ural Mountains*. John Murray, London.

Murchison, R.I., (1877) *The geological structure of the Parish of Harting* (In Gordon, H.D., *The history of Harting*, W. Davy & Son, London, 1-13.) [Murchison's essay dated 3 Jan. 1867]

Page, Leroy E., (1976) *The rivalry between Charles Lyell and Roderick Murchison.* Kansas State University.

Rudwick, M.J.S., (1974) R.I. Murchison *Dictionary of Scientific Biography,* **9**, 582-5

Secord, J.A., (1986) *Controversy in Victorian Geology. The Cambrian-Silurian dispute.* Princeton University Press, Oxford.

Thackray, J.C., (1978) R.I. Murchison's Geology of Russia (1845). *J. Soc. Biblphy nat. Hist.* **8** (4) 421-433.

Thackray, J.C., (1978) R.I. Murchison's Silurian System (1839). *J. Soc. Biblphy nat. Hist.* **9** (1) 61-73

Thackray, J.C., (1981) R.I. Murchison's Siluria (1854 and later) *Archives of Natural History* **10** (1) 37-43

Toghill, P., (2000) *The Geology of Britain – an Introduction.* Swan Hill Press, Shrewsbury.

Torrens, H.S., (1983) *Arthur Aikin's Mineralogical Survey of Shropshire 1796-1816 and the Contemporary Audience for Geological Publications,* **16** 111-53.

Trustees of the British Museum (Natural History) (1975) *British Palaeozoic fossils.*

Wilson, H.E. (1985) *Down to Earth – One hundred and fifty years of the British Geological Survey.* Scottish Academic Press, Edinburgh and London.

Index